ea
out in
pubs

Welcome to the first edition of this Guide

Our guide to dining pubs and inns is something of a new departure for Michelin. True, we've been picking out the best of British and Irish pubs in the Michelin Guide for seven years, and it's our same team of independent, professional inspectors who have compiled this selection. But for the first time, in-depth descriptive texts and specially commissioned photography bring out the character of each of the featured pubs, highlighting what's most charming and memorable about the place.

Eating out in pubs has changed a great deal over the last decade, as more and more establishments put the emphasis on dining. Now Michelin opens the door to a selection of some of the best places, so you can be confident in your choice: after all, we've been promoting and enjoying good food for over a century.

The five hundred pubs vary enormously in style, history and perso-nality and include not just Michelin award-winners but also other local favourites which deserve to be better known. Some chefs and landlords see themselves as part of a new "gastropub revolution", others are proud that their place has stayed unchanged for decades, even centuries, yet all of the pubs provide good food in enjoyable surroundings, and all of them make a really good meal out.

Michelin's readers contribute thousands of letters and e-mails every year, commenting on hotels and restaurants throughout the country. We hope you'll do the same for this new pub guide and help us to make the next edition even better than the first.

eating
out in
pubs

Michelin Travel Publications

Hannay House, 39 Clarendon Rd
Watford, Herts WD17 1JA
Tel: (01923) 205240
Fax: (01923) 205241
www.ViaMichelin.com
EatingOutInPubs-Gbirl@
uk.michelin.com

**Manufacture française
des pneumatiques Michelin**

Société en commandite par
actions au capital de
304 000 000 EUR.
Place des Carmes-Déchaux
63 Clermont-Ferrand (France)
R.C.S. Clermont-Fd B 855 200 507
© Michelin et Cie, Propriétaires-
Editeurs, 2004
Dépôt légal septembre 2004
ISBN 2-06-710963-4
Printed in France 09-04

Typesetting:

Nord Compo, Villeneuve-d'Ascq
Printing and binding:
IME, Baume-les-Dames

Photography

Picture Editor: Christine Chovet
Project manager: Alain Leprince
Agence ACSI - A Chacun Son
Image
2 r. Aristide Maillol
75015 Paris

Location Photographs:

Jérôme Berquez, Frédéric Chales,
Ludivine Boizard, Jean-Louis
Chauveau/ACSI

Thanks to:

John Bigelow Taylor/
Waddesdon, The Rothschild
Collection (The National Trust)
for the image of The Five Arrows
Hotel, Waddesdon

© Wales Tourist Board for the
image of Blue Anchor Inn

p8 : John A Rizzo/Photodisc Vert/
Getty Images

p3 - p12 : Consortium/
PHOTONONSTOP

p72 : Guy Durand/
PHOTONONSTOP

p534 : H. Champollion/MICHELIN

Contents

SHETLAND ISLANDS

ORKNEY ISLANDS

LANDS

EASTERN

NDON

TERN

ENGLAND

EAST MIDLANDS

EASTERN

LONDON

NORTH EASTERN

NORTH WESTERN

SOUTH EASTERN & I.O.W.

SOUTH WESTERN

WEST MIDLANDS

YORKSHIRE & HUMBER

IRELAND

NORTHERN IRELAND

REPUBLIC OF IRELAND

SCOTLAND

WALES

TOWN/VILLAGE NAME

COUNTRY/REGION & COUNTY NAMES

PICTURE OF THE ESTABLISHMENT

NAME, ADDRESS, TELEPHONE, E-MAIL AND WEBSITE OF THE ESTABLISHMENT

009
ENTRY NUMBER

Each pub or inn has its own entry number.

This number appears on the regional map at the start of each section to show the location of the establishment.

TEXT

COLOURED PAGE BORDER

Introduction

England

Scotland

Wales

Ireland

PAGE NUMBER

HOW TO GET THERE

Directions and driving distances from nearby towns, and indication of parking facilities and any other information that might help you get your bearings.

East - Cambridgeshire

Horningsea

009 Crown and Punchbowl
High St, Horningsea CB5 9JG
Tel: (01223) 860643 - Fax: (01223) 441814
E-mail: info@cambscuisine.com - Website: 222.cambscuisine.com

VISA AE

City of Cambridge Hobsons Choice

When is a pub not a pub? Answer: when it comes in the guise of the Crown & Punchbowl. This marriage of two buildings, one 17C, the other 19C, looks and feels like a pub, but doesn't actually have a bar, so anyone revisiting from 200 years ago would wonder what had happened to the village inn. It's certainly been given a modern makeover: wooden floors, farmhouse tables and chairs, rattan seats, neutral décor, contemporary lighting. Lovely old beams will take you back, though. Menus are a mixture of traditional, modern and international; favourite features include the sausage mix and match board and fresh fish blackboard. Clean, modern bedrooms keep the modish feel intact.

Food serving times:
Monday-Thursday:
12pm-2.30pm, 6.30pm-9pm
Friday-Saturday:
12pm-2.30pm
6.30pm-9.30pm
Sunday:
12pm-2.30pm
Closed 25 December and
dinner Bank Holidays
Prices:
Meals: 15.95 (fixed price lunch)
and a la carte 15.95/35.95
5 rooms : 49.95/69.95

Typical Dishes
Prawn and mushroom p...
pastry parcel
Lamb with rosemary
Sticky toffee pud...

4mi Northeast of Cambridge by A1303 and B1047 on Horningsea road. Parking.

24

6

SYMBOLS

🍽 Meals served in the garden or on the terrace

🍷 A good range of wines served by the glass

🍾 A particularly interesting wine list

Rest. Non-smoking dining room

🐕 No dogs allowed

VISA Visa accepted

AE American Express accepted

D Diners Club accepted

MC MasterCard (Eurocard) accepted

JCB Japan Credit Bureau accepted

REAL ALES SERVED

A listing to indicate the number and variety of regular and guest cask beers usually served.

OPENING HOURS FOOD SERVING TIMES PRICES ROOMS

Approximate range of prices for a three-course meal, plus information on booking and annual closures.

Some inns offering accommodation may close in mid-afternoon and only allow guests to check in during evening hours. If in doubt, phone ahead.

Room prices range from the lowest-priced single to the most expensive double or twin.

The cup and saucer symbol denotes breakfast; if no price is shown assume it is included in the price of the room.

Prices are given in £ sterling, except for the Republic of Ireland where Euro (€) are stated.

East - Cambridgeshire

The Pheasant
Village Loop Rd PE28 0RE
2) 710241 · Fax (01832) 710340
w.huntsbridge.co.uk

🍽 🍷 🍾 Rest. **VISA** **AE** **D** **MC** **JCB**

Adnams Best and 2 guest ales

tip for drivers tearing along the
A14 on the Cambridgeshire and
Northamptonshire borders: turn
Keyston and sample a taste of this
usly thatched inn, regularly awarded
helin Bib Gourmand. A dining pub
arge, The Pheasant consistently
s a range of good value, eclectic
in three agreeable dining areas.
ars mingle in the airy, timbered bar
ts open fire, muskets on the wall and
spaced wooden tables, but if the
g gets too busy there, then the rear
on – decorated with a mix of pictures
prints - is just as pleasant a place to
Interesting, modern a la carte menus
international influences are never
than accomplished and offer plenty of
anced flavour. Helpful, efficient service
given wherever you decide to eat.

Food serving times:
Monday-Sunday:
12pm-2pm, 6.30pm-9.30pm
(booking essential)
Prices:
Meals: a la carte 20.00/3

Typical Dishes
Smoked haddock, potato salad
Pork hock, potato and apple cake
Chocolate tart

5mi Southeast of Thrapston by A14
on B663.
Parking

25

THE BLACKBOARD

An example of a typical starter, main course and dessert, chosen by the chef.

Whilst there's no guarantee that these dishes will be available, they should provide you an idea of the style of the cuisine.

Beer
in the U.K.
and Ireland

As most pub-goers know, beers in Britain can be divided not only into Ales and Lagers – which differ mainly in their respective warm and cool fermentations – but also according to their means of storage. Keg beer is filtered, pasteurised and chilled, and then packed into pressurised containers from which it gets its name, while cask beer or "Real Ale", as it is often called, continues to ferment and mature in its barrel.

*B*rewers rightly insist that the final flavour of a beer depends on all sorts of elements, from the variety of yeast to the minerals in the local water, not to mention storage in the pub, but there are three stages of brewing which particularly influence the character of the beer in your glass.

The malting, the way the germinating barley is dried, roasted and milled to make it fermentable, affects the flavour, the 'body' and the colour of the drink: a hotter kiln means a darker malt. This malt is then soaked in hot water to form a porridge-like mash; time and temperature are crucial here.

Perhaps most importantly, the addition of hops gives a familiar, faintly astringent tang, with different strains of plant lending different overtones to the final pint. For extra aroma, bunches of hop flowers, called cones, can be added to the beer later, at the end of its vat fermentation or even in the barrel, a process known as "dry hopping".

Traditional Styles

Of the several distinct beer styles in the British Isles, **bitter** is the most popular traditional beer in England and Wales, although now outsold by lager.

No precise definition exists and the name is loosely used, but bitters are usually paler and dryer than Mild with a high hop content and, of course, a slightly bitter taste and bouquet, from flowery to citrus, depending on the hop variety. Seasonal drinks range from light-golden summer ales to strong, deep-toned winter brews.

Mild is largely found in Wales, the West Midlands and the North West of England. The name refers to the hop character as it is gentle, sweetish beer, generally lower in alcohol and often darker in colour.

The great dry **stouts** are brewed in Ireland and are instantly recognisable by their black colour and creamy head: they have a pronounced yeast flavour and sometimes a faint smoky taste. Reddish-black **porter** was revived by the renewed interest in real ale and is still something of a rarity.

Originally known as 'entire', this slightly lighter though still substantial beer was said to have been a favourite with London's market porters and delivery men when it was first brewed in the 18th century.

In Scotland the beers produced are typically full-bodied and malty and are often known simply as **Light, Heavy** or **Export,** which refers to the body and alcoholic content of the ale. The old shilling taxes were levied by roughly the same scale, at rates of 60/- to 80/- and beyond, and still survive in some beer names.

The Continental Connection

Many great European styles are now imitated by UK producers, with greater or lesser success, and publicans are also becoming increasingly discerning in their choices of European imports.

Drinkers in Britain's dining pubs might come across fizzy, hazy, tan-yellow **Weizenbier** from southern Germany which can accompany anything from full-flavoured white meats to seafood, or one of the crisp, bitter-edged **lagers** produced in the north, where they are sometimes served with fish.

Belgium's spontaneously fermenting **lambic** is aged in wine barrels for up to three years; when flavoured with fruit and bottle-matured it becomes **gueuze**, a sweet-sharp, bubbly beer quite unlike anything in the British tradition.

The great **abbey beers,** traditionally produced by the Belgian Trappist orders, are usually rich, effervescent and complex and need similarly robust flavours to complement them, while cloudy **white beers** make a refreshing accompaniment to light meals and summer salads.

Top-fermented then cold-stored like lagers, **bières de garde** from northern France and Wallonia are sometimes sealed with a Champagne-style wired cork.

These amber or nut-brown beers are typically strong and characterful and go well with cheeses or slow-cooked meats.

The Pub of the year

Of the 500 pubs and inns in the Guide, which have all been selected for the quality of their food, we wanted to choose a Pub of the Year which brings together all that's best about eating out in pubs: good cuisine, of course, but also atmosphere, setting, service, the choice of beers and wines and that intangible extra, something that makes a place really stand out.

The Michelin Pub of the Year is considered a great all-rounder, where drinkers and diners feel equally at home. Eating well here can mean a light snack or a full three-course meal, and has as much to do with the pub's style and atmosphere as it has with the food itself, although the cooking is fresh, flavourful and varied, and extremely popular. Pride and personality shine through in generous, friendly service, and the relaxed charm of the place – the X-factor of any great pub – makes you wish you lived closer to it. True to its roots in the beautiful Cotswold countryside, and still a firm favourite with the locals of Lower Oddington, the Pub of the Year is…

056 **Fox Inn**
Lower Oddington GL56 0UR
Tel: (01451) 870555 – Fax: (01451) 870666
e-mail:info@foxinn.net –Website:www.foxinn.net

See page 351 for more details.

*W*ith culinary tastes ranging from fresh samphire-shoots to cockles, smoked eel and Cromer crab, it's easy to get a flavour of the East of England. It's a region with strong brewing traditions and some of England's most charming pubs, but it's also a place of rich historic roots and a deep attachment to rural life. Here you'll find the medieval wool towns of Lavenham, Coggeshall and Saffron Walden and the old trading centres of Norwich and King's Lynn, Ely's distant tower and the Palladian splendour of Holkham Hall. Be part of the world-famous Aldeburgh music festival or the first Classics of the racing season at Newmarket; cast off into the waterways of the Norfolk Broads or lie back in a punt and drift down the Cam past the beautiful Cambridge colleges. Stroll through the fields of a lavender farm or strike out into the wilds, under the great open sky of the coast and the salt marshes, and spot basking seals, a flight of curlew or the rare wildlife of the broadland meadows. Wherever you go exploring, it's bound to be an inspiration. "They made me a painter and I am grateful", Constable once said of the walks along the Stour near his boyhood home. We can't guarantee the same for everyone, but you'll certainly work up an appetite along the way…

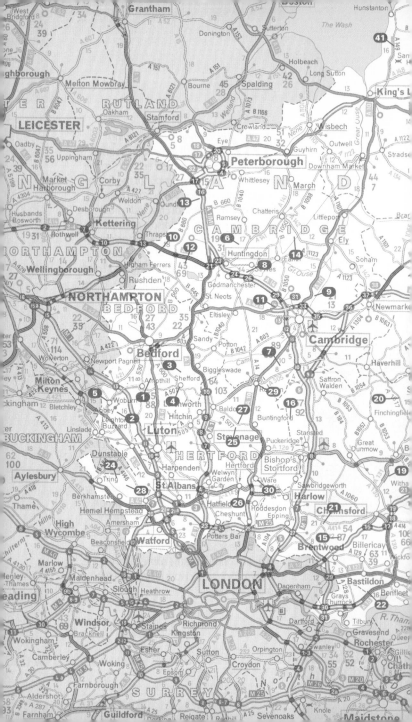

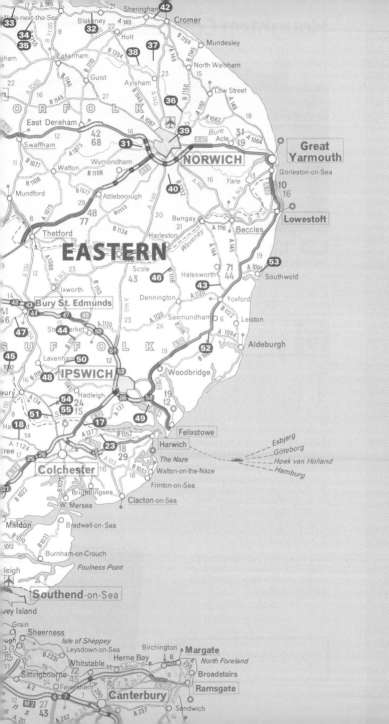

Houghton Conquest

001 Knife and Cleaver

The Grove, Houghton Conquest MK45 3LA
Tel.: (01234) 740387 - Fax: (01234) 740900
e-mail: info@knifeandcleaver.com - Website: www.knifeandcleaver.com

  rest **VISA** **AE** **①** **M ⓒ** **JCB**

 Fuller's London Pride, Batemans XB and Stowford Press Cider

This 17C redbrick inn is situated right opposite the church. It's lovely on a July day, when those in the know find a white metal table out in the garden, but the bar is also most inviting with a warm log fire, deep purple décor and black timbers - settle down on mahogany chairs, stools or even a small sofa. The area at the side – the old darts room – now looks rather contemporary, and minimalist, too, with just four tables. Menus go across the board from traditional to modern, light to substantial. Alternatively, a conservatory restaurant, which overlooks the garden, offers a fine choice of fish from an altogether more serious selection. Best produce is paramount. Pleasant bedrooms, in former stables, are individually styled and carefully furnished.

Food serving times:
Monday-Saturday:
    12pm-2.30pm, 7pm-9.30pm
Sunday: 12pm-2.30pm
Closed 27-30 December
(bar lunch Saturday)
Prices:
Meals: 14.95/22.00 and a la carte 19.70/27.95
9 rooms : 53.00/78.00

6.5mi South of Bedford by A6.
Near All Saints Church. Parking

Typical Dishes

Smoked chicken and mango terrine

Chargrilled tuna steak

Dark chocolate Marquise cake

Milton Bryan

002 **The Red Lion**

Toddington Rd, Milton Bryan MK17 9HS

Tel.: (01525) 210044 - Fax: (01525) 211564

    VISA **MC**

Greene King IPA, Abbot, Old Speckled Hen and 1 guest ale

You can't miss this place in early summer, when the white-gabled, redbrick pub is polka-dotted with a truly extravagant show of overflowing hanging baskets: the old English pub in Glorious Technicolor. Inside, the wood-floored, bare-brick public bar offers a tasty lunch menu of all-time pub favourites, but there's greater seasonal variety in the more formal restaurant, the friendly tenants gladly going the extra mile to find good ingredients for their Thai fishcakes, pheasant confit and a crisp and creamy leek and goat's cheese tart. For friendly neighbourhood atmosphere, it takes some beating, and there's real warmth and thoughtfulness to the service, too.

Food serving times:
Monday-Saturday:
  12pm-2.30pm, 7pm-9.30pm
Sunday: 12pm-2.30pm
Closed 25-26 December
Prices:
Meals: a la carte 17.20/28.30

Typical Dishes

Fried whitebait, lemon and garlic

Rump of lamb, spiced couscous

Lemon tart

Milton Bryan is South of Woburn by A4012. Parking

Old Warden

003 ## Hare & Hounds

Nr Biggleswade, Old Warden SG18 9HQ
Tel.: (01767) 627225 - Fax: (01767) 627029

 VISA **MC** JCB

Eagle IPA, Charles Wells Bombardier and 1 guest ale

Such a sincerely friendly welcome at the bar is always a good sign: you'd be welcome to stop here for a pint, but such enjoyable and fairly-priced food is just too good to miss. Three chic but cosy country dining rooms, newly refurbished in tweeds, floral patterns and soft autumnal colours, are an appropriate setting for rustic cooking with a good modern and traditional balance. Plentiful and full-flavoured dishes come and go – it all depends on the season and a handful of trusted local suppliers – but appealing blackboard specials supplement the menu: try a rich, crisp spiced duck confit with lentils and bacon or the Shuttleworth pork plate of fillet, belly and sausage. It's the staff who really make the difference, though: discreetly attentive and genuinely enthusiastic about the dishes they serve.

Food serving times:
Tuesday-Saturday:
  12pm-2pm, 6.30pm-9.30pm
Sunday: 12pm-2pm
Open Bank Holiday Mondays
Prices:
Meals: 20.00/25.00

Typical Dishes

Deep fried tiger prawns
Pan fried pigeon breast
Lemon tart

3.5mi West of Biggleswade by A6001 off B658. Parking

Shefford

004 **The Black Horse**
Ireland, Shefford SG17 5QL
Tel.: (01462) 811398 - Fax: (01462) 817238
e-mail: blackhorse@irelanduk.freeserve.co.uk

Fuller's London Pride, Bass and an IPA

You'd be hard put to find fault with this 17C white pub not far from the A1. For starters, it boasts a charming garden with bench seats and stylish patio, while inside the feel is no less comfortably rustic. The front bar's old and new beams are warmly off set by polished tables; an adjacent dining room boasts a stylish country feel. Main dining is at the rear in a 21C extension: again, very cool and contemporary, with an African theme predominating. The same menu is served throughout and changes every three months. Well-executed, modern dishes with a classic base ensure the Black Horse retains a serious dining tag. Two bedrooms, neat, up-to-date and compact, guarantee the satisfaction factor remains high.

Food serving times:
Monday-Saturday:
 12pm-2.30pm, 6.30pm-10pm
Sunday: 12pm-2.30pm
Closed 25-26 December and
1 January
Prices:
Meals: a la carte 22.95/26.95
🛏 **2 rooms :** 55.00

Typical Dishes

Field mushrooms, sun blushed tomato

Veal with Stilton mash and red wine jus

Amaretto cheesecake

1.75mi Northwest by B658 and Ireland rd.
Parking

Woburn

005 The Birch

20 Newport Rd, Woburn MK17 9HX
Tel.: (01525) 290295 - Fax: (01525) 290899

Adnams ales, Fuller's London Pride

This established dining pub, like much else in Woburn, sits confidently in the superior category. Locals and visitors mingle contentedly in an establishment that offers a very agreeable ambience, from the pleasant outside decking terrace to the stylish mix of furnishings within; these include mosaic and pine tables and rugs on the floors. At the back, the dining area covers two levels, not counting the conservatory extension: Mediterranean style décor gels comfortably with wooden chairs and tables. All eyes are on an open kitchen in the corner, where the satisfying modern dishes, particularly meat and fish, are conjured up from the grill. An interesting evening a la carte menu is balanced with lighter lunchtime dishes.

Food serving times:
Monday-Saturday:
12pm-2.30pm, 6.15pm-10pm
Sunday: 12pm-2.30pm
Closed 25-26 December and 1 January
(booking essential)
Prices:
Meals: a la carte 26.95/35.95

Typical Dishes

Pigeon Wellington

Cajun spiced catfish

Mango and passionfruit roulade

0.5mi North on A5130.
Parking

Broughton

006 The Crown

Bridge Rd, Broughton PE28 3 AY

Tel.: (01487) 824428 - Fax: (01487) 824428
e-mail: simon@thecrownbrougton.co.uk - Website: www.thecrownbroughton.co.uk

Elgoods Black Dog, Greene King IPA, City of Cambridge Hobson's Choice

This soft-hued brick pub nestles in the archetypal English country village scenario: next to the church, surrounded on all sides by rustic repose. Owned by the village, it boasts a large lawned garden and paved terrace with benches. Inside, the 21C has come calling: it's essentially one room divided by a fireplace, with modern tiled floor, pine furniture, bare tables and farmhouse chairs. The clean, uncluttered ambience is enhanced with bright bay windows, mustard walls and golden wood beams which create a sunny, open feel. Menus – which change monthly and feature blackboard specials at lunch and dinner – are keenly priced and modern with a classic French base.

Food serving times:
Wednesday-Sunday:
    12pm-2pm, 6.30pm-9pm
Prices:
Meals: a la carte 18.00/25.00

Typical Dishes

Venison carpaccio

Chicken, girolles and red wine

Lemon and sultana cheesecake

6mi Northeast of Huntingdon by B1514 off A141.
Opposite the village church. Parking

Fowlmere

007 The Chequers

High Street, Fowlmere SG8 7SR
Tel.: (01763) 208369 - Fax: (01763) 208944

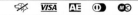

VISA AE ⦿ ⓜⓒ

No real ales offered

There's history at every turn in this fascinating 16C inn, built into the timbers and displayed on the walls: Spitfires and Mustangs are frozen in time in old photographs of Fowlsmere airfield and even the colours of the sign comemmorate the pub's finest hour, mirroring the chequerboard insignia of the British and American fighter squadrons who made this their local during the Second World War. Sound, satisfying cooking on a traditional base includes Dover sole, a hearty smoked haddock, cheese and tomato bake and homemade date pudding; you can eat in the conservatory, overlooking the garden, in the beamed and galleried dining room or in the bar itself. After dinner, settle down by the fire and try one – or more – of the thirty malt whiskies: the long-standing owners will be happy to recommend a personal favourite.

Food serving times:
Monday-Sunday:
    12pm-2pm, 7pm-9.30pm
Closed 25 December
Prices:
Meals: a la carte 13.70/38.00

Off B1368. Parking

Typical Dishes

King prawns, Thai sauce

Seafood in orange and pepper sauce

Hot date sponge

Hemingford Grey

008 The Cock

47, High St, Hemingford Grey PE28 9BJ
Tel.: (01480) 463609 - Fax: (01480) 461747
e-mail: info@cambscuisine.com - Website: www.cambscuisine.com

Woodfordes Wherry, Elgoods Black Dog Mild, City of Cambridge Hobson's Choice, JHB Oakham Ale

This lovely 17C village pub has been stripped back to basics by its owners, and given a new lease of life in the process. Locals flock to the pubby part, which revels in its original simplicity. A separate room, it specialises in real ale, and has won several accolades in this department. Don't expect food at the bar: if you're here to satisfy an appetite rather than slake your thirst, step into the main dining area, spacious and soft-toned with wooden floors and a comfy, traditional tables and chairs. A wood burning stove crackles, and saleable oil paintings might tempt you into a purchase. The menu is individual and offers a good choice of British and European dishes, on top of a well-priced light lunch selection. Specialities are fresh fish blackboard specials, and the hallmark sausage board.

Food serving times:
Monday-Saturday:
  12pm-2.30pm, 7pm-9.30pm
Sunday: 12pm-2.30pm,
             6.30pm-8.30pm

Closed 25 December

Prices:
Meals: 11.95 and a la carte 19.50/29.90

Typical Dishes

Chicken and red pepper terrine

Aberdeen Angus fillet, cheddar mash

Ginger crème caramel

5mi South East of Huntingdon by A1198 off A14. Parking

23

Horningsea

009 Crown and Punchbowl

High St, Horningsea CB5 9JG

Tel.: (01223) 860643 - Fax: (01223) 441814
e-mail: info@cambscuisine.com - Website: 222.cambscuisine.com

 VISA **AE** **M⊙**

 City of Cambridge Hobsons Choice

When is a pub not a pub? Answer: when it comes in the guise of the Crown & Punchbowl. This marriage of two buildings, one 17C, the other 19C, looks and feels like a pub, but doesn't actually have a bar, so anyone revisiting from 200 years ago would wonder what had happened to the village inn. It's certainly been given a modern makeover: wooden floors, farmhouse tables and chairs, rattan seats, neutral décor, contemporary lighting. Lovely old beams will take you back, though. Menus are a mixture of traditional, modern and international; favourite features include the sausage mix and match board and fresh fish blackboard. Clean, modern bedrooms keep the modish feel intact.

Food serving times:
Monday-Thursday:
 12pm-2.30pm, 6.30pm-9pm
Friday-Saturday:
 12pm-2.30pm, 6.30pm-9.30pm
Sunday: 12pm-2.30pm
Closed 25 December and dinner Bank Holidays
Prices:
Meals: 15.95 (fixed price lunch) and a la carte 15.95/35.95
🛏 **5 rooms :** 49.95/69.95

Typical Dishes

Prawn and mushroom puff pastry parcel

Lamb with rosemary risotto

Sticky toffee pudding

4mi Northeast of Cambridge by A1303 and B1047 on Horningsea road. Parking

Keyston

010 **The Pheasant**

Keyston, Village Loop Rd PE28 0RE

Tel.: (01832) 710241 - Fax: (01832) 710340
Website: www.huntsbridge.co.uk

Adnams Best and 2 guest ales

A tip for drivers tearing along the A14 on the Cambridgeshire and Northamptonshire borders: turn off at Keyston and sample a taste of this gloriously thatched inn, regularly awarded a Michelin Bib Gourmand. A dining pub writ large, The Pheasant consistently serves a range of good value, eclectic dishes in three agreeable dining areas. Regulars mingle in the airy, timbered bar with its open fire, muskets on the wall and well-spaced wooden tables, but if the going gets too busy there, then the rear section – decorated with a mix of pictures and prints - is just as pleasant a place to eat. Interesting, modern a la carte menus with international influences are never less than accomplished and offer plenty of balanced flavour. Helpful, efficient service is a given wherever you decide to eat.

Food serving times:
Monday-Sunday:
    12pm-2pm, 6.30pm-9.30pm
(booking essential)
Prices:
Meals: a la carte 20.00/30.00

Typical Dishes

Smoked haddock, potato salad

Pork hock, potato and apple cake

Chocolate tart

3.5mi Southeast of Thrapston by A14 on B663.
Parking

Madingley

011 Three Horseshoes

High St, Madingley CB3 8AB
Tel.: (01954) 210221 - Fax: (01954) 212043
Website: www.huntsbridge.com

Adnams Best and 2 guest ales

This picture-perfect thatched pub is an ideal bolt-hole for visitors slightly overwhelmed by tourist numbers in Cambridge. It's located in a village just to the west of the city, and presents an elegant, centuries-old exterior to the world: it used to be the local smithy. The interior, though, comes right up to date. There's a stylish, airy ambience, attributable in part to the pale floorboards, modern log fire and sage green walls, though the alert service has something to do with it too. Eat in the bar - which does a well-priced, short grill menu - or in the smartly set conservatory at the back. It has painted chairs and stylish cloth-clad tables, and menus are innovative, full of interesting combinations.

Food serving times:
Monday-Sunday:
  12pm-2pm, 6.30pm-9.30pm
Prices:
Meals: a la carte 25.00/35.00

Typical Dishes

Crab salad

Salmon with barley couscous

Caramelised lemon tart

4.5mi West of Cambridge by A1303. Parking

Spaldwick

012 The George

5, High St, Spaldwick PE28 0TD
Tel.: (01480) 890293 - Fax: (01480) 896847

🍷 ✂ 🚭 **VISA** Ⓜ©

Fuller's London Pride, Adnams Broadside, Theakstons Old Peculier

This early 16C inn is defined on the exterior by its characterful, crooked appearance, but inside refurbishment has been going on apace, and the renovated airy interior now has a bold, clean and uncluttered contemporary look. Lilac and aubergine walls blend with exposed black beams, tiled and wood floors, scrubbed wood tables, and leather armchairs around a lovely fireplace, with the inn's history framed above. The restaurant – also spacious – blends old ceiling timbers with pink hued leather banquettes and rich oil paintings: a stylish statement indeed. Menus here are modern European with solid British classics: sausage and mash, cod and chips, garlic and chilli prawns, fish soup. You can also take your pick from the blackboard.

Food serving times:
Monday-Sunday:
    12pm-3pm, 6pm-9.30pm
Prices:
Meals: a la carte 18.00/40.00

Typical Dishes

Pork belly and black pudding salad

Duck confit, lavender jus

Warm chocolate mousse

7.5mi West of Huntingdon by A141 off A14. Parking

Stilton

013 ## Village Bar (at Bell Inn)

Great North Rd, Stilton PE7 3RA
Tel.: (01733) 241066 - Fax: (01733) 245173

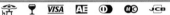

JHB Bitter, Greene King Abbot Ale, Fuller's London Pride, Adnams Best

You know you're in for a cheery experience the moment you come upon this part 16C inn with garden: its swinging red bell pub sign almost beckons you in off the street. The separate Village Bar is the heart and soul of the place, charmingly rustic in its appeal: rough stone walls, flag flooring, large wooden tables with benches and a mix of chairs. Local memorabilia all adds to the characterful mix. It shares its menu with the adjoining Courtyard bar. Expect robust cooking, international influences embellishing a firm traditional base. Hearty portions are guaranteed, and Stilton cheese turns up in soups, dumplings, quiche and dressings. Bedrooms are in the Bell Inn proper: some are deluxe, all are individually styled and well kept.

Food serving times:
Monday-Sunday:
 12pm-2pm, 6.30pm-9.30pm
Closed 25 December
Prices:
Meals: 14.95/24.95 and a la carte 15.00/25.00

Typical Dishes

Scallops, crab and crevettes

Mixed game pie

Stilton with warm plum bread

In centre of village.
Parking

Sutton Gault

014 **Anchor Inn**

Sutton Gault CB6 2BD

Tel.: (01353) 778537 - Fax: (01353) 776180
e-mail: anchorinn@btconnect.com - Website: www.anchor-inn-restaurant.co.uk

City of Cambridge Hobson's Choice, Fenland St Audrey's Ale

Standing by the bridge over the New Bedford River, this lovely, ever-popular inn can claim to be as old as the Levels landscape itself: the story goes that it was built to house Vermuyden's navvies, who ditched and drained the Cambridgeshire marshes back in the 1650s. Today, gas lamps and open fires light several charming little rooms, and a strong local reputation rests on the tasty cooking. Blackboard specials have a particularly seasonal flavour and the Modern British repertoire finds room for some ambitious Mediterranean touches: typical dishes include Cromer crab, halibut with spinach and artichoke risotto, and sticky toffee pudding with rum and raisin ice cream. Conscientious and personable staff certainly know their regulars, but see to it that everyone is well looked-after.

Food serving times:
Monday-Friday:
12pm-2pm, 7pm-9pm
Saturday: 12pm-2pm,
6.30pm-9.30pm
Sunday: 12pm-2pm,
7pm-9pm
Closed 26 December
(fixed price lunch only
Sunday)
Prices:
Meals: 19.95 and a la carte
22.00/28.00
2 rooms : 50.00/110.00

Typical Dishes

Dates in bacon, mustard cream sauce

Calves liver, Bayonne ham, cider

Banana tarte Tatin

Off B1381; follow signs to Sutton Gault from Sutton village. Pub is near the New Bedford River. Parking

Blackmore

015 **Leather Bottle**

The Green, Blackmore CM4 0RL

Tel.: (01277) 823538
Website: www.theleatherbottle.net

 VISA **MC**

Ridleys IPA, Adnams, Buntingford Strisselspalt, Wissey Valley Golden Rivet

A pleasant, well-run place and something of a family enterprise, the Leather Bottle has that confidence-inspiring neighbourhood feel to it: the guest beer mats decorating the walls of the little public bar will be invitation enough to any real ale converts and, in these welcoming surroundings, even sceptics might be tempted to try a half. Diners arriving in good time can choose between a table in the simply styled conservatory overlooking the garden or near the wood burner in the front bar, where a frequently changing menu blends traditional British and eclectic Mediterranean styles, with satisfying results: simple snacks and a handful of daily specials lend a touch of variety. Smooth but unpretentious service.

Food serving times:
Monday-Saturday:
　　　12pm-2pm, 7pm-9pm
Sunday:　　　12pm-2pm
Closed 26 December and 1 January
Prices:
Meals: a la carte 17.40/25.00

Typical Dishes

Wild mushrooms, poached egg

Salmon fishcakes

Bread and butter pudding

2.75mi Southeast of High Ongar by A414.
Parking in front of the pub

Clavering

016 **Cricketers**

Clavering CB11 4QT

Tel.: (01799) 550442 - Fax: (01799) 550882
e-mail: cricketers@lineone.net - Website: www.thecricketers.co.uk

Adnams Broadside, Tetleys

How many landlords could get Jamie Oliver to do the washing-up for pocket money? Mr and Mrs Oliver have been running this well-established local since The Naked Chef was in short trousers and not much has changed over the years: old beams, velour seats, a few newspaper cuttings and a lot of satisfied regulars. Gastro-pilgrims expecting an audioguide and photos of Jamie's dad inventing the Botham Burger will just have to like it for what it is, though that's easily done, and a nicely balanced menu is bound to put a smile on their faces – dishes range from dependable classics to a few recipes from the local hero. If you'd like to stay the night, the bedrooms in the pavilion are traditionally styled and those in the courtyard are more modern.

Food serving times:
Monday-Sunday:
    12pm-2pm, 7pm-10pm
Closed 25-26 December
Prices:
Meals: 26.00 (fixed price dinner) and a la carte 20.00/26.00
🛏 **14 rooms :** 70.00/100.00

Typical Dishes

Chicken and duck terrine

Pheasant with chestnuts and bacon

Peaches, mascarpone

On the B1038. Parking

Dedham

017 The Sun Inn

High St, Dedham CO7 6DF

Tel.: (01206) 323351 - Fax: (01206) 323964
e-mail: info@thesuninndedham.com - Website: www.thesuninndedham.com

⸰⸰room **VISA** **MC**

Adnams Broadside, Earl Soham Victoria, Arizona Phoenix, Crouch Vale Gold, St Peters Organic Ale

O pposite its contemporary, the 15C village church, this handsome inn is an understated blend of tradition and up-to-date style; despite recent renovations, it still feels surprisingly unspoilt. Behind a suitably cheery sunshine-yellow façade, polished period oak and bright modern bouquets fill the spacious front and back rooms. Pick a table, then choose from an affordable, well-sourced menu which changes day by day, adopting an original approach to Italian, Spanish and Maghreb traditions; antipasti platters are good for sharing, but you may find it hard to part with a forkful of chicken tagine, Tuscan sausage on spicy black beans or light and juicy cannellini and sage risotto. Thoughtfully appointed modern rooms include one with a four-poster bed. Walks up to the River Stour and Constable's beloved Flatford start right outside the door.

Food serving times:
Monday-Friday:
 12pm-2.30pm, 7pm-9.30pm
Saturday: 12pm-3pm, 7pm-10pm
Sunday : 12pm-3pm
Closed 25-26 December and 31 December
Prices:
Meals: a la carte 18.50/25.00
🛏 **4 rooms :** 55.00/110.00

Typical Dishes

Mushrooms, baby beetroot

Pork chop, salsa verde

Lemon and lime tart

In the centre of the village opposite the church. Parking

Earls Colne

018 Carved Angel

Upper Holt Street, Earls Colne CO6 2PG

Tel.: (01787) 222330 - Fax: (01787) 220013
e-mail: dining@carvedangel.com - Website: www.carvedangel.com

 ☂ ♀ ✗ **VISA** ⓜⓒ

Greene King IPA, Adnams Bitter and guest beers from Mighty Oak

Relaxed and full of character, this 15C inn has been stylishly updated to the last detail: a bright conservatory extention, subtle lighting, sprays of flowers, foodie pictures on the sage green walls and strings of little blackboard menu plaquettes hanging down from the beamed ceiling. These offer plenty of choice, detailing neatly presented modern gastropub standards and traditional dishes, some with a subtle continental influence – a typical selection might well include lamb chops, smoked haddock rarebit, roast poussin with a watercress sauce, crispy duck spring roll and pistachio crème brûlée. Service is unobtrusive and pleasant, but even at quieter times they stick rigidly to their rule about ordering everything from the bar.

Food serving times:
Monday-Friday:
　　　12pm-2pm, 7pm-9pm
Saturday:　12pm-2.30pm,
　　　　　7pm-10pm
Sunday:　12pm-2.30pm,
　　　　　7pm-9pm

Prices:
Meals: 9.95 and a la carte 15.00/25.00

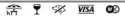

Typical Dishes

Goats cheese brûlée

Lamb rump, sauteed spinach

Chocolate tart, Guinness ice cream

On sharp bend just outside of the town. Parking

Fuller Street

019 ## Square & Compasses

Fuller Street CM3 2BB

Tel.: (01245) 361477

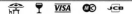

Ridleys IPA, Nethergate Suffolk County

For those who like their pubs with plenty of character, this is an absolute gem. Bringing a little piece of Cold Comfort Farm eccentricity to the wilds of Essex, a bizarre collection of rural odds and ends includes a stuffed owl, old riding tackle, in fact, almost everything but a square and compasses. Ancient farm implements hang from the walls and the photo of a farmer who used them also tells a story. It could so easily feel unnerving or "over-local", but it turns out to be welcoming and extremely cosy, thanks in part to the polite staff behind the bar. A blackboard and a printed menu list lots of dishes available in either starter or large size portions, with local game and traditional British recipes well represented; a simpler menu on Sunday evenings concentrates on pies and quiches.

Food serving times:
Tuesday-Sunday:
12pm-2.30pm, 7pm-9.30pm
Open Bank Holiday Mondays
Prices:
Meals: a la carte 14.00/27.50

Typical Dishes

Coconut chilli prawns

Ribeye steak with Stilton

Lemon curd cheesecake

Between Chelmsford and Braintree off A131.
Parking

Great Yeldham

020 White Hart

Poole St, Great Yeldham CO9 4HJ

Tel.: (01787) 237250 - Fax: (01787) 238044

e-mail: reservations@whitehartyeldham.co.uk - Website: www.whitehartyeldam.co.uk

      VISA **AE** **D** **MC**

Adnams and various guest ales

You'd have difficulty missing this prominent, Grade I listed pub, and you wouldn't want to – its imposing black and white timbers are an outward sign of 16C glories within. Spacious areas proudly display timbers, mighty log-filled inglenooks, brick walls and flagstone floors. The overall effect is, quite simply, an ultra-relaxing country pub. You can dine in traditional surroundings – at the bar, in the lawned garden or served by waiters in bow-ties in the sparklingly smart restaurant – but you'll eat accomplished and very tasty modern dishes with global coverage, backed up by bold British staples: the range goes from steamed steak and kidney pie to mouth-watering Thai curry.

Food serving times:
Monday-Sunday:
12pm-2pm, 6.30pm-9.30pm
Prices:
Meals: 14.50 and a la carte
20.00/30.00

Typical Dishes

Swordfish, chilli and mango salsa

Guinea fowl, prune and apricot farce

Baileys crème brûlée

6mi Northwest of Halstead by A1124 on A1017. On the banks of the River Colne. Parking

High Ongar

021 ## The Wheatsheaf

King St, High Ongar CM5 9NS
Tel.: (01277) 822220 - Fax: (01277) 822441

Greene King IPA

Pretty and well-restored it may be, but The Wheatsheaf wouldn't be half the place it is without its hard-working staff; cordial, well-informed and eager to please, but in a very genuine, down-to-earth way. They serve four rooms – decorated with ornaments, bric-a-brac and floral fabrics – surrounding a central bar, but if you feel like an open-air summer lunch, ask them if there's a free table in the garden. A classically based British menu, notable for its well-combined but nicely defined flavours, varies from one day to the next, but past dishes have included a rich and fluffy goat's chees and pecan soufflée, cod with a cheese and bacon crumble crust and rhubarb jelly and ice cream, with caramelised oranges for a zingy foil.

Food serving times:
Tuesday-Friday:
12pm-1.45pm,
6.30pm-8.45pm
Saturday: 6.30pm-9.30pm
Sunday: 12pm-3pm
Closed from 26 December for 2 weeks and 15-22 June (booking essential)
Prices:
Meals: a la carte 23.00/35.00

Typical Dishes

Scallops, guacamole and bacon

Roast guinea fowl, honey and garlic

Banoffee crumble tart

2mi East by A414 on Blackmore road. Parking

Horndon-on-the-Hill

022 Bell Inn

High Rd, Horndon-on-the-Hill SS17 8LD

Tel.: (01375) 642463 - Fax: (01375) 361611
e-mail: info@bell-inn.co.uk - Website: www.bell-inn.co.uk

 Greene King IPA, Bass, Crouchvale Brewers Gold, Adnams Broadside, Archers Golden

Monkfish with veal and snail fritters, ox cheek ravioli with crab sauté and truffle froth: there's no doubting the high culinary ambition behind The Bell's daily-changing modern European menu. At its most complex, the cooking can seem a little overwrought, but there's no denying that the extra effort and attention raise simpler dishes – like Caesar salad or ribeye with parsley sauce – comfortably above pub average. The rather serious approach to good eating sits surprisingly well with the comfy, traditional décor and a long family history, and this characterful and well-established place is efficient, upbeat and busy, particularly at lunchtime.

Food serving times:
Monday-Sunday:
12pm-1.45pm, 7pm-9.45pm
Closed for food 25-26 December and Bank Holidays
Prices:
Meals: a la carte 18.50/26.00
🛏 **5 rooms :** 85.00
☕ 9.00

Typical Dishes

Lobster risotto
Lambs liver with meatballs
Liquorice jelly and sherbet

3mi Northeast of Grays by A1013 off A13.
Parking

Mistley

023 ## The Mistley Thorn

High Street, Mistley CO11 1HE

Tel.: (01206) 392821 - Fax: (01206) 390122
e-mail: info@mistleythorn.co.uk - Website: www.mistleythorn.com

Adnams, Greene King IPA, St Peters Organic

Though the exceptionally likeable young staff are only too happy for people to drop in for a drink – and maybe a plate of oysters – you're missing a real treat if you don't stay for dinner in the strikingly contemporary setting of this restyled Georgian pub. Well-composed menus of carefully presented cooking – with conspicuous depth and freshness of flavour – make a strong case for sourcing imaginatively, locally and organically, and include dishes like East Anglian asparagus, shrimp and herb mousse, tender lamb chops on a borlotti and artichoke stew, and a light Chez Panisse chocolate cake: the owner's cookery classes in "the Mistley Kitchen" reveal some, but not all of the secrets. Of the five bedrooms, two front-facing ones look out towards the Stour.

Food serving times:
Monday-Sunday:
12pm-2.30pm,
6.30pm-9.30pm
Closed 25 December
Prices:
Meals: 12.95 and a la carte
15.50/22.50
5 rooms : 60.00/87.00

On B1352.
Not far from Mistley Towers. Parking

Typical Dishes

Smoked salmon, mustard fennel sauce

Seafood stew

Jack Daniels pecan tart

Aldbury

024 **Valiant Trooper**

Trooper Rd, Aldbury HP23 5RW

Tel.: (01442) 851203 - Fax: (01442) 851071

 VISA **M©**

 A selection of up to 5 real ales offered

This is another traditional pub that benefits from its close proximity to the Ridgeway Path, so a healthy gathering of walkers can be guaranteed at most times. Even closer than the Ridgeway is the local duck pond; the pub's red, black and white bulk is a short walk away. The rustic bar boasts not only a real fire but also a welcoming wood burner; quarry tiled floors and scrubbed tables and chairs enhance the effect. Dining happens in an area at the back, which has seen a modicum of modernisation: the newer feel is accentuated by minimalist décor. Blackboard plaques announce traditional menus with some international influence, at a reasonable price. There's a good selection of lighter dishes, too: many a rambler has felt the benefit of one of the pub's hearty jacket potatoes.

Food serving times:
Monday-Saturday:
  12pm-2pm, 6.30pm-9.15pm
Sunday: 12pm-2.30pm
Closed 25 December
Prices:
Meals: a la carte 17.00/21.00

In centre of village.
Parking

Typical Dishes

Crab and crayfish cocktail

Pork with aubergine and mushroom

Brandy chocolate torte

Ardeley

025 **The Jolly Waggoner**

Ardeley SG2 7AH

Tel.: (01438) 861350

 VISA

 Green King IPA

A lovely, welcoming inn – as pretty and well cared-for as Ardeley itself – which has been keeping the village fed and watered for years; the trim, uncluttered but still pleasantly cosy feel of the place seems to have spread through from the old Rose Cottage next door, now part of the pub restaurant. It's easy to see why it's a neighbourhood favourite: the wholesome, freshly sourced meals are familiar and dependable; not an eye-opening gastronomic statement, but a natural choice for an easy midweek supper or a leisurely Saturday lunch with beers, friends and a big spread of the weekend papers. Cheery bar staff keep things ticking over, pointing out the daily specials and keeping up a steady chat with the regulars.

Food serving times:
Tuesday-Saturday:
  12pm-2pm, 6.30pm-9.30pm
Sunday: 12pm-2pm
Open Bank Holiday Mondays
Prices:
Meals: a la carte 13.25/29.25

Typical Dishes

Fresh dressed crab

Monkfish, cheese and tomato sauce

Chocolate truffle torte

1.5mi South of Cottered by B1037. Parking

Cottered

027 **The Bull**

Cottered SG9 9QP
Tel.: (01763) 281243

   VISA   M©

Greene King IPA and Abbot Ale

In a pretty village blighted by a busy A road, you need somewhere to keep your spirits up. The Bull is that place: a well looked-after neighbourhood pub in the old tradition that's genuinely eager to please and worth a visit for its understated friendliness. If you're stopping by at lunchtime, don't expect anything more elaborate than blue cheese and celery soup, baked potatoes, plates of carved ham or pork and leek sausages – good "beer-friendly" pub meals, in other words. Dinner, though, sees the addition of tasty and sustaining seasonal British dishes like steak, Stilton and Guinness pie or rack of lamb, plus a couple of daily specials. If The Bull is your kind of place, you'll probably like their sister pub, the Jolly Waggoner, just down the road in Ardeley.

Food serving times:
Monday-Sunday:
   12pm-2pm, 6.30pm-9.30pm
Closed Tuesday dinner
Prices:
Meals: a la carte 20.00/25.00

Typical Dishes

Smoked salmon and prawn parcels

Roast beef, bacon, Stilton and Madeira

Brandy bread pudding

On A507.
Parking at the front of the pub

Frithsden

028 The Alford Arms

Frithsden HP1 3DD

Tel.: (01442) 864480 - Fax: (01442) 876893
e-mail: info@alfordarms.co.uk

   VISA AE MC

Marstons Pedigree, Flowers Original, Brakspear, Morrell's Oxford Blue

The quiet hamlet of Frithsden has a frequent tendency to see its population inflate like the hot-air balloons floating over its beautiful surrounding countryside. This is due in part to the popularity of this attractive brick pub, which is based quite close to the Ridgeway Path and regularly offers pints, sustenance and a comfy seat to walkers and saddle-sore cyclists. It's a small and stylish inn, and a good neighbourhood feel pervades the place with a confident, modern gastropub style much in evidence. There's a "free-for-all" drinking area at the front bar, but tables are reserved in the rear dining area. Well-priced menus change seasonally, and the fresh ingredients are evident in a tasty, varied dining pub selection.

Food serving times:
Monday-Saturday:
    12pm-2.30pm, 7pm-10pm
Sunday: 12pm-3pm,
                        7pm-10pm
Closed 25-26 December
Prices:
Meals: a la carte 17.50/26.25

Typical Dishes

Smoked bacon, bubble and squeak

Cod on saffron mash

Rocky road chocolate bar

4.5mi Northwest of Hemel Hempstead by A4146.
By the village green. Parking

Hertford

026 The Hillside

45, Port Hill, Bengeo, Hertford SG14 3EP

Tel.: (01992) 554556 - Fax: (01992) 583709
e-mail: justine624@hotmail.com - Website: www.thehillside.co.uk

      VISA AE ⓪ Ⓜ️Ⓒ JCB

Fuller's London Pride

Put on the brakes as you head out of Hertford and pay a visit to this cosy, intimate, recently refurbished 17C pub, nestling contentedly – as its name suggests – on a hillside. The small beamed bar with comfy leather sofa is a charming haven for drinkers; for diners, there's a sunny, surprisingly airy restaurant with leather banquettes and bare tables decorated with bright flowers. Paintings – for sale – brighten the walls. Contemplate what takes your fancy while waiting for chef's cheery wife to serve a modern menu of brasserie dishes with pronounced global reach alongside more traditional staples. There's also an interesting little organic deli and farm shop next door.

Food serving times:
Monday-Sunday:
 12pm-2.30pm, 6.30pm-10pm
Prices:
Meals: a la carte 25.00/40.00

Typical Dishes

Spiced crab mayonnaise

Breast of duck, braised cabbage

Chocolate fondant

North 0.25mi on B158. Parking

Reed

029 The Cabinet at Reed

High St., Reed SG8 8AH

Tel.: (01763) 848366 - Fax: (01763) 849407
e-mail: thecabinet@btopenworld.com - Website: www.thecabinetinn.co.uk

🍷 🖊 ✂ **VISA** **AE** **MC**

Greene King IPA, Adnams, Ruddles, Nethergate Augustinian

This pretty 16C clapboard inn suits Reed to perfection, but since its refurbishment it's more than just a village pub in the traditional sense. So while the bar proper still has all the charm of a rustic local, with a little snug to one side, the real focal point is the quietly chic, contemporary dining room beyond, with elegant tables featuring outsize glassware – the red wine glasses actually hold a whole bottle, although that's not really the idea. An enthusiast and populariser to the core, the owner, Paul Bloxham, makes a natural TV chef, sometimes continuing the performance in his demonstration kitchen on the terrace: his interesting, upmarket Modern British menu would not look out of place in a West End restaurant. Jazz Brunch gets summer Sundays off to a leisurely, chilled-out start.

Food serving times:
Tuesday-Saturday:
    12pm-3pm, 6pm-11pm
Sunday: 12pm-3pm
Closed 25-26 December
Prices:
Meals: 19.95 and a la carte 24.00/39.00

3mi South of Royston, just off the A10 London to Cambridge road. Parking

Typical Dishes

Ham hock terrine

John Dory with Israeli couscous

Pineapple tarte Tatin, banana ice cream

Ware

030 Jacoby's

Churchgate House, 15 West St, Ware SG12 9EE

Tel.: (01920) 469181 - Fax: (01920) 469182
e-mail: info@jacobys.co.uk - Website: www.jacobys.co.uk

    VISA **AE** **MC**

 No real ales offered

Carefully renovated into a modern bar and restaurant, this Grade II listed timber framed house, dating back to the late 15C, boasts tremendous history and character: in its time, it's been an inn, a bakery and maltings and even a motorcycle repair shop. It stands opposite St Mary's church; in the summer, you'll want to look for a place on the pleasant pavement terrace which faces the square. The stylish front bar has leather armchairs and sets a buzzy tone for the rest of the place. Dining is on two levels: go upstairs for the more intimate tables. Menus change frequently, providing well-executed, mix and match options: good British classics with strong Mediterranean influences alongside dishes with a wider global reach. Service is prompt, young and keen; booking's advisable at weekends.

Food serving times:
Monday-Saturday:
    12pm-3pm, 6pm-9.30pm
Closed 25 December-2 January
Closed Monday lunch
Prices:
Meals: a la carte 23.00/34.00

Typical Dishes

Leek and potato soup

Seared tuna steak, chilli salsa

Apple and toffee crumble tart

In the town centre, just off the High St. Public car park opposite

Bawburgh

031 Kings Head

Harts Lane, Bawburgh NR9 3LS

Tel.: (01603) 744977 - Fax: (01603) 744990
e-mail: anton@kingshead-bawburgh.co.uk - Website: www.kingshead-bawburgh.co.uk

     VISA **AE** **MC** **JCB**

 Adnams, Woodfordes Wherry, Greene King IPA and guest beers

Only a short drive out of Norwich but already well into the countryside, this traditional place has plumped for Edward VII as its royal figurehead, the under-represented pub monarch perhaps getting the nod here for his generous appetite and his Sandringham connections. The old bon vivant would be baffled by the fruit machines, but drawn instinctively to the casual but comfortable dining room leading off from one side of the main bar. Here, the menu changes with the seasons: an equal mix of traditional and modern recipes might offer anything from bangers and burgers to potted crab, chicken salsa verde with pasta and peppers or maple and pecan cheesecake. Once the woodburning stove is fired up on winter afternoons, it's also pleasant enough for a quiet pint.

Food serving times:
Monday-Saturday:
  12pm-2pm, 6.30pm-9.30pm
Sunday: 12pm-2pm
Closed dinner 25 December
Prices:
Meals: a la carte 15.00/25.00

Typical Dishes

Roquefort, chicory and pecan salad

Cod with grilled vegetables

Chocolate pot

5mi West of Norwich by B1108.
Parking

Blakeney

032 White Horse

4 High St, Blakeney NR25 7AL

Tel.: (01263) 740574 - Fax: (01263) 741303
e-mail: enquiries@blakeneywhitehorse.co.uk - Website: www.blakeneywhitehorse.co.uk

  rest **VISA** AE M©

Adnams Broadside, Woodfordes Wherry, Nelsons Revenge

Estuary, saltings, quayside, and a gaggle of tourists from the Capital make up much of the character of 21C Blakeney. It's further defined by this popular part-17C pub of flint-and-brick which draws in the locals and weekenders a-plenty. They gather round a split-level bar and sup good real ale at wooden tables, chairs and banquettes – an appealing conservatory provides a smart alternative. Go to the rear, to the former stables, to eat: naturally enough, seafood is the staple here. It's proudly local in nature; particularly worth tucking into is the smoked cod with leek and Parmesan tart, followed by fillet of sea bass with Italian sausage sauce, an unusual but successful addition. For those not climbing back into their 4X4s, there's the option of small, cosy bedrooms.

Food serving times:
Tuesday-Sunday:
    12pm-2pm, 6pm-9pm
Closed 2 weeks mid January
Prices:
Meals: a la carte 17.00/30.00
10 rooms : 40.00/100.00

Typical Dishes

Seared tuna with marinated artichokes

Grilled sea bass, capers and prawns

Iced caramel mousse

Off A149 following signs for the Quay, beside the church.
Parking

East - Norfolk

47

Brancaster Staithe

033 **The White Horse**

Main Rd, Brancaster Staithe PE31 8BY

Tel.: (01485) 210262 - Fax: (01485) 210930
e-mail: reception@whitehorsebrancaster.co.uk - Website: www.whitehorsebrancaster.co.uk

    VISA

 Adnams Best, Regatta, Fuller's London Pride, Woodfordes Wherry

This popular North Norfolk inn is the place to go for views: from the sun deck or the big conservatory there are stunning vistas of the distant tidal marshes that stretch flat as dinner plates to the horizon. Weekenders up from London appreciate the palette here: muted colours with pastel tints. Fresh flowers abound and modern paintings light up the walls. There's a bar area at the front, which is solely for drinkers, with cushioned wicker armchairs and sofas, but the rest of the open-plan interior is set up for dining, and menus are full of tasty local seafood, such as oysters, potted shrimps, cod, crabs and mussels. Norfolk meats also make a appearance. Spacious, uncluttered bedrooms are worth it for the views; the North Norfolk Coast Path meanders along the bottom of the garden.

Food serving times:
Monday-Sunday:
   12pm-2.30pm, 6pm-10pm
Prices:
Meals: a la carte 25.00/28.00
⊨ **15 rooms :** 72.00/132.00

Typical Dishes

Foie gras with quince

Sea trout, broad beans and thyme

Hazelnut and ricotta torte

On A149.
Parking

Burnham Market

034 The Hoste Arms

The Green, Burnham Market PE31 8HD

Tel.: (01328) 738777 - Fax: (01328) 730103
e-mail: reception@hostearms.co.uk - Website: www.hostearms.co.uk

    VISA MC

Greene King IPA, Abbot, Woodfordes Wherry

The popularity of this bright yellow coaching inn has almost come to define the charming north Norfolk town of Burnham Market: set on the picturesque Green, its 17C quirks have been fully restored; in startling contrast, there's an intriguing wing decorated in Zulu style, and a new Moroccan garden terrace. The bar is an invariably bustling place, and the sound of champagne corks popping is not uncommon; you'll find similar levels of volume and bonhomie in the restaurant. The staff respond well to being busy, and are invariably attentive and friendly, with good attention to detail. Menus offer a mix of global styles, with much local produce in evidence, and earn a Michelin Bib Gourmand for their quality and fair prices. There's an excellent wine selection featuring 180 bins.

Food serving times:
Monday-Sunday:
     12pm-2pm, 7pm-9pm
(booking essential)
Prices:
Meals: a la carte 20.00/35.00
36 rooms : 78.00/236.00

Typical Dishes

Scallops, artichoke purée, salad

Sea bass, roast almond pesto

Assiette of desserts

Overlooking the green. Parking

Burnham Thorpe

035 ### The Lord Nelson

Walsingham Rd, Burnham Thorpe PE31 8HL
Tel.: (01328) 738241 - Fax: (01328) 738241
e-mail: enquiries@nelsonslocal.co.uk - Website: www.nelsonslocal.co.uk

      VISA MC JCB

Greene King IPA, Abbot, Woodfordes Wherry, Nelsons Revenge and guest beers

Named in honour of Burnham Thorpe's most illustrious son, and perhaps Britain's first modern celebrity, this 17C inn honours the Victor of the Nile with just enough in the way of pictures and memorabilia: too much swashbuckling nauticalia would clutter up this shipshape little place. Three low-ceilinged parlours, one with a Battle of Trafalgar mural, lead off from a firelit taproom with a tiny cubby-hole of a bar: the landlord opens up the timbered barn, with chunky pine tables and benches, if the pub itself starts to feel overcrowded. Simple, fresh, good-value dishes, both classic and modern, could include grilled red mullet with tapenade or chicken with a red wine and parsley sauce.

Food serving times:
Monday-Saturday:
    12pm-2.30pm, 7pm-9pm
Sunday: 12pm-3pm
Closed dinner 25-26 December, 1 January and Monday October-June except Bank Holidays
Prices:
Meals: a la carte 19.65/25.65

Typical Dishes

Wells crab salad

Steak with whisky and haggis

Lemon tart

2mi South of Burnham Market.
Parking

Coltishall

036 **King's Head**

26 Wroxham Rd, Coltishall NR12 7EA

Tel.: (01603) 737426 - Fax: (01603) 736542

 🍷 ❌ **_VISA_** **AE** **M©**

Adnams Best, Regatta, Broadland Harvest

One of the nicest things about this rather ordinary looking pub in deepest Norfolk is its attractive setting – diners with window tables can look out onto the meandering River Bure. Elsewhere within, a relaxed air pervades. Open fires crackle beneath solid timbers and pieces of fishing and boating memorabilia hang from the ceiling, lending a particularly atmospheric air at night: meals can be ordered in the bar as well as the dining room. Seafood specialities take pride of place with the Norfolk catch freshly served each day - recent recommendations include crispy fried sea bass on a bed of watercress and spinach, or, as an alternative to fish, chef's special lamb served on ratatouille with gnocchi and a rich sauce. Pine fitted bedrooms allow merely the faintest murmur of the Bure.

Food serving times:
Monday-Sunday:
    12pm-2pm, 7pm-9pm
Closed 26 December and 1 January
Prices:
Meals: 9.95 and a la carte 20.00/30.00
🛏 **4 rooms :** 27.00/59.00

Typical Dishes

Herring in red wine and bacon

Fillet of sea bass with scallops

Frangipane torte

7mi North of Norwich on B1150. Parking

Erpingham

037 Saracen's Head

Wolterton, Erpingham NR11 7LX

Tel.: (01263) 768909 - Fax: (01263) 768993
e-mail: saracenshead@wolterton.freeserve.co.uk - Website: www.saracenshead-norfolk.co.uk

 ⊱room 🚭 *VISA* AE MC

🍺 *Adnams Best Bitter, Woodfordes Wherry*

Charmingly faded and quirky by turns, this individualistic 19C former coaching inn is in the middle of nowhere and loses nothing by its isolation. It contains an impressive walled garden and courtyard set back from two busy, bustling bar rooms and a boldly red-painted parlour filled with odd pictures, bric-a-brac and little wooden tables and chairs with plastic tablecloths. Traditional dishes come dressed in local ingredients such as mussels from Morston and crab from Cromer: unpretentious, country dishes that draw in regular shoals of satisfied customers from miles around. Simple, modest bedrooms nevertheless share the owner's mild and endearing eccentricity.

Food serving times:
Monday-Sunday:
  12.30pm-2pm, 7.30pm-9pm
Closed 25 December and dinner 26 December
Prices:
Meals: a la carte 16.50/25.00
 6 rooms : 45.00/80.00

Typical Dishes

Mussels in cider and cream

Medallions of venison and red fruits

Treacle tart

West 1.5mi on Ittergham rd.
Parking

Itteringham

038 Walpole Arms

The Common, Itteringham NR11 7AR

Tel.: (01263) 587258 - Fax: (01263) 587074
e-mail: goodfood@thewalpolearms.co.uk - Website: www.thewalpolearms.co.uk

Adnams Bitter, Broadside, Woodfordes Walpole, Wherry

Blickling Hall sets an awesome architectural benchmark in this part of Norfolk; in its more modest way, the nearby part-18C Walpole Arms reaches out in empathy. It's hugely characterful, with roaring fires, exposed brick walls and heavy timbers marking out the bar as a great place to eat modern, Michelin Bib Gourmand meals, such as confit of duck with a stew of haricot blanc; saddle of rabbit wrapped in bacon with butter beans, mushrooms and chocolate; or paella of jointed chicken, rabbit, chorizo and prawns. Extensive use is made of local and seasonal ingredients; the owners heartily take on board recommendations from their fishmonger and game supplier. There's a more formal restaurant upstairs, but no let-up on the character front, with linen-clad tables and exposed roof trusses lending it an appealing air.

Food serving times:
Monday-Saturday:
    12pm-2pm, 7pm-9.30pm
Sunday: 12.30pm-2.30pm
Closed dinner 25 December
Prices:
Meals: a la carte 19.00/24.00

5mi Northwest of Aylsham by B1354. Parking

Typical Dishes

Baked sardines

Salt pork belly, chickpea and chorizo

Almond chocolate torte

Norwich

039 Mad Moose Arms

2 Warwick St, Norwich NR2 3LD

Tel.: (01603) 627687 - Fax: (01603) 633945
e-mail: madmoose@animalinns.co.uk

 📶 🚫 **VISA** **AE** **OD** **MC**

Adnams Broadside, Greene King IPA, Abbott Ale, Wolf Brewery Golden Jackal

Just eccentric enough to stand out from the suburban herd, this Victorian tavern wears its bright, cheerful modern refit surprisingly well, particularly in the simply styled first-floor dining room, which feels a little cut off, for better or worse, from the young, full-volume crowd in the bar downstairs. Flavourful modern cooking at a fair price takes in dishes like seared scallops with chilli jam, roast duck in cinnamon jus, served on spring greens, and banana tart – if you've ever eaten at the Wildebeest Arms across the city, you'll have an idea of what to expect. The chatty service from a smart, black-shirted team is well organised and evenly paced.

Food serving times:
Monday-Sunday:
     12pm-2pm, 6pm-10pm
Closed 25 December
Bar meals only Saturday lunch and Sunday dinner
Prices:
Meals: 14.95/16.50 and a la carte 16.50/25.00

Typical Dishes

Ham hock and morcilla terrine

Steak, thyme fondant

Chocolate brownie with cherries

In residential area West of city centre. Designated parking bays lunchtime, street parking in the evening

Snettisham

041 ## The Rose and Crown

Old Church Rd, Snettisham PE31 7LX

Tel.: (01485) 541382 - Fax: (01485) 543172
e-mail: info@roseandcrownsnettisham.co.uk - Website: www.roseandcrownsnettisham.co.uk

  ⚐room *VISA* ⓂⒸ

 Adnams Broadside, Greene King IPA, Fuller's London Pride, Bass

A buzzing, convivial place at its best, though first-time guests may struggle to get their bearings in a maze of cosy, rustic bars and brightly styled rooms, where quirky decorative details and bric-a-brac give just a hint of well-composed muddle. Whatever you do, don't plan on a quick dinner – for all its good intentions, the service can start to unravel on busy evenings, leaving some diners feeling slightly lost – but go prepared to flag down waitresses and allow time for a drink and a chat between courses. The menu is a conversation piece in itself. Asian influences mingle with Modern European dishes and the out-and-out traditional: try satay terrine followed by smoked paprika chicken on chorizo risotto or fish and chips. Tidy, interestingly appointed bedrooms, in a colourful style you'll recognise from downstairs, and good breakfasts.

Food serving times:
Monday-Sunday:
12pm-2pm, 6pm-9pm
Prices:
Meals: a la carte 17.50/27.50
🛏 **11 rooms :** 60.00/100.00

Typical Dishes

Asian beef carpaccio

Cod, kabanos, pea and pesto risotto

Crème brûlée

11mi North of King's Lynn by A149.
Parking

Stoke Holy Cross

040 Wildebeest Arms

82-86 Norwich Rd, Stoke Holy Cross NR14 8QJ

Tel.: (01508) 492497 - Fax: (01508) 494353
e-mail: mail@animalinns.co.uk

 VISA AE M© JCB

Adnams Best Bitter

Dark wooden furniture and sunny yellow walls, allied to soft lighting, give a homely, comfortable feel to this smoothly run rural pub. The invariably friendly and efficient service is a notable plus; the meals are served at substantially proportioned "tree-trunk" tables or, if preferred on brighter days, in the garden. Cooking is of a modern style, and has both the quality and price to earn it a Michelin Bib Gourmand. Recently recommended are smooth foie gras and chicken liver parfait with mango and quince chutney, roast fillet of cod with sautéed cabbage and chorizo, and, for dessert, frozen chocolate parfait with hazelnuts and roasted bananas.

Food serving times:
Monday-Sunday:
    12pm-2pm, 7pm-10pm
Closed 25-26 December
Prices:
Meals: 14.95/18.50 and a la carte 20.00/32.50

Typical Dishes

Scallops, apple and avocado

Ballotine of chicken, Parma ham

Chocolate fondant

5.75mi South of Norwich by A140. Parking

West Runton

042 The Village Inn

Water Lane, West Runton NR27 9QP

Tel.: (01263) 838000 - Fax: (01263) 838999

🍄 🚭 VISA ⓂⓌ JCB

Bass, Adnams, Broadside and 1 guest beer

West Runton's sand and shingle beach – good for rock pool paddling and fossil hunts along the foreshore – is only a short walk away, making the neatly kept Village Inn an extremely popular choice in high season, so arrive early to secure a place in the comfortable, dark-toned rear dining room or in one of the cosy corners around the bar, or a picnic table on the lawn. A really reasonably priced menu on a traditional base ranges from lunchtime sandwiches and baguettes to tasty crab and leek tartlet on a light roquette salad, crispy, pink liver with sautéed pancetta and green beans, and delicately creamy cheesecake. The formal restaurant – "The Nineteenth" – serves a more elaborate dinner menu from Tuesday to Saturday.

Food serving times:
Monday-Sunday:
    11am-2.30pm, 6pm-9pm
Prices:
Meals: a la carte 15.00

Typical Dishes

Vegetable samosas

Honey sausages, black pudding

Tia Maria and chocolate chip parfait

On A149.
Parking

Bramfield

043 Queen's Head

The Street, Bramfield IP19 9HT

Tel.: (01986) 784214 - Fax: (01986) 784797
e-mail: qhbfield@aol.com - Website: www.queensheadbramfield.co.uk

   ⚒≈rest **VISA** **AE** **MC** **JCB**

Adnams Bitter, Broadside, Crones Organic Cider

Organic food is the name of the game at this neat and tidy, 'proper' pub not far from Southwold and the Suffolk coast. Nobody seems to know quite how old the Queens Head is, but going by the exposed roof trusses and mighty fireplaces in one of the hugely rustic rooms – a former barn – we're talking about a few hundred years at least. Good value menus take a particular delight in showing off the organic nature of extremely local ingredients: pork, venison and beef are from nearby farms. Settle down to eat at scrubbed pine tables and chairs. In the summer months, the pretty garden is worth discovering with its dome-shaped willow bower, but at colder times of the year settle down in front of a blazing fire with a pint of ale from down the coast road.

Food serving times:
Monday-Saturday:
    12pm-2pm, 6.30pm-10pm
Sunday: 12pm-2pm,
                7pm-9pm

Closed 26 December
Prices:
Meals: a la carte 14.85/23.70

Typical Dishes

Grilled dates in bacon

Chicken supreme with lemon and tarragon

Mango, banana and coconut pavlava

3mi South of Halesworth on A144.
Parking

Buxhall

044 The Buxhall Crown

Mill Road, Buxhall IP14 3DW

Tel.: (01449) 736521 - Fax: (01449) 736528
e-mail: trevor@buxhallcrown.fsnet.co.uk - Website: www.thebuxhallcrown.co.uk

Greene King IPA, Tindalls Best Bitter, Mauldons, Woodfordes Wherry

Without a sixth sense for country pubs, you'd do well to find the Crown by chance, but all the more reason to seek it out, especially on a quieter weekday. One half of the pub is always set for dining, with plenty of intimate corners and a big fire, but you can also eat in the classic old bar, where many of the regulars drop in for a pint of the usual and a quiet smoke. There's an almost homely, family feeling to the place as gently helpful staff shuttle between the bar and kitchen, bringing out well-heaped plates of hearty cooking: notwithstanding a few modern touches, it's the traditional foundations that come across in dishes like Bailey's cheesecake with strawberries and raspberries or thick, pink lamb cutlets with pea purée and plenty of seasonal veg.

Food serving times:
Tuesday-Saturday:
    12pm-2pm, 6.30pm-9pm
Sunday: 12pm-2pm
Closed 25-26 December
Prices:
Meals: a la carte 18.00/30.00

Typical Dishes

Crab tart with rocket

Rack of lamb, red pepper relish

Mint chocolate bavarois

From Stowmarket, follow the road to Buxhall across Rattlesden Junction. Parking in Mill Bar Restaurant

Cavendish

045 The George

The Green, Cavendish CO10 8BA

Tel.: (01787) 280248 - Fax: (01787) 281703

e-mail: reservations@georgecavendish.co.uk - Website: www.georgecavendish.co.uk

 ⟨⟩rest *VISA*

 Nethergate Augustinian Ale, Woodfordes Wherry

A new-style village inn that strikes the right balance: the hard work of restoration shines through without obscuring of the pub's original, late-medieval character and though the three main rooms are designed for destination dining rather than session drinking, the animation and busy chat around the bar suggests the locals have taken to the place. It's easy to see why. A glance across at the open kitchen reveals a focussed team, hard at work on an appetising, precisely prepared modern repertoire which cuts no corners with its raw ingredients; choice and variety run deep, presentation is careful but unshowy, and sensible prices make it easy to talk yourself into a return visit. Comfortable, well-maintained bedrooms offer dependability and the same good value for money.

Food serving times:
Tuesday-Saturday:
   12pm-3pm, 6.30pm-10pm
Sunday: 12pm-3pm
Closed dinner 25 December and dinner 1 January
Prices:
Meals: a la carte 15.00/40.00
🛏 **5 rooms :** 48.00/110.00

Typical Dishes

Scallops and chorizo, sherry
Roast Moroccan spiced lamb
Bitter chocolate tart

In the centre of the village, opposite the green. Parking

Fressingfield

046 **The Fox & Goose Inn**

Church Rd, Fressingfield IP21 5PB

Tel.: (01379) 586247 - Fax: (01379) 586106
e-mail: foxandgoose@uk2.net - Website: www.foxandgoose.net

 Adnams Best, Broadside, Regatta

In the heart of the countryside, this capacious black and white pub with fine leaded windows has become something of a favourite with Suffolk diners. Its well-established credentials guarantee a bustling ambience. Drinkers are catered for with a few tables near the entrance, but the main hub centres around the most welcoming two-roomed dining area of wooden floors, black beamed ceiling and fine floral drapes. There's an extensive menu choice, both fixed price and à la carte, and the pricing is reasonable. Local ingredients are used where possible on traditional menus overlaid with modern twists: dishes might include duck, chorizo and artichoke salad with honey and cumin dressing or sea trout, crushed potatoes, ricotta tortelli with pea and sorrel sauce.

Food serving times:
Tuesday-Sunday:
12pm-2pm, 7pm-9pm
Closed 27-30 December and 2nd week in January
(booking essential)
Prices:
Meals: 13.95 and a la carte 25.00/35.00

Typical Dishes

Scallops with artichoke risotto

Beef fillet, thyme jus

Elderflower panna cotta

4mi South of Harleston on B1116. Parking

Horringer

047 **The Beehive**

The Street, Horringer IP29 5SN

Tel.: (01284) 735260

Greene King IPA, Abbot Ale

Staggeringly rich and deeply eccentric, even by the standards of the Regency gentry, the 4th Earl of Bristol spared no expense on Ickworth House and its Italianate gardens, now owned by the National Trust. His ideal local would probably have been a neoclassical gastro-folly, but The Beehive, just down the road, brings us back down to earth in the very best sense. An attractive, traditional brick and flint house, its old timbers and flagstones set off nicely with a bright, modern décor, it always seems to have one last inviting corner waiting and an old wooden table free. A good-sized blackboard menu, with its share of lighter dishes, combines predominantly British themes with a subtle taste for the modern and the exotic – perhaps His Lordship would have approved after all. Well run by long-standing landlords.

Food serving times:
Monday-Saturday:
    12pm-2pm, 7pm-9.30pm
Sunday: 12pm-2pm
Closed 25-26 December
Prices:
Meals: a la carte 17.00/25.00

Typical Dishes

Duck breast salad

Braised lamb with tomato and oregano

Apple and blackberry meringue pie

3.5mi South West of Bury St. Edmunds by A143

Lavenham

048 **Angel**

Market Pl, Lavenham CO10 9QZ

Tel.: (01787) 247388 - Fax: (01787) 248344
e-mail: angellav@aol.com - Website: www.lavenham.co.uk/angel

Nethergate Suffolk County, Adnams, Greene King IPA, Abbot Ale

History's timbered face appears at every turn in the gorgeous old town of Lavenham, and the Angel wears one of its more delightful countenances. This charming inn has stood in the market square since 1420 and receives a never-ending stream of curious tourists and relaxed locals. There's a pubby bar with several dining areas including lots of timbers, simple wooden tables and a log fire. On the first floor is the Solar, which contains a rare fully pargetted ceiling constructed in the early 1600s, featuring the remains of early wall paintings on some of its beams. This has great views of the Guildhall and Church and is now a residents' sitting room. Hearty, varied menus employ seasonal, local produce, while well-kept bedrooms provide effortlessly comfortable accommodation.

Food serving times:
Monday-Sunday:
12pm-2.15pm,
6.45pm-9.15pm
Closed 25-26 December
Prices:
Meals: a la carte 14.25/20.95
🛏 **8 rooms :** 55.00/85.00

In town centre.
Parking

Typical Dishes

Asparagus with hollandaise sauce

Steak and ale pie

Steamed syrup sponge pudding

Levington

049 Ship Inn

Church Lane, Levington IP10 0LQ
Tel.: (01473) 659573 - Fax: (01206) 397504

  VISA

Adnams Best, Broadside, Greene King IPA

In an age of rebranding, some pub names still go deeper. The salt of the Suffolk marshes is in the very timbers of this part 14C thatched inn, which stands in sight of the estuary. Though built from the broken-up hulks on the coast and full of seafaring pictures, curiosities and keepsakes, it now feels just too neat and cosy ever to have been a smugglers' haunt, but read the old newspaper cutting on the wall and you'll find the atmosphere of excisemen and contraband hangs about you a little more thickly. Relaxed, smiling and attentive service recalls you to the present for an appetizing menu with a good balance tilted in favour of the traditional: seafood includes Cromer crab and fresh griddled plaice with crispy salad. Save a space for homemade puddings like apple and rosemary crumble with custard.

Food serving times:
Monday-Saturday:
　12pm-2pm, 6.30pm-9.30pm
Sunday:　　　　　12pm-3pm
Closed 25-26 December and 1 January
Prices:
Meals: a la carte 14.50/25.00

Typical Dishes
Toasted crayfish, prawn and salmon

Venison, brandy and mushroom sauce

Chocolate brownie

6mi Southeast of Ipswich by A14. Parking

Monks Eleigh

050 Swan Inn
The Street, Monks Eleigh IP7 7AU
Tel.: (01449) 741391

 ♀ ⋈ ⊗ *VISA* MC

Adnams Best, Broadside and one guest ale

Heading, perhaps, for the Tudor delights of Lavenham, there's every chance you'll come across this attractive little 16C roadside pub with its thatched roof and honey yellow façade. Stop off and step inside. The interior is as fresh as the country air, with rustic olive tones and shiny wooden floors. It's a charming mix of the old and the new, undertaken with understated style. You won't be let down by the food, either. The chef and landlord specialises in innovative menus that treat local ingredients with the utmost respect: fish, for instance, is the day's catch from the coast. Early dinners come at bargain prices – a great time to sample the homemade seasonal game dishes. When you've left the pub, remember to look round the quaint little streets of Monks Eleigh itself.

Food serving times:
Wednesday-Sunday:
    12pm-2pm, 7pm-9.30pm
Closed 25-26 December
Prices:
Meals: a la carte 16.50/28.00

Typical Dishes

Scallops, sage and grapefruit
Lamb, baby vegetables
Panna cotta, summer berries

3.5mi Southeast of Lavenham on A1141.
Parking

Nayland

051 White Hart Inn

11 High Street, Nayland CO6 4JF

Tel.: (01206) 263382 - Fax: (01206) 263638
e-mail: nayhart@aol.com - Website: www.whitehart-nayland.co.uk

Greene King IPA

Floodlit at night, this very pleasant, well-run part-15C former coaching inn has a charming position on the high street of a typically homely Suffolk village, amid colour washed houses, overhanging timbers and patches of cobblestone. Dining is really what the White Hart is all about, and the smooth, considerate service certainly reflects this as much as the layout. Exposed beams divide the welcoming, terracotta-tiled dining room into three distinct areas, with a cosy back bar for pre-prandial relaxation. Menus are modern and accomplished, and may include millefeuille of baby spring vegetables with tomato and basil butter sauce, or rolled loin of suckling pig with seasonal greens and Calvados sauce; the bread and butter pudding is made to the chef's mother's own secret recipe! Beamed bedrooms are pleasantly creaky but very comfortable.

Food serving times:
Monday-Sunday:
12pm-2.30pm,
6.30pm-9.30pm
Closed 26 December-9 January
Prices:
Meals: 12.95/21.50 and a la carte 18.95/27.00
6 rooms : 69.00/95.00

Opposite the church. Parking

Typical Dishes

Salmon mousse, crayfish bouillon

Salt marsh lamb with basil jus

Crème brûlée, lychees

Snape

THE CROWN INN

052 Crown Inn

Bridge Rd, Snape IP17 1SL
Tel.: (01728) 688324

Adnams Broadside, Regatta, Old Ale

This gem of a Suffolk pub, with its origins firmly entrenched in the 15C, draws in visitors from upmarket Aldeburgh and The Maltings. They come for the Suffolk ale, the pubby atmosphere enhanced enormously by standing timbers and rafters, old brick flooring and horseshoe-shaped high-backed settles around a grand brick inglenook, and the heart-warming popular dishes served from the blackboard menu. These have a sharp emphasis on fresh fish, game and organic vegetables supplied by local producers, and might include Cromer crab risotto or confit of honey-roast duck on red cabbage and apple with wild mushroom jus. Quaint bedrooms continue the aged theme, complete with sloping floors, beams and some low, low doorways.

Food serving times:
Monday-Sunday:
      12pm-3pm, 7pm-9pm
Closed 25 December and dinner 26 December
Prices:
Meals: a la carte 17.00/25.00
3 rooms : 60.00/80.00

Typical Dishes

Crayfish tails in Thai sauce

Rack of lamb, celeriac mash, wine jus

Sticky toffee pudding

6mi West of Aldeburgh by A1094 on B1069.
Parking

Southwold

053 The Randolph

Wangford Rd, Reydon, Southwold IP18 6PZ

Tel.: (01502) 723603 - Fax: (01502) 722194
Website: www.therandolph.co.uk

♟ ⅹ-rest ⅹ **VISA** **AE** **MC**

 Adnams Southwold, Bitter, Broadside and up to 10 regularly changing ales

It's a wrench setting foot out of glorious Southwold, but a mile up the road is this sturdy old Victorian stalwart, built by the grandfather of the chairman of the local brewery. It's been given a startling and successful 21C makeover, the big, open-plan bar is suffused with light and furnished with contemporary wicker chairs and leather sofas; deep, bold colours lead you into the dining room where the emphasis is on extremely local produce: those who supply fish, game and the like often stay on for a pint of ale in the bar. Food is traditional and robust: apart from the aforementioned, you might tuck into steaks or toad-in-the-hole. If you're not staying in one of the comfy bedrooms, then what could be better than a post-prandial walk round the greens, beach huts and lighthouse of Suffolk's finest…

Food serving times:
Tuesday-Saturday:
12pm-1.30pm,
6.30pm-8.30pm
Sunday: 12pm-1.30pm
Prices:
Meals: 13.50 and a la carte 25.00/32.00
🛏 **10 rooms** : 55.00/90.00

1mi Northwest of Southwold by A1095 on B1126.
Parking ➤➤

Typical Dishes

Randolph smoked salmon
Sea bass in herb crust
Stem ginger crème brûlée

Stoke-by-Nayland

054 Angel Inn

Polstead St, Stoke-by-Nayland CO6 4SA

Tel.: (01206) 263245 - Fax: (01206) 263373
e-mail: the.angel@tiscali.co.uk - Website: www.horizoninns.co.uk

    VISA

No real ales offered

Parts of this 16C inn in the heart of Constable country creak with age: not surprisingly, a traditional air is worn with pride. It's heavily beamed and timbered, with exposed brickwork and roaring fires, and a cheerily informal bar that leads through to a sitting room where you can recline in deep sofas. Dine in the main bar or repair to the Well Room, which contains the house's original well and a superb beamed ceiling. Menus here are the same as elsewhere, but the pervading atmosphere is a touch more tranquil and formal. Seasonally influenced dishes abound with locally sourced meat, fish and game prepared in a modern British style. It's the kind of place you might not want to leave, so stay on in one of the traditionally and individually styled bedrooms.

Food serving times:
Monday-Saturday:
    12pm-2pm, 6pm-9.30pm
Sunday: 12pm-5pm,
                5.30pm-9.30pm
Closed 25 December and 1 January
Prices:
Meals: a la carte 15.25/26.70
🛏 **6 rooms :** 60.00/85.00

Typical Dishes

Avocado, prawn salad

Roasted lemon and thyme poussin

Malibu panna cotta, mango compote

On B1068.
Parking

Stoke-by-Nayland

055 The Crown

Stoke-by-Nayland CO6 4SE
Tel.: (01206) 262001 - Fax: (01206) 263910
e-mail: crown.eoinns@btopenworld.com

 🍷 🍺 **VISA** MC

Adnams Best, Greene King IPA, Timothy Taylor Landlord, Ringwood 49er, 2 guest beers

"1530" is stamped on the outside of this promising-looking pub, but its comfortable and stylish interior – with a mis-match of sofas, leather armchairs and farmhouse chairs at broad tables – owes much to a recent sympathetic refit. Such is its local reputation that several spacious dining rooms soon fill with a mix of couples, friends and families, particularly for long lunches at weekends and holidays, so booking really is a must. With a new menu every fortnight, the hearty cooking keeps pace with the seasons and brings a regional touch to a couple of daily specials – plus a catch of the day – and a wider range of surefire gastropub classics: a handful of these come in either starter or main portions. The Crown is owned by a firm of wholesale vintners, and its wine shop sells an interesting selection, as well as local homemade chocolates.

Food serving times:
Monday-Saturday:
 12pm-2.30pm, 6pm-9.30pm
Sunday: 12pm-3.30pm,
 6pm-9pm
Closed 25-26 December and
1 January
(booking essential)
Prices:
Meals: a la carte 16.95/26.50

Typical Dishes

Crab, avocado timbale

Roast halibut steak, sorrel sauce

Pecan and praline cheesecake

Village centre at the junction of B1068 and B1087. Parking

☐ a.   ✗✗   *A comfortable restaurant?*
☐ b.   ❀   *A very good restaurant in its category?*
☐ c.   😋   *Good food at moderate prices?*

**Can't decide?
Then immerse yourself in the
Michelin Guide!**

In this collection the Michelin
inspectors recommend and describe
more than 45,000 hotels and
restaurants across Europe ranging
from new 'Bib Gourmand' 😋
bistros to luxury 3 star ❀❀❀
restaurants. There are also 300 maps
and 1600 town plans to help you find
each establishment.

**Discover the pleasure of travel
with the Michelin Guide.**

A tour of the region begins with a well-kept secret: the rural beauty of the east. Towards the coast lie acres of silent fens, the gentle countryside of the wolds, and the magnificent silhouette of Lincoln Cathedral, rising above the old city. Nottingham, Derby and the nearby towns shot to fame as centres of industry and science and remain the powerhouses of the region. With Leicester they form an old industrial heartland, regenerated by the first plantings of the National Forest and bordered by rural Rutland, "independent" again since 1997. Then to the west, sombre moors, the pretty "White Peak"" downlands, the Derwent and dramatic Dovedale form some of the country's most picture-perfect landscapes, while Peak architecture reflects every mood and era of its history: Matlock's mills and the moving monuments of Eyam village, Georgian Buxton and the stately archetypes of Chatsworth and Haddon Hall. In the region's pubs, there's a strong local flavour on tap – even Rutland brews its own beer – as well as on the plate. Bakewell tarts, or puddings, are a point of local pride, while only the rich, blue-veined cheese from three East Midlands counties can lay claim to the name of Stilton.

Ashbourne

001 Bramhall's

6 Buxton Rd, Ashbourne DE6 1EX

Tel.: (01335) 346158
e-mail: info@bramhalls.co.uk - Website: www.bramhalls.co.uk

  VISA M© JCB

 Bass

D on't be put off by the rather dreary façade, just off Ashbourne's cobbled market square; once inside, it's a different picture. Pick a table in one of the four or five little rooms and snugs and let a well-drilled team do the rest. Keen and helpful staff in denim uniforms serve an appetising menu rounded out with daily specials on the board: cream of white onion soup, monkfish with gnocchi and asparagus and rasperry crème brûlée are typical of a sound modern-classic style. At the back, an enclosed terrace for dining looks down over a stepped garden. If you're planning on staying the night, the usefully equipped bedrooms range from plain to contemporary.

Food serving times:
Monday-Sunday:
12pm-2.30pm,
6.30pm-9.30pm
Closed Sunday dinner
November-Easter
Prices:
Meals: a la carte 20.00/30.00
🛏 **10 rooms :** 27.50/65.00

Typical Dishes

Seared scallops, pak choi, chilli oil

Rack of lamb with parsnip mash

Vanilla brûlee

In centre of town.
Parking

Hognaston

002 Red Lion Inn

Main Street, Hognaston DE6 1PR

Tel.: (01335) 370396 - Fax: (01335) 372145
e-mail: redlion@hognaston.com - Website: www.lionrouge.com

Marstons Pedigree, Old Speckled Hen, Bass, Hartington Bitter

Nestling in a pretty village in the foothills of the Derbyshire Peaks, this cream-washed extended late 17C inn has a cosy, comfortable appeal, typified by a bar full of objets d'art and ornaments. A 'real' pub ambience predominates, with the warmth of the surroundings enhanced with open fires and a rugged old stone floor. You'll want for nothing: the owner is chatty and enthusiastic, and very much on hand to recommend drinks or dishes from the menu. Classic pub meals here have been given a modern twist: typically, pork sausages with mustard mash and red wine jus. Dine at a candle-lit mix of older wooden tables and chairs. Stay overnight in beamed, individually decorated bedrooms.

Food serving times:
Tuesday-Saturday :
    12pm-2pm, 6.30pm-9pm
Sunday: 12pm-2pm
Closed 25 December

Prices:
Meals: a la carte 12.85/24.45
3 rooms : 55.00/85.00

4.5mi Northeast of Ashbourne by B5035.
Parking to rear

Typical Dishes

Tomato, mozzarella and pesto tart

Crispy duck, plum sauce

Sticky toffee pudding

Hope Valley

003 **Chequers Inn**

Froggatt Edge, Hope Valley S32 3ZJ

Tel.: (01433) 630231 - Fax: (01433) 631072
e-mail: info@chequers-froggatt.com - Website: www.chequers-froggatt.com

     VISA

 Charles Wells Bombadier, Greene King IPA

Located at the eastern end of the Peak District, and just in front of the woods that lead to Froggatt Edge, this attractively set pub - a Grade II listed building - is quite a find. It dates back to the 16C and was originally four houses; it's been extensively refurbished yet retains many period features, such as the old stables. The spacious interior has a welcoming feel, typified in the bar by a well-chosen selection of wines by the glass, chalked up on blackboard slates hung around the richly varnished panelled ceiling; chunky stone walls with antique prints all add to the rustic atmosphere. Sit at simple, polished wooden tables and tuck into tasty meals with a distinctive modern feel, backed up by efficient, friendly service. Walkers may be delighted to finish the evening tucked up in very pleasant, cosy bedrooms.

Food serving times:
Monday-Friday:
12pm-2pm, 6pm-9.30pm
Saturday: 12pm-9.30pm
Sunday: 12pm-9pm
Closed 25 December
Prices:
Meals: a la carte 16.00/25.00
5 rooms : 85.00

Situated on the edge of the village.
Parking

Typical Dishes

Scallops with noodles, chilli sauce

Venison, walnut pickle and beetroot

Chocolate mousse

Marston Montgomery

004 Bramhall's at The Crown Inn

Rigg Lane, Marston Montgomery DE6 2FF

Tel.: (01889) 590541
e-mail: info@bramhalls.co.uk - Website: www.bramhalls.co.uk

Draught Bass, Marstons Pedigree

Just up the road from Alton Towers is a far more relaxing and certainly less energetic alternative: a pleasant pub, hidden away in the village centre. Locals are drawn by the warm and welcoming atmosphere, not to mention the splendid selection of real ales and wines by the glass; exposed rafters and an open fire all add to the happy mix. This simple, cosy interior is further enhanced by plenty of comfy seats and distressed wooden tables. The food served here, off a daily blackboard menu, seamlessly matches its surroundings: tasty and unfussy, with modern twists thrown in for good measure. Bedrooms do the trick, too: they're warm, cosy and contemporary.

Food serving times:
Monday-Saturday:
   12pm-2.30pm, 6.30pm-9pm
Sunday: 12pm-2.30pm
Closed 25 December
Prices:
Meals: 12.95 and a la carte 20.00/30.00
7 rooms : 40.00/65.00

Typical Dishes

Mango chilli prawns

Rack of lamb, paprika vegetables

Cranberry and orange pudding

7.5mi Southeast of Ashbourne by A515.
Parking

Bruntingthorpe

005 Joiners Arms

Church Walk, Bruntingthorpe LE17 5QH

Tel.: (0116) 2478258 - Fax: (0116) 2478258

e-mail: stephen@joinersarmsbruntingthorpe.co.uk - Website: www.joinersarms-bruntingthorpe.co.uk

 VISA

 Greene King IPA

B e warned: you might not even recognise the Joiners Arms as a hostelry at all: its smart little whitewashed 18C exterior only bears the most discreet of pub signs. Once inside, any lingering doubts are soon banished: there's a surprising amount of contemporary design, married successfully to wooden beams, recently returned to their natural oak. Drinkers relax on velvet-upholstered furniture; diners can recline on cushioned pews at closely-spaced wood tables. The menu choice is quite small but appealingly formed, incorporating daily changing blackboard specials that are good value, tasty and accomplished, making the most of seasonal ingredients. Service is friendly and polite.

Food serving times:
Tuesday-Saturday:
  12pm-2pm, 6.30pm-9.30pm
Sunday: 12pm-2pm
Closed 25 December and
Bank Holidays
(booking essential)
Prices:
Meals: a la carte 20.00/27.50

Typical Dishes

Smoked haddock, leek and Gruyère tart

Sea bass, chilli sauce

Lemongrass and coconut panna cotta

Between Leicester and Husbands Bosworth off A5199.
Parking

Castle Donington

006 Nags Head

Hill Top, Castle Donington DE74 2PR

Tel.: (01332) 850652
e-mail: idavison@aol.com

Y ✗ *VISA* AE M©

Marstons Pedigree, Banks Mild, Mansfield Bitter

In an area renowned for speed, with the Grand Prix Collection, Donington Park circuit and East Midlands airport all on the doorstep, it's advisable to engage a lower gear in order to appreciate the charms of this snug and cosy pub. A welcoming and professional team oil the wheels; you'll find it hard to drag yourself away from the crackling open fires, but a trip to the dining room is recommended. The walls here are filled with French style posters and prints and the semi-open kitchen allows you a view of the chefs preparing a daily changing blackboard menu which offers a wide range of tasty dishes with the emphasis very much on abundant local ingredients.

Food serving times:
Monday-Saturday:
12pm-2pm, 7pm-9.15pm
Closed 26 December-3 January
(booking essential)
Prices:
Meals: a la carte 22.40/27.85

Typical Dishes

Warm cheese pudding, mustard crust

Lambs liver, bacon, black pudding

Chocolate tart

0.5mi North of Castle Donington. Parking

Hallaton

007 Bewicke Arms

1 Eastgate, Hallaton LE16 8HB
Tel.: (01858) 555217 - Fax: (01858) 555598

Flowers IPA and beers from the Grainstore Brewery

Visit Hallaton on Easter Monday and you won't forget the experience in a hurry. That's the day of the annual Bottle Kicking and Hare Pie Scramble when locals jostle for pieces of pie and teams of men from Hallaton and neighbouring Medbourne engage in a manic free-for-all trying to capture three wooden casks. The 17C Bewicke Arms provides a pleasant change of pace from the strange goings-on. It is rusticity itself: solid stone floor, hop bines, open fires and exposed rafters. Produce from the region, selected on a seasonal basis, forms the hearty backbone to the weekly changing blackboard menus; chatty, friendly service is guaranteed.

Food serving times:
Monday-Saturday:
    12pm-2pm, 7pm-9.30pm
Sunday: 12pm-2pm
Closed October-May
(booking essential)
Prices:
Meals: a la carte 15.95/19.50

8mi Northeast of Market Harborough by B664.
Parking

Typical Dishes

Mushrooms, goat's cheese and tomato

Chicken in cheese and cream sauce

Cappuccino meringue

Stathern

008 **Red Lion Inn**

2 Red Lion St, Stathern LE14 4HS

Tel.: (01949) 860868 - Fax: (01949) 861579

e-mail: info@theredlioninn.co.uk - Website: www.theredlioninn.co.uk

Grainstore Olive Oil Bitter, Brewster's VPA and guest ales

Though it's hard to put your finger on what makes the Red Lion such a quietly likeable place, the comfortable sitting room, with today's papers over the arms of the leather sofas, is a nice, understated invitation to make yourself at home. A rural inn to the core, filled with wooden antiques, rustic ornaments and bunches of dried flowers, its able, well-priced Bib Gourmand cooking easily steps out of old pub convention and manages to keep its well-defined contemporary country style while still rotating its dishes day by day: it's a winning formula, but never comes across as formulaic. Try an appetising lemon and herb risotto or herb-crusted cod, served at neat, gingham-clad tables in what was once the pub's skittle alley, or in the little courtyard at the back.

Food serving times:

Monday-Saturday:
12pm-2pm, 7pm-9pm

Sunday: 12pm-2pm

(booking essential)

Prices:

Meals: 13.50/15.50 and a la carte 19.00/27.00

Typical Dishes

Warm smoked haddock and leek tart

Lamb, aubergine, tomato, mozzarella

Local ale cake

8mi North of Melton Mowbray by A607.
Parking

Thorpe Langton

009 Bakers Arms

Main St, Thorpe Langton LE16 7TS

Tel.: (01858) 545201

e-mail: tim@thebakersarms.co.uk

  VISA

Tetleys, Langton Bakers Dozen

This pleasantly relaxed pub hidden away in a Leicestershire village has a wonderfully appealing 16C thatched appearance; inside, the appeal also harks back to olden days. Scrubbed pine tables - candlelit in the evenings - exposed timbers, pew seats, oriental rugs, all of them surrounded by rich red walls, ensure that the atmosphere is intimate and most convivial. It's not really a drinker's pub, though if you want a pint, you're certainly welcome. The Bakers is aimed more for the dining fraternity, who, judging by their numbers, are well satisfied by their experience here. Menus are innovative and well executed, with good use made of seasonal Leicestershire ingredients.

Food serving times:
Tuesday-Friday:
6.30pm-9.30pm
Saturday-Sunday:
12pm-2pm, 6.30pm-9.30pm
(booking essential)
Prices:
Meals: a la carte 18.00/30.50

Typical Dishes

Chicken with avocado

Monkfish wrapped in Parma ham

Chocolate torte with Tia Maria anglaise

3.75ml North of Market Harborough by A4304 via Great Bowden. Parking

Grimsthorpe

010 **Black Horse Inn**

Grimsthorpe PE10 0LY

Tel.: (01778) 591247 - Fax: (01778) 591373
e-mail: dine@blackhorseinn.co.uk - Website: www.blackhorseinn.co.uk

      VISA AE MC JCB

Guest ales from small local breweries

Originally built as a coaching halt, the Black Horse remains very much an inn, in spite of the changes over the last three centuries: overnight guests have the run of a residents' lounge and their choice of practical, pleasantly chintzy bedrooms. Plenty of people come just for the food, though: exposed stone walls, candlelight and period ornaments add to the traditional ambience of the dining room, but you can also eat in the more modern bar, where the menu is slightly simpler. Hearty, carefully prepared cooking blends old and new, giving pride of place to local seasonal game. The inn stands in the grounds of Grimsthorpe Castle - with a North Front by Vanburgh - and you could hardly leave without a walk in the gardens or a visit to the family home of many Lord Chancellors, who furnished it with a few thrones from the old House of Lords!

Food serving times:
Monday-Saturday:
　　　　12pm-2pm, 6pm-9pm
Sunday:　　　　12pm-2pm
Prices:
Meals: a la carte 18.15/23.75
6 rooms : 55.00/70.00

Typical Dishes

Mushroom and shallot tartlet

Lamb rump, blue cheese risotto

Raspberry cheesecake

> 3.5mi Northwest of Bourne on A1151. Parking at front or back of pub

Lincoln

011 Wig & Mitre

First Floor, 30-32 Steep Hill, Lincoln LN2 1TL

Tel.: (01522) 535190 - Fax: (01522) 532402

e-mail: email@wigandmitre.com - Website: www.wigandmitre.com

Ruddles Best, Marstons Pedigree, Black Sheep, Castle Rock Pale Harvest

Superior and diverse: two words which readily spring to mind when describing this 14C hostelry, now a most welcoming café, bar and restaurant. It's close to the cathedral, a natural resting place after climbing Steep Hill, where it's perched. Walk in past the handsome broad-windowed exterior to the relaxed café: newspapers to read, sofas and pews to lounge in, exposed stone walls, oak floorboards, simple tables, appealing bistro style menus. Upstairs, the dining room has a medieval air about it, with an open fire, shelves of old books, antique prints and banquette seats. Wide ranging menus with much appeal might include roast sausages with garlic and black pudding mash and apple cream sauce; or steamed brill with red wine butter.

Food serving times:
Monday-Friday:
8am-12am

Prices:
Meals: 13.95 (fixed price lunch) and a la carte 20.00/31.00

Typical Dishes
Cheese soufflé
Rack of lamb, redcurrant jus
Raspberry and mascarpone brûlée

Close to the Cathedral

Sleaford

012 **Tally Ho Inn**

Aswarby, Sleaford NG34 8SA

Tel.: (01529) 455205 - Fax: (01529) 455773
Website: www.tally-ho-aswarby.co.uk

 VISA

| *Bass, Everards Tiger, Adnams* |

Even as you pull up to this smart roadside coaching inn and reach for the door, you might just catch the sound of chatter and laughter from the bar: a real local meeting place, it's the kind of pub that feels best with the regulars in, warming up by the fire or leaning on the counter, calling the odds for the next round. There's a frequently changing blackboard menu here and a reminder next door, where recycled glassware and stripped tables give the dining room a nice, unfussy, farmhouse feel. Traditional cooking with a touch of Fenland character certainly keeps the cold out, and the generous platefuls are "popular with the shooters". Try dishes like roast cod with Parma ham and pea purée or grilled ribeye and peppercorn sauce.

Food serving times:
Monday-Sunday:
    12pm-2pm, 6pm-9.30pm
Prices:
Meals: a la carte 12.65/25.85
 6 rooms : 40.00/60.00

Typical Dishes

Stuffed pepper, bacon and mushroom

Lamb, apricot and brandy sauce

Strawberry roulade

4.5mi South of Sleaford on A15. Parking

Woolsthorpe-by-Belvoir

013 ## The Chequers

Main Street, Woolsthorpe-by-Belvoir NG32 1LU

Tel.: (01476) 870701 - Fax: (01476) 870085
e-mail: justin@chequers-inn.net - Website: www.chequers-inn.net

Kimberly Best, Adnams, Fuller's London Pride, Timothy Taylor Landlord, Olde Trip

In the gentle Lincolnshire countryside near 19C Belvoir Castle, this sizeable old coaching inn is made up of traditionally styled lounges, snugs and bar as well as a slightly more formal restaurant. The same menu is served throughout, the variations on a classic British theme including a salad of black and white puddings with poached egg and ham hock in mustard sauce; it's worth asking about the lunchtime set menu. A gravel petanque strip in the back garden should stimulate some healthy competition, and the cricket pitch in the pub grounds hosts village matches from May to September. Alternatively, friendly local staff can also point you in the right direction for a walk towards Grantham. Out in the converted stable block, four neat, pine-furnished rooms in cottage patterns offer useful facilities.

Food serving times:
Monday-Sunday:
   12pm-2.30pm, 7pm-9.30pm
Closed dinner 25-26 December and dinner 1 January
Prices:
Meals: 12.50 and a la carte 16.25/25.90
🛏 **4 rooms:** 49.00/59.00
🍽 5.00

7.5mi West of Grantham by A607. Parking

Typical Dishes

Peppers, feta and olive bruschetta

Calves liver, polenta

Poached apricots and plums

Lowick

014 Snooty Fox

16 Main St, Lowick NN14 3BH

Tel.: (01832) 733434 - Fax: (01832) 733931
e-mail: thesnootyfox@btinternet.com

  VISA

Adnams Southwold, Oakham JHB, Old Speckled Hen, Jennings Cumberland Ale, Hopback Summer Lightning

This spacious inn dates back to 16C; it started life as the local Manor House, and is reputedly haunted by a horse and its rider killed in the Battle of Naseby, a dozen or so miles to the west. Its carved beams are of particular note, but then again, for those who've tasted them, so are the locally renowned rotisserie grill menus and home-made favourites like pasties and cottage pies. You can eat around the sizable bar or in the elegant main dining room. If you're going for meat, select the size of your cut from a nicely stocked chilled cabinet, but if you're after the vegetarian option, then you won't be disappointed either. Prices are keen and the cooking's very good. It's all run, most unsnootily, by experienced and welcoming owners.

Food serving times:
Monday-Sunday:
  12pm-2pm, 6.30pm-9.30pm
Closed dinner 25-26 December and 1 January
Prices:
Meals: a la carte 16.80/23.95

Typical Dishes

Serrano ham with Spanish peppers

Blade of Scotch beef

Hot banana tart with caramel sauce

Village off A6116. Parking

Oundle

015 ## The Falcon Inn

Fotheringhay, Oundle PE8 5HZ

Tel.: (01832) 226254 - Fax: (01832) 226046
Website: www.huntsbridge.com

Adnams Best, Greene King IPA and 2 guest ales

Richard III and Mary Queen of Scots aren't a bad couple of names to help draw in the punters: one was born here, one died here (not in the pub, you understand, but in the village of Fotheringhay). Those not aware of the history will still succumb to the warmth of this characterful place, run with professionalism and great personality. Though modernised, it still feels like a all-round good pub: open fires, spindle back chairs, fresh flowers, framed prints picking up on the history, and tubby wood tables. A spacious conservatory offers a formal air, Lloyd Loom chairs, and some impressive cooking from the modern British repertoire: Greek feta burger with light raita and crisp chips, or smoked haddock with potato and chive tart.

Food serving times:
Monday-Sunday:
12pm-2pm, 6.30pm-9.30pm
Prices:
Meals: 15.75 and a la carte
22.00/30.00

North 3.75mi of Oundle by A427 off A605.
Parking

Typical Dishes

Duck spring rolls

Calves liver with spinach and bacon

Sticky toffee pudding

Caunton

016 Caunton Beck
Main Street, Caunton NG23 6AB

Tel.: (01636) 636793 - Fax: (01636) 636828
e-mail: email@wigandmitre.com - Website: www.wigandmitre.com

Ruddles Best Bitter, Springhead Bitter, Castle Rock Pale Harvest

With the parish church opposite and the beck itself running alongside, this end of Caunton wouldn't look quite right without a neat village pub to complete the picture. Spacious and airy, with exposed brick walls, open fires and a big counter bar, this sympathetically designed modern place is actually bigger than it looks; a smart dining room offering a more formal alternative and soundly prepared lunches and dinners on a traditional base. A typical selection might take in leek and cheese soufflé or monkfish with crispy pancetta, but don't overlook the bar menu, particularly if you're after something a bit lighter or simpler: a keen young team are on hand if you just can't decide.

Food serving times:
Monday-Sunday:
8am-12am

Prices:
Meals: 13.95 and a la carte
21.00/29.50

Typical Dishes

Duck leg in Parma ham

Lemon and thyme chicken breast

Ricotta crème brûlée

Located on the A616, 6mi past the sugar beet factory. Parking

Colston Bassett

017 **Martins Arms**

School Lane, Colston Bassett NG12 3FD

Tel.: (01949) 81361 - Fax: (01949) 81039

 A selection of regularly changing ales

Blessed indeed are the cheesemakers, for we're right in the heart of "Stilton country", and the owners of the Martins Arms are as proud as anyone of Nottinghamshire's most famous culinary export. Tucked away at the heart of this sleepy rural village, the big pub with the warm and welcoming atmosphere varies its appealing modern menu with the seasons, but cheese connoisseurs will want to try the generous ploughmans lunches or a tasty starter of Stilton rarebit: other dishes from a wide-ranging repertoire, generally with a more complex and contemporary edge, might include pigeon with mushroom ravioli or strawberry mousse. Lunches and dinners are served in a smart, semi-panelled dining room with lovely Queen Anne style chairs, but the spacious bar is equally appealing, with a carved wooden fireplace and rustic brickwork and furnishings.

Food serving times:
Monday-Saturday:
        12pm-2pm, 6pm-10pm
Sunday: 12pm-2pm
Closed dinner 25 December
Prices:
Meals: a la carte 18.75/28.50

East of Cotgrave off A46.
Parking

Typical Dishes

Scallop, leek and smoked bacon tartlet

Panfried sea bass with confit tomato

Pineapple tarte Tatin

Halam

018 Waggon and Horses

Mansfield Rd, Halam NG22 8AE

Tel.: (01636) 813109 - Fax: (01636) 816228
e-mail: w-h@btconnect.com

⤫rest **VISA** ⓂⒸ

Thwaites Best, Lancaster Bomber, Thoroughbred

Between Nottingham and Mansfield, just to the east of Sherwood Forest, the Waggon and Horses draws in an appreciative mix of East Midlanders and passers-by, many of whom have heard about its good local reputation. It's no more than due recognition for the owners, who are members of the Campaign for Real Food and try to offer as much fresh, local produce as possible. The pub itself is quite small with low-beamed ceilings and heavy wooden tables; cricket memorabilia betrays the fact you're not so far from Trent Bridge. The dining area, adjacent to the bar, is the place to try out extensive menus: blackboard specials change daily, and the modern, style of the cuisine, allied to the freshness of the ingredients, guarantees a legion of fans.

Food serving times:
Monday-Saturday:
  12pm-2.30pm, 6pm-9.30pm
Sunday: 12pm-2.30pm
Closed 25-26 December
Prices:
Meals: 11.00/12.00 and a la carte 20.00/28.00

1.75mi West of Southwell, opposite the school.
Parking

Typical Dishes

Scallops and tiger prawns in bacon

Calves liver, belly pork, ale jus

Chocolate fondant

Clipsham

019 **The Olive Branch**

Main St, Clipsham LE15 7SH

Tel.: (01780) 410355 - Fax: (01780) 410000

e-mail: info@theolivebranchpub.com - Website: www.theolivebranchpub.com

     VISA

Shepherd Neame Spitfire, Brains Dark, Belgian beers: Rochefort, Gulden Draak, Timmermans Gueuzes

Followers of Michelin starred establishments will have their taste buds suitably satiated at this rurally located inn. But, as Rutland residents have appreciated for some years now, there's so much more to this cosy firelit pub than the admittedly first-rate cooking. For instance, the neat pergola doubles as a terrace in good weather, while back inside there's an irresistible mix of country style attractions – church pew seats, open wood fires, and roughly painted walls with sepia prints, cookery books and assorted curios. And the food? Perfectly judged, seasonally inspired dishes – a flavourful mix of the old and new, with plenty of flexibility and originality in the end result. Three charmingly endowed dining areas enrich the enjoyment factor.

Food serving times:
Monday-Sunday:
    12pm-2pm, 7pm-9pm
(booking essential)
Prices:
Meals: 15.00 and a la carte 24.50/28.00

Typical Dishes

Caramelised onion tart

Spring lamb, olive boulangere

Queen of puddings, lemon sorbet

9.5mi Northwest of Stamford by B1081 off A1.
Parking

Hambleton

020 Finch's Arms

Oakham Rd, Hambleton LE15 8TL

Tel.: (01572) 756575 - Fax: (01572) 771142
e-mail: finchsarms@talk21.com - Website: www.finchsarms.co.uk

    VISA

 Timothy Taylor Landlord, Oakham ales, Grainstore ales

It doesn't matter why you come to the Finch's; you're not likely to find the experience unrewarding. Some tourists want to see its location: alone, surrounded by the vast expanse of Rutland Water. Others want to relax on the splendid hillside terrace and check out the views from another angle. But many arrive wanting to enjoy the pub's atmosphere: an inviting rusticity in keeping with its surroundings; there are open fires, coir carpets, scrubbed, candle-lit wooden tables, and pew-style benches. The more formal rear dining room has solid stone-topped tables. Rather complex menus have an appealing quality full of fresh, seasonal ingredients: typically, ballottine of guinea fowl with prunes. A weekly changing blackboard menu is more down-to-earth. Impressive bedrooms have a French country feel.

Food serving times:
Monday-Saturday:
   12pm-3pm, 6.30pm-9.30pm
Sunday: 12pm-9pm
Closed 25 December
Prices:
Meals: 11.50 and a la carte
14.95/24.00
6 rooms : 65.00/75.00

Typical Dishes

Anise flamed tiger prawns

Pork medallions in cider sauce

Ice cream

3mi East of Oakham by A606.
Parking

Knossington

021 **The Fox and Hounds**

6 Somerby Road, Knossington LE15 8LY

Tel.: (01664) 454676 - Fax: (01664) 454031

 rest **VISA** **MC**

No real ales offered

This lovely, ivy clad 18C former coaching inn makes an ideal refuelling stop after a visit to Rutland Water. Set in a small, pretty village, it's the very picture of a rural Rutland pub, with low ceilings, beams and wood tables at the front for al fresco meals. Drinkers relax on stools at the bar; diners make for one of two coir-carpeted rooms with polished wood tables and a choice of cushioned chairs or pew-style banquettes. Daily changing menus comprise good value, modern rustic dishes with local produce in much evidence. Try, perhaps, breast of chicken with chick peas, broad beans and lentils, or grilled calves liver with green beans and tapenade. Warm attentive service is a pleasant plus.

Food serving times:
Tuesday: 7pm-9.30pm
Wednesday-Saturday:
  12pm-2.30pm, 7pm-9.30pm
Sunday: 12.30pm-3.30pm
(booking essential)
Prices:
Meals: 13.95 (fixed price Sunday lunch only) and a la carte 17.50/25.00

Typical Dishes

Chicken liver parfait, balsamic onion

Calves liver, leeks, bacon and sage

Colston Basset Stilton

4mi West of Oakham by A606 and Braunston rd. Parking

Lyddington

022 Old White Hart

51 Main Street, Lyddington LE15 9LR

Tel.: (01572) 821703 - Fax: (01572) 821965

 VISA **MC**

Timothy Taylor Landlord, Greene King Abbott, IPA

A mong the happy throng of drinkers at this wonderfully unstuffy, unfussy pub you'll find a surprising number of petanque players, drawn by the – probably unique – 10-lane boules court. Of course, you don't need to be a sporty type to appreciate the delights of this pretty Rutland village inn. The gardens offer plenty of outdoor seats, but in winter you'll prefer the roaring fires, welcoming beamed bar and nice feeling of intimacy which ensues. When you're hungry, dine on good value lunch menus or, later, a seasonal à la carte with plenty of choice. The daily changing blackboard fish specials are tasty and renowned: try, perhaps, the Grimsby haddock or mussels in white wine and garlic. Well-kept bedrooms await those staying overnight.

Food serving times:
Monday-Saturday:
　　12pm-2pm, 6.30pm-9pm
Sunday:　　　　　　　12pm-2pm
Closed 25 December
Prices:
Meals: 12.95 and a la carte
21.00/30.00
🛏 **5 rooms :** 55.00/80.00

Typical Dishes

Foie gras, fig compote

English lamb, redcurrant jus

Jam roly poly, custard

1.5mi south of Uppingham off A6003.
By the village green. Parking

Oakham

023 **The Admiral Hornblower**

64 High St, Oakham LE15 6AS

Tel.: (01572) 723004 - Fax: (01572) 722325
e-mail: enquiries@hornblowerhotel.co.uk - Website: www.hornblowerhotel.co.uk

    VISA M©

 Grainstore Cooking, Triple, Bass

A handsome, creeper-clad building, the inn's foursquare proportions and spacious interior might remind you of a converted country schoolhouse, but the only blackboards list the daily specials and the atmosphere is definitely that of a popular, county-town pub: three main rooms – with scrubbed wooden dining tables and exposed brickwork – feel busy, lively and comfortable. Set well apart from the bustle of the bar, the pleasingly traditional Garden Room restaurant fits the bill for a more formal dinner, but certainly doesn't regard itself as just a "special occasions" place, and a well-prepared classic menu makes no distinction. It's worth knowing that they also offer accommodation in the old stable block: practical, pine-fitted rooms with spotless ensuites and power showers.

Food serving times:
Monday-Sunday:
      12pm-3pm, 6pm-9.30pm
Closed 25 December
Prices:
Meals: a la carte 18.00
🛏 **10 rooms :** 59.50/125.00

Typical Dishes

Chicken liver parfait
Pork loin with Stilton
Crème brûlée

In the town centre ⟩⟩

Oakham

024 The Whipper-In

Market Pl, Oakham LE15 6WT

Tel.: (01572) 756971 - Fax: (01572) 757759
e-mail: whipper.in@brook-hotels.co.uk - Website: www.brook-hotels.co.uk

 🍷 rest VISA AE ◐ MC

Grainstore Triple B

As fondly regarded a part of the Market Place as the Castle hall, the fine ironstone buildings of Oakham School and the sturdy spire of All Saints', this smart coaching inn reflects the same steady, market-town prosperity, particularly in the open, comfortable public bar and rear drawing room, and its two dining rooms are really variations on a pleasantly familiar British theme. An extremely popular brasserie adds a light dash of simple modern style – and some striking flower arrangements - to the inn's traditional cosiness, offering very fresh-tasting, carefully prepared dishes like Omelette Arnold Bennett or panna cotta with strawberry compote. A weekend favourite with the county set, The George moves the formality up a notch while steering well clear of any stuffiness. Appealing bedrooms, many furnished with an eye for period décor.

Food serving times:
Monday-Sunday:
 12pm-2pm, 7.30pm-9.30pm
Prices:
Meals: 12.95/19.95 and a la carte 16.50/30.00
🛏 **24 rooms :** 75.00/85.00
☕ 9.95

In the town centre.
Parking

Typical Dishes

Avocado, tomato and Parma ham tart

Chicken with thyme, lemon cress

Fruit crème brûlée

Stretton

025 The Jackson Stops Inn

Rookery Rd, Stretton LE15 7RA
Tel.: (01780) 410237 - Fax: (01780) 410280
e-mail: james@jacksonstops-inn.fsnet.co.uk

    VISA

   Adnams Broadside, Oakham Ales JHB

When estate agent Jackson Stops sold off the Stretton Estate in 1955, their sign was outside what was then The White Horse pub for so long that it became known as the Jackson Stops. An interesting little anecdote which goes some way to explaining why a 17C, rurally set thatched inn should end up with such an unusual name. It's a wonderfully characterful place, rustic down to its Rutland wellies; a low wooden bar is frequented by regulars, but this then gives way to a surprising four dining areas, minimalist with plain décor and vintage scrubbed tables, silver chargers glinting in welcome. A very pleasant atmosphere prevails; the constantly evolving menus offer good value, rustic British cooking to Bib Gourmand standards.

Food serving times:
Tuesday-Saturday:
            12pm-2pm, 7pm-10pm
Sunday: 12pm-2pm
Closed 25 December and New Year. Open Bank Holiday Mondays
Prices:
Meals: a la carte 17.75/25.50

Typical Dishes

Crab risotto

Wild mushroom pancakes, mixed salad

Apricot and fig crème caramel

8mi Northwest of Stamford by B1081 off A1.
Parking

Wing

026 Kings Arms

13 Top St, Wing LE15 8SE

Tel.: (01572) 737634 - Fax: (01572) 737255

e-mail: enquiries@thekingsarms-wing.co.uk - Website: www.thekingsarms-wing.co.uk

&=room

Timothy Taylor Landlord, Marston Pedigree, Grainstore Cooking, Ten Fifty and 1 guest

Built in the early days of Cromwell's Britain, this delightful place gave the Restoration time to settle before becoming "The Kings Arms", but the cosy bar can't have changed much over the last 350 years or so. Flagstone floors, ancient beams and a big open fire lend true period warmth, while more recent prints and paintings of Rutland and around reflect a local pride that comes across just as clearly on the menu. Fresh and substantial dishes on a traditional base make good use of seasonal produce from our smallest county, and the landlord and team chip in well with relaxed, conversational service. All well away from the main bar, the bedrooms are warm and immaculately kept. Rutland Water is a short drive away.

Food serving times:
Monday-Sunday:
11am-9pm

Prices:
Meals: a la carte 20.00/30.00
🛏 **8 rooms :** 55.00/75.00

5mi South of Oakham by A6003.
Parking

Typical Dishes

Scallops with caramelised apples

Lamb in Parma ham with turnip mash

Gateau Marceaux

*I*t's Britain's cultural centre, a business superpower and a fashionista's paradise, but where do you go to find the heart of London itself? Amid the money and the power of Westminster and the City, the mini-Manhattan of Canary Wharf or the bars and studios of Shoreditch and Hoxton in between? Down by Tate Modern and The Globe on rejuvenated Bankside, in the Thames meadows of Richmond and Kew or at the top of the London Eye? The boutiques on New Bond Street or the market stalls of Borough and Billingsgate? Dreaming in the Pavillion End at Lord's or paddling on the Serpentine? In leafy Greenwich, chic Kensington and Chelsea or the glitzy streets of Soho? Wherever you start within this changing patchwork of neighbourhoods, somewhere between The Mall and Metroland, the capital's pubs are moving with the times. Away from the bright lights, brassy Victorian gin-palaces, quiet mews bars and old local boozers are being restored and reborn as London's newest gastronomic gems, bringing good-value informal dining closer to home...

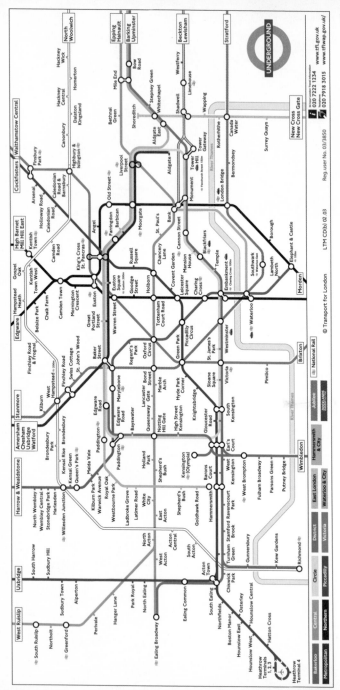

UNDERGROUND

www.tfl.gov.uk
www.tflwap.gov.uk/

☎ 020 7222 1234
☎ 020 7918 3015

New Cross
New Cross Gate

LTh CD(b) 02.03

Reg. user No. 03/3850

© Transport for London

National Rail

Bakerloo
Metropolitan
Central
Northern
Circle
Piccadilly
District
Victoria
East London
Waterloo & City
Jubilee
DOCKLANDS
Hammersmith & City
Wimbledon
Brixton
Morden

Reg. user No 04/4039

Kensal Rise

002 **The Greyhound**

64-66 Chamberlayne Road, Kensal Rise NW10 3JJ

Tel.: (020) 8969 8080 - Fax: (020) 8969 8081
e-mail: thegreyhoundnw10@aol.com

 Charles Wells Bombardier, Adnams Broadside, Courage Directors, London Pride

Once the London campus for the School of Hard Knocks, Kensal Rise is on the up, helped along by enterprising efforts like this. The old neighbourhood pub stood derelict for a year before a group of young friends – with a big picture of a greyhound, but nowhere to hang it – set to work on its restoration. To one side it's a bar, with club chairs and comfy chesterfields for slow drinking and snacking, and on the other side, it's more like a classic gastropub, with reclaimed furniture and black leather banquettes setting a slightly more formal tone. Enjoyable cooking in tried-and-tested, Modern British style takes in crispy belly pork, roast cod on pea purée and caramelised pork chops with lemon and rosemary. Sheltered rear terrace.

Food serving times:
Monday-Friday:
12.30pm-3pm, 6.30pm-10.30pm
Saturday: 12.30pm-4pm, 6.30pm-10.30pm
Sunday: 12.30pm-4pm, 6.30pm-10pm
Closed 25-26 December and 1 January
Closed Monday lunch
Prices:
Meals: a la carte 18.00/28.50

Typical Dishes

Chicken liver and pigeon crostini

Shoulder of lamb

Passion fruit custard tart

Nearest tube: Kensal Green

Willesden Green

001 ▸ The Green

110a Walm Lane, Willesden Green NW2 4RS

Tel.: (020) 8452 0909 - Fax: (020) 8452 0774
e-mail: patrick@thegreennw2.com - Website: www.thegreennw2.com

VISA

 No real ales offered

Actually a converted Conservative Club snooker room, The Green has kept its airy period proportions, but green baize is out and leather banquettes and stripped wood are in: a bustling but pleasantly low-key bar in the modern gastropub manner, its dining room a touch smarter than out front. The chef and co-owner's Caribbean heritage and an Anglo-French fine dining apprenticeship are both discernable in the generous modern cooking, but the influence is more subtle, and the balance more natural, than you might expect: bream with fried plantain and salsa appears next to duck confit on pak choi or chicken liver parfait, while the lighter selection served in the bar and on the front terrace might feature jerk chicken and coleslaw or gastropub staples like Caesar salads and steak sandwiches. Bright, spontaneous and "au fait" service.

Food serving times:
Monday-Friday:
12pm-3pm, 6.30pm-10.30pm
Saturday-Sunday:
12pm-3.30pm,
6.30pm-10.30pm
Prices:
Meals: a la carte 14.95/28.50

Typical Dishes

Scallop and ackee fricassee

Supreme of salmon, fried plantain

Baked Alaska

Nearest tube: Willesden Green ▸

Hampstead

006 The Hill

94 Haverstock Hill, Hampstead NW3 2BD

Tel.: (020) 7267 0033
Website: www.geronimo-inns.co.uk

VISA MC

No real ales offered

Haverstock Hill, to be precise, where this substantial Victorian pub has been turned around from a workaday drinking haunt to something far trendier: strings of fairy lights twinkle against oxblood-red walls and stylish twentysomethings make themselves at home in old armchairs and sofas. One half of the big, high-ceilinged bar is given over to dining and a smaller room to one side – with one wall covered in black and white photos – is also just for food. Chatty, T-shirted staff serve a good choice of modern Mediterranean cooking with the odd Far Eastern touch: tiger prawns are mixed with coriander and paw-paw salad; prosciutto-wrapped chicken and mozzarella comes with tasty Parmentier potatoes. Laid-back yet lively – a good evening out.

Food serving times:
Monday-Thursday:
7pm-10pm
Friday-Sunday:
12pm-4pm, 7pm-10pm
Closed 25-28 December and 1 January
Prices:
Meals: a la carte 16.00/24.00

Typical Dishes

Sauteed squid with chilli

Roast duck breast, garlic French beans

British cheeses

Nearest tube: Belsize Park/Chalk Farm

Hampstead

007 The Magdala

2A South Hill Park, Hampstead NW3 2SB
Tel.: (020) 7435 2503 - Fax: (020) 7435 6167

Greene King IPA, Abbot Ale, Fuller's London Pride

A stroll on Hampstead Heath reaches a perfect finale with a visit to this deliciously characterful pub, with its two surprisingly rustic bars, appealing neighbourhood ambience - and one rather dark secret, in that it's the place in the 1950s where Britain's last execution victim, Ruth Ellis, shot her lover. Original stained glass windows allow the sunshine to flood through; flickering candles lend a more romantic evening glow. You can eat downstairs or up: the former has an open kitchen, the latter an elegant, formal feel, but it's only open at weekends. Interesting, honest cooking with well-sourced ingredients provides the backbone of a solid dining-pub menu.

Food serving times:
Monday-Friday:
      12pm-2.30pm, 6pm-10pm
Saturday: 12pm-10pm
Sunday: 12pm-9.30pm
Closed 25 December
Prices:
Meals: a la carte 17.50/26.00

Typical Dishes

Pan fried mackerel, paprika and garlic

Chicken, butternut squash risotto

Chocolate parfait

Street parking or nearby Heath car park. Nearest tube: Belsize Pk/ Hampstead Heath National Rail

Hampstead

009 ## The Wells
30 Well Walk, Hampstead NW3 1BX

Tel.: (020) 7794 3785 - Fax: (020) 7794 6817
e-mail: info@thewellshampstead.co.uk - Website: www.thewellshampstead.co.uk

 Adnams Broadside, Fuller's London Pride

This attractive 18C inn sits very easily in a smart part of Hampstead equidistant between the High Street and the Heath. Wander in and relax instantly into one of the dark leather sofas arranged in cosy corners; drinks are ordered from a smart modern bar running centrally across the room. Upstairs it's a bit more formal, with three adjoining rooms linked by burgundy walls and linen covered tables. Menus are from a classical French repertoire, carefully prepared and well balanced. Recent recommendations include roast monkfish minestrone or loin of hare with red cabbage and celeriac purée. What we have here is not quite a pub, not quite a restaurant, but something satisfying in-between.

Food serving times:
Monday-Sunday:
     12pm-3pm, 7pm-10pm
Closed 25-26 December and 1 January
Prices:
Meals: 19.50/29.50

Typical Dishes
Smoked haddock, creamed leeks
Rump of lamb, fondant potato
Tarte Tatin, ice cream

Parking at the end of the street near the Heath. Nearest tube: Hampstead

Highgate

004 ## Rose & Crown
86 Highgate High St, Highgate N6 5HX
Tel.: (020) 8340 6712 - Fax: (020) 9340 0770
e-mail: johnkrimsonbars@aol.com - Website: www.roseandcrownhighgate.com

Greene King Abbot Ale

In the midst of Highgate's lifestyle shops and restaurant chains, the 300 year old Rose and Crown often passed unnoticed until its recent makeover, now signified by the "RC" monogram sign swinging above the door and the calm palette of reds and creams inside. Smaller, less hectic and more neighbourly than many, the bar now does a stronger line in Pimm's cocktails than in session pints, while a little dining room and secluded garden terrace are similarly relaxed. Here, sound, subtly seasonal cooking on a familiar modern theme adds classic French ideas and a light Asian influence: as well as the balanced à la carte, an accesibly priced lunch and early dinner menu make this a good spur-of-the-moment choice.

Food serving times:
Tuesday-Saturday:
    12pm-2.30pm, 6pm-10pm
Sunday: 12pm-3.30pm,
        6pm-10pm

Prices:
Meals: 15.95 and a la carte
17.95/35.50

Typical Dishes

Tuna tartare

Fillet of beef, friture of horseradish

Apple tart, pistachio ice cream

On street parking, free except for between 10am-12pm. Nearest tube: Highgate/Archway

Primrose Hill

005 The Engineer

65 Gloucester Ave, Primrose Hill NW1 8JH

Tel.: (020) 7722 0950 - Fax: (020) 7483 0592
e-mail: info@the-engineer.com - Website: www.the-engineer.com

     VISA

Adnams Broadside, Fuller's London Pride

A mid tall terraces in an ever-smarter part of town, this elegantly remodelled Victorian tavern is a neighbourhood pub of a very modern kind. Locals lounge over late lunch and pints in a front bar, filled with light from the broad windows, and even with the intimacy of linen and candlelight, there's an easy, come-as-you-are style about the chic dining room. There's also a little walled terrace at the back. Eclectic cooking, in gratifyingly massive portions, draws freely on global influences: dishes with a robust Pacific Rim or Modern European edge might include quail with polenta or squid on papaya, cucumber and mint salad. Efficient and friendly service.

Food serving times:
Monday-Friday:
12pm-3pm, 7pm-11pm
Saturday-Sunday:
12.30pm-3.30pm, 7pm-11pm
Closed 25 December
Prices:
Meals: a la carte 20.75/28.75

Typical Dishes

Pork and cherry terrine

Smoked duck salad

Champagne jelly, poached strawberries

Parking meters outside. Nearest tube: Camden Town/Chalk Farm

Primrose Hill

008 The Queens

49 Regent's Park Rd, Primrose Hill NW1 8XD

Tel.: (020) 7586 0408 - Fax: (020) 7586 5677

e-mail: mail@thequeens49.fsnet.co.uk - Website: www.geronimo-inns.co.uk

Youngs Bitter, Special and 1 guest ale

Chief among the places that defined the style, and substance, of the capital's gastropubs, this surprisingly down-to-earth local landmark continues as buzzing as ever, and not dining out on past successes, either. With its gauze of hazy blue-grey smoke and the Premiership highlights on in the corner, the basement bar remains an everyday-chic, urbanite drinking den and upstairs the balcony overlooking Primrose Hill is still one of the most popular square metres in North London. In the dining room, simple, close-set linen and paper-clad tables give half a glimpse of jars and rolling pins in the open kitchen, which serves up robust, almost rustic, modern classics like steak and chips and moules portugaise: a regularly changing choice is chalked up on the boards.

Food serving times:
Monday-Sunday:
12pm-3pm, 7pm-10pm
Prices:
Meals: a la carte 22.00/30.00

Nearest tube: Chalk Farm

Typical Dishes

Game and foie gras terrine

Roast lamb chump,
red wine jus

Baileys crème brûlée

Tufnell Park

003 ## Junction Tavern

101 Fortess Rd, Tufnell Park NW5 1AG
Tel.: (020) 7485 9400 - Fax: (020) 7485 9401

    VISA **MC**

Fuller's London Pride, Deuchars IPA and weekly changing guest ales

Halfway between Tufnell Park and Kentish Town stands this noble Victorian edifice, now given a modern makeover, guaranteeing swarms of North Londoners making a beeline for its doors: it's become so popular that it could be worth booking at weekends. This is a typical grand 19C metropolitan pub, with a high ceiling and ornate wood panelling and though it still has its split, two-room bar, you're free to eat in either. One is more an informal bar with a conservatory extension; the other a proper dining area with a stainless-steel, open-plan kitchen and array of mis-matched tables. Cheerful young staff serve generous portions of robust dishes with tasty, fresh ingredients sourced from local markets.

Food serving times:
Monday-Friday:
 12pm-3pm, 6.30pm-10.30pm
Saturday: 12pm-4pm,
                  6.30pm-10.30pm
Sunday: 12pm-4pm,
                  6.30pm-9.30pm
Closed 24-26 December and
1 January
Prices:
Meals: a la carte 16.50/25.00

Typical Dishes

Duck liver parfait

Organic salmon, vegetables

*Honey crème caramel,
roast pear*

On-street parking after 6.30pm
Monday-Friday and all day
weekends. Nearest tube: Tufnell Park

City of London

010 The White Swan

108 Fetter Lane, City of London EC4A 1ES

Tel.: (020) 7242 9696 · Fax: (020) 7242 9122
e-mail: info@thewhiteswanlondon.com · Website: www.thewhiteswanlondon.com

 Greene King IPA, Fuller's London Pride and 2 regularly changing guest ales

Just off Fleet Street, the old Mucky Duck has completed an elegant transformation. A lively, free-spending after-work crowd can make the ground floor a busy press of suits and pints, but the vast mirror, reflecting the white sweep of the mezzanine and the big blackboards, makes this handsome, part-panelled bar feel bigger than it really is. In the quieter dining room upstairs, a long mirrored ceiling again gives a sense of space, while elegant, close-set tables and low-backed leather chairs lend a smart brasserie atmosphere. The bar menu with pub classics and a few earthier Old English dishes – pheasant pie, pork cheeks on mash and pints of prawns – makes way for a European and British daily repertoire that might include monkfish fricassee or lamb with gnocchi and root veg. Tidy if rather formal service. Good value for The City.

Food serving times:
Monday-Friday:
        12pm-3pm, 6pm-10pm
Closed Bank Holidays
Prices:
Meals: 25.00/28.00

Typical Dishes

Calves brain assiette

Roast pigeon, confit leg, choux farci

Chocolate millefeuille

NCP car park nearby or free on street parking after 6pm. Nearest tube: Chancery Lane

Ealing

011 **Ealing Park Tavern**
222 South Ealing Rd, Ealing W5 4RL

Tel.: (020) 8758 1879 - Fax: (020) 8560 5269
e-mail: keooi@btconnect.com

   VISA **AE**

Timothy Taylor Landlord, Fuller's London Pride

The M4 thunders along close by, but visitors to the Ealing Park Tavern are oblivious to its presence. This typically Victorian pub looks large on the outside, and is cavernous within. It's split into two, with a large, pubby bar, and a high-ceilinged dining area, and light floods through large windows looking out onto the road. Despite its London location, there's a modern-rustic flavour to the cooking, which lures the locals in droves. The buzzy atmosphere is enhanced with an open-plan kitchen, old wooden tables and chairs and colourful modern artwork on the walls. Daily changing menus might offer goats cheese with mixed bean salad for a starter, with rump of lamb, rösti and rosemary jus next up.

Food serving times:
Monday-Sunday:
  12pm-3pm, 6pm-10.30pm
Closed Monday lunch
Prices:
Meals: a la carte approx. 22.00

Typical Dishes

Ox tongue with salsa verde

Roast pumpkin ravioli

Rhubarb and orange sorbet

On street parking. Nearest tube: South Ealing

Winchmore Hill

012 The Kings Head

1 The Green, Winchmore Hill N21 1BB

Tel.: (020) 8886 1988
Website: www.geronimo-inns.co.uk

 VISA M©

Greene King IPA, Bass

Facing the green at the top of the town, this informally run place is still King of the Hill; 19C eclecticism gives three cheers for itself in the imposing façade, an endearing combination of suburban tavern and stately home. Stylishly contemporary inside, it feels vastly Victorian in scale and, decorated with accumulated odds and ends, it's still no place for minimalists, but the mood overall is casual and friendly: beers, sofas, unhurried conversation. Split half and half, there's plenty of room for drinking on one side and eating on the other: a jumble of tables and chairs includes a couple of truly regal thrones, and decently sourced cooking, while holding few surprises, offers reliable theme and variation on modern classics.

Food serving times:
Monday-Sunday:
12pm-3pm, 7.30pm-10pm
Prices:
Meals: a la carte 18.00/25.00

Typical Dishes

Mussels, herb glaze

Seared tuna with French
bean salsa

Pink Champagne jelly,
summer berries

Nearest tube: Winchmore Hill
National Rail/Southgate

Fulham

015 The Salisbury Tavern

21 Sherbrooke Rd, Fulham SW6 7HX

Tel.: (020) 7381 4005 - Fax: (020) 7381 1002
e-mail: thesalisburytavern@longshotplc.com

 Fuller's London Pride, Charles Wells Bombardier plus one guest, often Black Sheep

Assured of a special place in the affections of many Fulhamites, this stylish, smartly modernised corner pub remains the locals' preferred choice for a spur-of-the-moment midweek beer or a little leisurely brasserie eating. Without aspiring to be the neighbourhood's communal living room, The Salisbury mixes in a touch of relaxing, take-us-as-you-find-us spirit with its efficiency and good management, and though it starts busy and gets busier, a natural split between the dining room and the sofas and easy chairs of the bar means there's generally no need for anxious seat–bagging. A tasty, neatly done gastropub repertoire proves just familiar enough: spring rolls with prawns and beetroot might be followed by minute steak-frites with Béarnaise and apple and cinnamon mousse with ice cream.

Food serving times:
Monday-Friday:
12.30pm-2.30pm, 7pm-10.45pm
Saturday: 12pm-3.30pm, 7pm-10.45pm
Sunday: 12pm-2.30pm, 7pm-10.30pm

closed 25, 26 and 31 December

Prices:
Meals: 18.50 (Served Monday-Saturday) and a la carte 22.50/30.00

Typical Dishes

Foie gras and chicken liver parfait

Salmon and smoked haddock fishcake

Chocolate fondant

Street parking nearby. Nearest tube: Fulham Broadway/Parsons Green

Hammersmith

013 **Anglesea Arms**
35 Wingate Rd, Hammersmith W6 0UR
Tel.: (020) 8749 1291 - Fax: (020) 8749 1254

 Fuller's London Pride, Greene King IPA, Old Speckled Hen and regularly changing guest ales

Though hidden away in deepest Hammersmith, the secret of one of London's original gastropubs is long since out, and a wait at the bar, and at table, is not uncommon on busier days, though decent service smooths things over well. Undoubtedly food-focused, there's still something of the residential street-corner pub about the place, with a sizeable bar at the centre and its dozen close-spaced dining tables kept off to one side, expectantly facing a bustling open kitchen. Capable and full-flavoured cooking in distinctly modern style encompasses dishes like home-cured gravadlax, duck with roast figs and celery and a smooth summer fool with biscotti.

Food serving times:
Monday-Sunday:
12.30pm-2.45pm,
7pm-10.30pm
Closed 23-31 December
(bookings not accepted)
Prices:
Meals: 12.95 and a la carte 19.00/24.00

Typical Dishes

Pigeon terrine

Liver on horseradish mash

Brittany cake, caramelised apple cream

Nearest tube: Ravenscourt Park/ Goldhawk Road

Shepherd's Bush

014 **Havelock Tavern**
57 Masbro Rd, Brook Green, Shepherd's Bush W14 0LS
Tel.: (020) 7603 5374 - Fax: (020) 7602 1163
Website: www.thehavelocktavern.co.uk

 Brakspear, Marstons Pedigree, Fuller's London Pride

It may not look too enticing on the corner of this unassuming West London street, but inside, the Havelock is buzzing. Formerly two shops, there are still big windows looking out onto the street. It gets very, very busy here, so for drinkers or diners, the message is simple: arrive early. Many come for the rather classy food to be had, and most tables are snapped up by seven o'clock. Menus change daily and might include pork with lentils, spinach and mash; Thai fish cakes with chilli dipping sauce; or smoked salmon with soft flour tortillas, avocado salsa, coriander and lime. Despite the bustling atmosphere, staff are friendly and attentive and obviously used to being at full stretch.

Food serving times:
Monday-Sunday:
12.30pm-2.30pm, 7pm-10pm
Closed 22-26 December and Easter Sunday
(bookings not accepted)
Prices:
Meals: a la carte 18.00/24.00

Typical Dishes

Rabbit, foie gras and prune terrine

Beef with mustard and horseradish

Treacle apple tart

Pay and display parking during the week, free parking at weekends.
Nearest tube: Kensington Olympia

Chiswick

016 **The Bollo**

13-15 Bollo Lane, Chiswick W4 5LR
Tel.: (020) 8994 6037

 Greene King IPA, Abbot

Already a popular neighbourhood meeting-place, this handsome redbrick tavern is at its best on bright summer days, when a buoyant crowd of drinkers and diners fill the spacious bar and make themselves at home on the terrace. There's a slightly smarter rear dining room – its wood panelling, burgundy walls and tan leather banquettes rather suit the pub's Victorian dimensions – but the full menu is served throughout. A core of suitably generous gastropub favourites needs no introduction, but the daily changing menu finds room for more eclectic and original dishes in the same forthright, full-flavoured style: their tasty, medium-rare tuna with braised peas, chorizo and celery is worth looking out for.

Food serving times:
Monday-Saturday:
    12pm-3pm, 7pm-10pm
Sunday: 12.30pm-4pm,
        7pm-10pm
Closed 1 January
Prices:
Meals: a la carte 20.00/26.00

Typical Dishes

Prawns, garlic, chilli

Monkfish, cinnamon and tomato sauce

Gnocchi; honey and rum sauce

Parking meters outside. Nearest tube: Chiswick Park

Chiswick

017 **The Devonshire House**

126 Devonshire Rd, Chiswick W4 2JJ

Tel.: (020) 8987 2626 - Fax: (020) 8995 0152
e-mail: info@thedevonshire.co.uk - Website: www.thedevonshirehouse.co.uk

No real ales offered

At the quiet residential end of a West London road close to the A4, this Victorian pub has reaped the benefits of a pleasant conversion: a young crowd creates a bustling atmosphere in what is now a stylish dining pub. Some of the original character is retained by way of the high ceiling and large windows. Elsewhere, the feeling is contemporary and spacious, with wooden floors, navy blue banquettes and chocolate brown leather chairs. Interesting, contemporary menus offer a succinct but balanced choice and might include, for starters, summer salad with smoked haddock brandade, tomato and chive vinaigrette; for mains, escalope of pork Milanese; and, as a refreshing dessert, nougatine glace with fresh raspberries. Obliging and efficient service.

Food serving times:
Tuesday-Friday:
 12pm-2.30pm, 7pm-10.30pm
Saturday: 12pm-3pm,
 7pm-10.30pm
Sunday: 12pm-3pm,
 7pm-10pm
Closed 25 December-1 January
Prices:
Meals: a la carte 23.40/31.95

Typical Dishes
Rabbit confit niçoise
Sauteed bream, basil and herb gnocchi
Chocolate marquise with raspberries

Parking available on the street.
Nearest tube: Turnham Green

Archway

 St John's

91 Junction Rd, Archway N19 5QU
Tel.: (020) 7272 1587 - Fax: (020) 7687 2247
e-mail: coppershack@excite.com

🍷 *VISA* **AE** **MC**

Up to 3 real ales served

This one-time scruffy, edgy boozer, down from Archway tube, looks sharp and bright again as a smartly run gastro-local. Broad picture windows light up the long counter bar, its real buzz provided by a lively mix of regulars and others at stools and scrubbed tables, but squeeze your way through to the big double doors on the right to see the place at its best. The high-ceilinged former snooker hall, in fine period proportion, is now a bustling dining room and open kitchen, hung with tall mirrors and big blackboard menus; laid-back, convivial and modestly stylish, it's just the place for varied, fresh-tasting dishes in decent quantity, including some tasty chargrills. Spirited staff in t-shirts and aprons shuttle to and fro with baskets of fresh bread, providing swift and friendly service.

Food serving times:
Monday-Sunday:
12pm-3pm, 6.30pm-10.30pm
Closed Monday lunch
Prices:
Meals: a la carte 20.00/25.00

Typical Dishes

Borscht, sour cream

Caramelised duck, watercress salad

Dark chocolate tart, Columbian rum

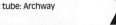
Nearest tube: Archway

Canonbury

018 Centuria

100 St Paul's Rd, Canonbury N1 2QP
Tel.: (020) 7704 2345 - Fax: (020) 7704 2204

   VISA **MC**

 No real ales offered

Without destination-bar glitz or culinary overstatement, Centuria is the unassuming gastropub we'd all like to have at the end of the road, if only for the easy-going atmosphere and the friendly mix of young regulars. The open kitchen caters well for N1's love of all things Italian: fresh, crisp frito misto – the pick of the starters – and hearty and dependable Mediterranean-influenced mains, often with a subtle Moroccan edge. Considerate staff divide their time between a busy front bar and a nicely casual, high-ceilinged dining room where you'll find a little more space.

Food serving times:
Monday-Friday:
6pm-10.30pm
Saturday-Sunday:
12pm-10.30pm
Closed 25 December and 1 January
Prices:
Meals: a la carte 20.00/30.00

Typical Dishes

Mussels, ginger and mustard sauce

Cod with spicy yoghurt crust

Assiette of desserts

Nearest tube: Highbury and Islington/Canonbury National Rail

Finsbury

024 The Peasant

240 St John St, Finsbury EC1V 4PH
Tel.: (020) 7336 7726 - Fax: (020) 7490 1089
e-mail: eat@thepeasant.co.uk - Website: www.thepeasant.co.uk

Charles Wells Bombardier, Archers of Swindon and 1 monthly changing guest ale

No-one charting the rise of the gastro-revolution could miss out The Peasant. This upmarket founding father between Smithfield and The Angel is a landmark pub in more ways than one, and if the cooking has evolved over time, the recipe for success has stayed the same: daily changing menus of robust, well-presented cooking combine fresh ingredients and a marked Mediterranean influence. The pub's original glory days came over a century ago and hints of handsome, high-Victorian style remain, from the broad arched windows and lofty ceilings to the tiled floor, but the defining quality is the bustling atmosphere of happy Londoners at full volume. Even when it's packed out, more often than not, well-organised staff keep their cool and their smiles, but head for the linen-laid tables upstairs if you want quieter, more intimate dining.

Food serving times:
Monday-Friday:
    12pm-4pm, 6pm-11pm
Saturday: 6pm-11pm
Sunday: 12pm-4pm
Closed 1 week Christmas and Bank Holiday Mondays (booking essential)
Prices:
Meals: a la carte 15.00/30.00

Typical Dishes

Smoked haddock and crab cakes

Grilled calf's liver, warm potato salad

Selection of cheeses

Parking meters opposite. Nearest tube: Farringdon/Angel

Islington

019 Drapers Arms

44 Barnsbury St, Islington N1 1ER
Tel.: (020) 7619 0348 - Fax: (020) 7619 0413

Old Speckled Hen, Courage Best and 1 guest ale

An impressive and substantial stone façade announces this proud looking Georgian pub tucked away in one of fashionable Islington's quiet side streets. It was once a ramshackle boozer, but in the last few years has undergone something of a "gastropub" rebirth: rough wooden floors, plenty of space to air-kiss, shiny leather sofas, tables and booths sited along walls made over with a contemporary palette. A delightful rear courtyard terrace is great for summer smooching, and food comes with the guarantee of a light, precise touch: white gazpacho with chilli tiger prawns; gnocchi with Gorgonzola; salmon and cod fishcake with spinach and tartare sauce.

Food serving times:
Monday-Sunday:
    12pm-3pm, 7pm-10.30pm
Closed 25-26 December
Prices:
Meals: a la carte 21.00/30.35

Typical Dishes

Fish soup, cheese and croutons

Lamb chermoula

Bitter chocolate and ginger tart

Nearest tube: Highbury and Islington

Islington

021 The Barnsbury

209-211 Liverpool Rd, Islington N1 1LX
Tel.: (020) 7607 5519 - Fax: (020) 7607 3256
e-mail: info@thebarnsbury.co.uk - Website: www.thebarnsbury.co.uk

VISA **MC**

Timothy Taylor Landlord, Fuller's London Pride and 1 monthly guest ale

A block or so back from busy Upper Street, The Barnsbury takes things at a more laid-back pace than its larger neighbours. Easy to spot in summer, with a line of flowering lavender fringing the front railings, this agreeable gastrobar keeps up the same downplayed chic on the inside. It's appealingly simple, with a central counter bar surrounded by pews, old stripped tables and chairs, cool cut-glass goblet chandeliers and quarterly changing tableaux on the walls, which are painted in signature shades of dusky duck-egg blue. Genuinely helpful staff, as smiling and at ease as the regulars, happily make the effort to talk you through the menu, a selection of robust modern pub dishes served in unstinting portions.

Food serving times:
Monday-Sunday:
   12pm-3pm, 6.30pm-10pm
Closed 25-26 December
Prices:
Meals: a la carte 25.00/35.00

Typical Dishes

English asparagus, hollandaise sauce

Skate wing, capers and rocket leaves

Gratin of soft fruits

On-street parking after 6.30pm.
Nearest tube: Highbury and Islington

Islington

022 The House

63-69 Canonbury Rd, Islington N1 2DG

Tel.: (020) 7704 7410 - Fax: (020) 7704 9388
e-mail: info@inthehouse.biz - Website: www.inthehouse.biz

  VISA MC

 Adnams ales

Around the back of the Town Hall in residential Islington, a pleasant and unassuming bar which is popular with the locals. There's a subtle change of tone in the dining room, however: smart linen, flowers, candlelight and even the artwork should prepare you for similar aspiration and attention to detail in a menu that shows the chef's West End restaurant experience. From the open kitchen come carefully composed and full-flavoured dishes: good-sized slices of crispy duck on a soy-dressed watercress salad, herb-crusted cod with noodles and a creamy mustard and chive velouté, and rich, smooth chocolate and orange parfait. A lunchtime list includes shepherd's pie and a modern take on the all-day breakfast.

Food serving times:
Monday-Friday:
  12pm-2.30pm, 6pm-10.30pm
Saturday: 12pm-3.30pm,
                6pm-10.30pm
Sunday: 12pm-3.30pm,
                6pm-9.30pm
Closed 24-26 December and
1 January
Closed Monday lunch
Prices:
Meals: 14.95 (fixed price lunch)
and a la carte 21.00/40.00

Typical Dishes

Salad of scallops

Rib of beef with a shallot crust

Chocolate pudding, vanilla ice cream

Parking meters outside or free after 6.30pm. Nearest tube: Highbury and Islington

Islington

023 **The Northgate**

113 Southgate Rd, Islington N1 3JS
Tel.: (020) 7359 7392 - Fax: (020) 7359 7393

 Adnams Best, Fuller's London Pride and weekly changing guest ales

The Northgate looks like the kind of ordinary corner pub you walk past every day, but ask around and you won't want to pass up a visit to this neighbourhood stalwart. A traditionally proportioned front room mixes scrubbed tables and wood floors with eye-catching works of modern art; a big central bar separates it from a slightly smarter dining room to the back. There's no hard and fast split, though, and locals who pull up a stool for a half may well end up staying for one of the daily specials; you can also eat out on the street-side terrace. Blackboard menus offer a cross-section of modern cooking, often working in Mediterranean ideas and flavours to good effect: unusually for a London pub, they also bake their own bread.

Food serving times:
Monday-Friday:
6.30pm-10.30pm
Saturday: 12pm-4pm,
6.30pm-10.30pm
Sunday: 12pm-4pm,
6.30pm-9.30pm
Closed 24-26 December and 1 January
Prices:
Meals: a la carte 17.50/26.50

Typical Dishes

Asparagus, anchovy and egg salad

Sea bass, fennel and potato gratin

Fig and almond tart

Unrestricted street parking Sunday, after 6.30pm Monday-Saturday. Nearest tube: Essex Road/ Canonbury National Rail

Islington

025 The Social

33 Linton St, Islington N1 7DU
Tel.: (020) 7354 5809 - Fax: (020) 7354 8087
e-mail: managers@thesocial1.com - Website: www.thesocial.com

Charles Wells Bombardier, Eagle IPA, Erdinger Weißbräu

Don't be put off by the slightly confusing sign here. It says "Hanbury Arms" on the outside because it's a listed building; look beneath that for "The Social", a name with a seriously fashionable reputation that rests on the DJ's choice of music and a spark of Islington chic as much as on the appetising food. An open-plan kitchen divides the restaurant and a buzzing bar: lots of Japanese lager is drunk, but the über-cool ambience is softened by wood panelled walls. Modern pub menus make the place worth a visit: a good range covers everything from steak sandwiches to confit of duck, and prices have a sensible look about them.

Food serving times:
Monday-Friday:
6pm-10.30pm
Saturday-Sunday:
12.30pm-5pm, 6pm-10.30pm
Closed 25-30 December
(booking essential)
Prices:
Meals: a la carte 15.00/25.00

Typical Dishes

Chicken liver pâté

Lemon chicken breast, mustard sauce

Strawberry cheesecake

Street parking available after 6.30pm and weekends. Nearest tube: Essex Road/Angel

Chelsea

026 ## Admiral Codrington

17 Mossop St, Chelsea SW3 2LY

Tel.: (020) 7581 0005 - Fax: (020) 7589 2452

 Charles Wells Bombardier, Old Speckled Hen

This well-established, fashionably located pub is something of a traditional gathering point for the well-heeled neighbours. Its main bar is invariably packed in the evenings, when a pair of shoulder pads can prove a useful fashion accessory. Lightly push your way to the back and you'll find a very pleasant small dining area with wood floor, soft lighting and even a retractable glass roof. Large banquettes, in a modern floral fabric resembling tapestry, can be a haven after the scrum through the bar. The menus are changed quarterly and provide a very good choice: there's strength in depth in the fine range of modern dishes. Pleasant, efficient service is a certainty.

Food serving times:

Monday-Friday:
    12pm-2.30pm, 7pm-11pm

Saturday: 12pm-3.30pm, 7pm-11pm

Sunday: 12pm-4.30pm, 7pm-11pm

Closed 25-26 December

Prices:

Meals: a la carte 22.75/35.00

Typical Dishes

Foie gras and chicken liver parfait

Cod in soft herb crust

Passion fruit cheesecake

Nearest tube: South Kensington ❯❯

Chelsea

027 Builders Arms

13 Britten St, Chelsea SW3 3TY

Tel.: (020) 7349 9040

♀ *VISA* ⓂⓈ

Fuller's London Pride, Adnams

Down a quiet Chelsea side street, just off the King's Road, this little terraced bar can seem impossibly crowded in the early evening, but squeeze through to the less smoky back rooms where bookshelves, wing-back armchairs and slightly surreal oil paintings create an easy, offbeat lounge ambience for the young King's Road set. Relaxed but super-efficient staff haven't let the pub's popularity go to their heads, serving up modern standards like rib-eye and fries, rocket and Parmesan salad and bangers and mash in endless succession, and somehow it all works. Home-made ice creams are a speciality and well worth a try.

Food serving times:
Monday-Friday:
   12pm-2.30pm, 7pm-9.45pm
Saturday-Sunday:
   12pm-3pm, 7pm-9.30pm
Closed 25-26 December and
1 January
(bookings not accepted)
Prices:
Meals: a la carte 17.00/28.00

Typical Dishes

Pea, mint and lemon risotto

Rump of lamb, gnocchi, tapenade

Peach panna cotta

Parking meters available on adjacent roads. Nearest tube: South Kensington

Chelsea

028 **Chelsea Ram**

32 Burnaby St, Chelsea SW10 0PL

Tel.: (020) 7351 4008

 🍷 *VISA* **MC**

🍺 *Youngs Bitter, Special, Waggledance and seasonal guest ales*

Standing out like a hardy reminder of old London near the rather soulless enclaves of Chelsea Harbour, this solid citizen of a dining pub draws in the punters like a magnet: it's on a corner so it's hard to miss it. Walk in and a feeling of good cheer is instantly awakened. This could be something to do with the bright, airy interior with warm yellow hued walls, or the light that pours in through the etched glass windows. Maybe it's just the knowledge that good beer is on handpump and interesting menus lurk round the back in intimate dining alcoves - an internationally influenced choice of dishes is up for grabs: start off, maybe, with Thai duck salad and follow it up with smoked haddock, black pudding and crushed potato. The shelves of old books might serve to remind you that in a past incarnation this was a junk shop.

Food serving times:
Monday-Saturday:
12.30pm-3.30pm,
6.30pm-10pm
Sunday: 12pm-9.30pm
Closed 25 December
Prices:
Meals: a la carte 16.85/25.85

Typical Dishes

Carpaccio of beef

Sea bass ratatouille, saffron sauce

Pear and chocolate Bakewell tart

Pay and display parking available nearby. Nearest tube: West Brompton

Chelsea

029 **Cross Keys**

1 Lawrence St, Chelsea SW3 5NB

Tel.: (020) 7349 9111 - Fax: (020) 7349 9333
Website: www.thexkeys.co.uk

  VISA AE

Wadworth 6X, Courage Directors

At a fashionable address just up from Cheyne Walk, this is more than just a local pub, whatever the inn sign and 200 year-old façade might suggest on first sight. A spacious bar, brightened by tall windows, mirrors and a curly iron chandelier and open to the gallery above, caters well for drinkers, but the glass–roofed dining room is in a style of its own: tables are spread beneath the branches of a tree, while wicker hurdles, sheaves of grass and a frieze of farming tools are best described as Chelsea Ironic-Rustic. Upstairs, you'll either love or try to ignore a faintly kitsch mix of modern and neo-Classical: the gaping Bacchus-head fireplace on the top floor is particularly impressive. More importantly, though, flavourful, generous standards and specials from the open kitchen strike a real chord with a smart crowd of local diners.

Food serving times:
Monday-Sunday:
    12pm-3pm, 7pm-11pm
Closed 25 December, 1 January and Bank Holidays
Prices:
Meals: 15.00 and a la carte 22.00/31.00

Typical Dishes

Oysters with shallot vinegar

Ribeye steak, chips and Choron sauce

Home-made ice cream

Nearest tube: Sloane Square

Chelsea

031 Lots Road Pub & Dining Room

114 Lots Rd, Chelsea SW10 0RJ

Tel.: (020) 7352 6645 - Fax: (020) 7376 4975

e-mail: lotsroad@thespiritgroup.com - Website: www.thespiritgroup.com

♀ *VISA* AE MC JCB

London Pride, Wadworth 6X, Adnams

Tucked away between Chelsea Harbour's flats and offices and the old gasworks, this refitted gastropub is a friendly, informal and surprisingly busy place – if you happen to be passing, the logic seems to go, you've every right to make yourself at home. Old schoolroom chairs and tables follow the curve of a quadrant-shaped bar-room, and while you can also get a good plate of something and a cold beer sitting at the metal counter, the most intimate place to dine is easily missed, with smart tables off to the other side; a few deep armchairs also beckon for a slow drink. Young, T-shirted staff stay on the move from table to open kitchen, serving a daily changing menu of contemporary dishes like sea bream with fennel.

Food serving times:
Monday-Friday:
12pm-3pm, 5.30pm-10.30pm
Saturday-Sunday:
12pm-10.30pm

Prices:
Meals: a la carte 15.00/25.00

Typical Dishes

Celeriac and shallot soup

Chicken and pork brochette

Sticky toffee pudding

Nearest tube: West Brompton

Chelsea

032 **Swag and Tails**

10-11 Fairholt St, Knightsbridge, Chelsea SW7 1EG

Tel.: (020) 7584 6926 - Fax: (020) 7581 9935

e-mail: theswag@swagandtails.com - Website: www.swagandtails.com

 VISA AE MC JCB

 Marstons Pedigree, Charles Wells Bombardier

Just a two-minute walk from Harrods, down a charming mews, hides this cosy little inn with its colourful hanging baskets and smart blue shutters. It makes a neat contrast to the more garish pubs in this part of London. Despite the compact proportions, it falls into two distinct sections: a front half, embellished with wood and pine, brick walls and eponymous swagged curtains; and a rear tiled conservatory with imposing posters and swish down-lighting. Seasonal modern dishes please sophisticated palates: try, perhaps, pot roasted shoulder of lamb with crushed root vegetables and jus, or smoked haddock, mustard mash, brown butter and soft poached egg.

Food serving times:
Monday-Friday:
12pm-3pm, 6pm-10pm
Closed Christmas-New Year and Bank Holidays
Prices:
Meals: a la carte 26.00/30.00

Typical Dishes

Foie gras, pear jam

Skate with lentils and goat's cheese

Stawberry and Champagne soup

Parking meters at the end of the street, or on single yellow line after 6.30pm. Nearest tube: Knightsbridge

Earl's Court

030 **Hollywood Arms**
45 Hollywood Rd, Earl's Court SW10 9HX
Tel.: (020) 7349 7840 - Fax: (020) 7349 7841

🍷 *VISA* 𝖠𝖤 Ⓓ Ⓜ©

Timothy Taylor Landlord, Charles Wells Bombardier, Fuller's London Pride

An intelligent renovation of this handsome old pub seems to have struck just the right balance: original glasswork has been preserved while fine fabrics, neo-Gothic arches and even the period-patterned wallpaper pay discreet modern homage to the more restrained school of Victorian design. Beyond the stylish bar - polished tables and club chairs - is a softly lit dining room serving a concise, Mediterranean influenced menu with some original touches: flavourful dishes include tender veal with a piquant lemon and caper sauce and a warm salad of artichokes, butter beans, aïoli and soft-boiled egg. Smooth, helpful service really adds to the enjoyment.

Food serving times:
Monday-Sunday:
12pm-11pm
Prices:
Meals: a la carte 20.00/30.00

Typical Dishes

Beef carpaccio, rocket
Grilled fillet of sea bass
Rhubarb crème brûlée

Pay and display parking nearby.
Nearest tube: West Brompton

Wimbledon

033 The Fire Stables

27-29 Church Rd, Wimbledon SW19 5DQ

Tel.: (020) 8946 3197 - Fax: (020) 8946 1101
e-mail: thefirestables@thespiritgroup.com

  VISA **AE** **MC** **JCB**

 London Pride and a selection of guest ales

Amongst the trendy natives of Wimbledon, this is seen as a rather smart and stylish addition to the eateries of SW19. They're not wrong: The Fire Stables is handily set in the centre of the village, and is a dining pub writ large, the contemporary décor being modish but not clinical. There's a high vaulted ceiling with a startling abstract painting on the wall. Furniture is a pleasing mix of modern and retro: leather sofas, dark wooden artefacts and floorboards, a coal fire. The rear restaurant serves locally renowned, heart-warming menus. How about the moist, fresh, tasty lamb burger with herbs, light mayonnaise and thick cut, home cooked chunky chips? Followed by feather light panna cotta with caramelised blood orange salad? Enough people are smitten, even though it's not the cheapest place around, so get there early.

Food serving times:
Monday-Friday:
    12pm-3pm, 6pm-10.30pm
Saturday: 11.30am-4.00pm,
                6pm-10.30pm
Sunday: 11.30am-4.30pm,
                6pm-10pm

Closed 25 December

Prices:
Meals: 15.50/23.00 and a la carte 18.00/28.00

Pay and display parking outside.
Nearest tube: Wimbledon

Typical Dishes

Scallops with fennel salad

Beef fillet, beetroot and horseradish

Lemon tart

Barnes

034 The Bridge

204 Castelnau Road, Barnes SW13 9DW

Tel.: (020) 8563 9811 - Fax: (020) 8748 9421
e-mail: thebridgeinbarnes@btinternet.com - Website: www.thebridgeinbarnes.co.uk

  rest **VISA**

 Charles Wells Bombardier, Marstons Pedigree, Ruddles Best

Smartly refurbished a few years back, The Bridge's smart gold lettering and sign proclaim a welcome change of direction for this reformed boozer. With polished tables and chairs dotted around a horseshoe counter bar, the original proportions remain, while the old fireplace and the arch of the ceiling fit the cool but casual look of the retro lounge and its palms, leather sofas and chandelier. Even in the more formal dining area, however, the hint of smartness is less important than the approachable, pleasantly lived-in feel of the place. There's also a neat decked terrace set aside for summer dining and a light seasonal shift in the menu of contemporary gastropub favourites. Though it's set back from the river, don't go expecting a slow, peaceful pint on Boat Race day!

Food serving times:
Monday-Saturday:
 12pm-3pm, 5.30pm-10.30pm
Sunday: 12pm-10.30pm
Closed 25 December
Prices:
Meals: a la carte 20.00/40.00

Typical Dishes

Baked Spanish chorizo

Red snapper, coconut and tomato

Poached plums baked on flaky pastry

Near Hammersmith Bridge, opposite Lonsdale Road. Parking in Arundel Terrace. Nearest tube: Hammersmith

East Sheen

035 The Victoria

10 West Temple Sheen, East Sheen SW14 7RT

Tel.: (020) 8876 4238 - Fax: (020) 8878 3464
e-mail: bookings@thevictoria.net - Website: www.thevictoria.net

  🍷 ✕ ✕ *VISA* AE M©

No real ales offered

The age-of-empire pub sign still hangs outside The Victoria, but any resemblance to a suburban boozer stops at the door. Restyled in clean lines and natural colours, a conservatory with linen-clad tables leads out to a terrace and children's play area: it's ideal for diners who like a quick slide or clamber between courses, but a post-lunch family ramble across nearby Richmond Park is better for really letting off steam. Daily changing evening menus combine traditional and Mediterranean-inspired dishes like walnut and rocket penne, brandade-stuffed peppers and sea bass with a bouillabaise sauce; there are one or two weekend lunch specials and understanding staff can suggest a few smaller failsafe options for young gastronomes. It's worth knowing that they're also open for morning coffee and buns: a big hit with mums and toddlers alike.

Food serving times:
Monday-Friday:
    12pm-2.30pm, 7pm-10pm
Saturday: 12pm-3pm,
          7pm-10pm
Sunday: 12pm-4pm,
          7pm-9pm
Closed 4 days at Christmas
Prices:
Meals: a la carte 17.50/30.00
🛏 **7 rooms:** 98.00

Parking. Nearest station: Mortlake/ North Sheen National Rail

Typical Dishes

Tapas plate

Spit roast beef with garlic butter

Chocolate Nemesis, cherries

Bermondsey

037 **The Hartley**

64 Tower Bridge Road, Bermondsey SE1 4TR

Tel.: (020) 7394 7023

e-mail: enquries@thehartley.com - Website: www.thehartley.com

 No real ales offered

It's already a bit of a sleeper hit with the upwardly mobile young neighbours and local after-work diners, and Bermondsey may soon wonder how it ever got on without the new version of this Victorian redbrick pub, a little one-room place with close-set, rickety bistro tables, an open kitchen and a lightly quirky taste in decoration. No points for guessing the origin of the name: the converted Hartley's factory across the road is remembered in old nanny-knows-best adverts, black and white photos showing a hard day at the marmalade vats and even jars of jam above the spirits rack. Fight down the urge to order toast and choose instead from a concise menu – terrines, steaks, roast poussin and salsa rosso, salmon cakes and chips – or half a dozen daily specials. Friendly staff, and efficient with it.

Food serving times:
Monday-Friday:
    12pm-3pm, 6pm-10pm
Saturday: 12pm-5pm,
        6pm-10pm
Sunday: 12pm-6pm
(Sunday lunch - roast menu only)
Prices:
Meals: a la carte 20.00/30.00

Typical Dishes

Baby octopus, brown shrimps, aïoli

Scallops, honey braised pig's head

Lavender crème brûlée

On street parking. Nearest tube: Borough

Waterloo

036 The Anchor & Hope

36 The Cut, Waterloo SE1 8LP

Tel.: (020) 7928 9898
e-mail: anchorandhope@btconnect.com

VISA   *MC*

   Charles Wells Bombardier, Eagle IPA

Those in the know queue round the bar and out the door for dinner at one of London's most talked-about dining pubs, where a stylish and convivial no-frills attitude extends to communal tables and boiled eggs and celery salt on the bar, yet avoids the charge of inverse pretension. A tiny open kitchen serves up simply presented but very satisfying cooking which is indebted to the French regional traditions and the earthy, rustic cuisine of St John, Clerkenwell, but remains seriously original for all that: try smoked herring with beetroot and horseradish, lamb in hay with braised peas and a sharp rhubarb jelly with vanilla ice cream. When you add impressively calm, well-timed service, even under pressure, and wines by the tumbler and carafe, this represents conspicuously good value for money.

Food serving times:
Monday-Saturday:
  12pm-2.30pm, 6pm-10.30pm
Closed Christmas-New Year,
last 2 weeks August and
Bank Holidays
Closed Monday lunch and
Tuesday lunch after Bank
Holidays
Prices:
Meals: a la carte 21.00/35.00

Nearest tube: Southwark

Typical Dishes

Smoked herring and lentils

Roast pigeon, gnocchi

Panna cotta and nectarines

Bayswater and Maida Vale

040 ## The Waterway
54 Formosa St, Bayswater and Maida Vale W9 2JU
Tel.: (020) 7266 3557 - Fax: (020) 7266 3547
e-mail: info@thewaterway.co.uk - Website: www.thewaterway.co.uk

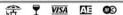 🍽 🍷 *VISA* AE M©

 Fuller's London Pride, Courage

With bright-painted barges moored along the canal, the trees in full leaf and the church spire beyond, the deck terrace of this smart gastrobar seems far removed from the pressures and cares of Travelcard zones 1 and 2. Cool young locals chat, clink beers and Pinot Grigio and relax on garden chairs and slatted benches; heaters take the last chill out of the spring air. To the right of the bar, a smart team provides relaxed and efficient restaurant-style service, coasting around a chic dining room where leather banquettes, blond wood and elegant lights set the tone. A concise but nicely weighted modern menu offers dishes like braised lamb with Parmesan polenta, crisp, golden salt cod cakes with aioli, or coffee and praline brulée. Civilised fun.

Food serving times:
Monday-Sunday:
12.30pm-4pm,
6.30pm-10.15pm
Closed 25-26 December
Prices:
Meals: a la carte 22.00/30.00

Typical Dishes
Black pudding with poached egg
Roasted salmon, peas
Ice creams with seasonal fruits

Parking. Nearest tube: Warwick Avenue

Victoria

039 ## The Ebury (Brasserie)
Ground Floor, 11 Pimlico Rd, Victoria SW1W 8NA

Tel.: (020) 7730 6784 - Fax: (020) 7730 6149
e-mail: info@theebury.co.uk - Website: www.theebury.co.uk

🍷 🍴 **VISA** **AE** **MC**

 Marstons Pedigree

The ground floor of this refurbished Victorian redbrick pub is now a rather smart meeting place, with floor-to-ceiling windows looking out to the pavement, and a striking and sizable walnut bar being the centre of attention for those who want to look in: it does have just a hint of the "place to be seen" about it. Much of the space is laid out as a comfortably modern room with stylish tables and chairs, but one end is set aside with small leather sofas, another has become a smart seafood bar. Cooking covers the spectrum, and you can get anything from Welsh rarebit and salads to full modern menus blending the continental brasserie and Modern British kitchen. Service is attentive and quite formal, but pleasantly so. More metropolitan good living from the people who brought you The Wells and The Waterway.

Food serving times:
Monday-Sunday:
12pm-4pm, 6pm-10.30pm
Closed 25-26 December and 1 January
Prices:
Meals: a la carte 22.00/35.00

Typical Dishes °

Salmon ceviche

Calves liver, marjoram potato gnocchi

Hot chocolate pudding

On street parking after 6.30pm.
Nearest tube: Sloane Square

Regent's Park & Marylebone

038 ## The Abbey Road
63 Abbey Road, St John's Wood, Westminster NW8 0AE
Tel.: (020) 7328 6626 - Fax: (020) 7625 9168
e-mail: abbey.road@btconnect.com

♉ *VISA* AE *M©*

Greene King IPA and Abbott Ale

The Beatles may have made the name famous, but owners Nick and Rob have built up a loyal following of their own with this rather grand gastropub down the road from the recording studios. Its corner location guarantees conspicuousness; so does its striking columned façade. A patio terrace with wooden benches, canopy and heaters brings out summer drinkers in swarms. Inside, the bustling front bar leads through to a snazzy duck-egg blue main dining room, with French posters, high ceiling and ornate mirrors: large windows let you see and be seen. Modern menus are in the Mediterranean style; on Sundays a roast and brunch is up for grabs. Everyday dishes might include courgette and pine nut ravioli with saffron for starters, followed by roast cod with mixed pepper coulis and spinach; to finish, perhaps, deliciously moist chocolate torte.

Food serving times:
Monday: 7pm-10.30pm
Tuesday-Saturday:
                12.30pm-3.30pm,
                7pm-10.30pm
Sunday: 12pm-4pm,
                7pm-10pm
Closed New Year's Eve
Prices:
Meals: 25.00 (dinner only) and a la carte 17.00/30.00

Typical Dishes

Beef carpaccio

Rack of lamb, pea purée, vine tomatoes

Mango with yoghurt and lemon mousse

Some on-street parking, free after 6pm. Nearest Tube: St John's Wood/ Maida Vale

A. Leprince / Michelin

- ☐ a. *Charming guesthouse?*
- ☐ b. *Room for € 40 or less per night?*
- ☐ c. *That little extra, not to be missed?*

Can't decide?
Then simply open a copy of
Michelin Charming Places to Stay!

From a remote country farmhouse to a mansion surrounded by vineyards, from a tiny rustic B&B to a château amid acres of parkland, this guide offers a selection of hotels and guesthouses for each region in France, chosen for their character, peace and quiet and hospitality to suit all budgets.

Discover the pleasure of travel with the Michelin Charming Places to Stay.

A better way forward

*S*trenghtened by the iconic BALTIC Centre, the Millennium Bridge and the Angel of the North, the sense of identity which binds Newcastle, Gateshead and the region around them has made northeastern unity a modern reality. In the days of the mighty border fiefdom, Northumbria's independent spirit took shape in the castles of Bamburgh and Alnwick and the splendour of Durham Cathedral, though the most celebrated symbols of the region date back still further. The ruins of Lindisfarne Priory and lonely Inner Farne, just off the beautiful Northumberland coast, recall the austerity and learning of the first monastic settlers, and from Housesteads to Wallsend, Hadrian's Wall is the cornerstone of Northern history. But the North East doesn't stop here – to the surprise of many visitors from further south! Some of England's most impressive working countryside can be found in the vast man-made pinewoods of Kielder Forest and the rolling line of the Cheviots: these weathered volcanic slopes are renowned for flavourful Cheviot lamb, while Kielder is known for its venison. Other specialities include fresh and smoked fish and, of course, Newcastle's famous Brown Ale, the national beverage of the "Geordie Nation"!

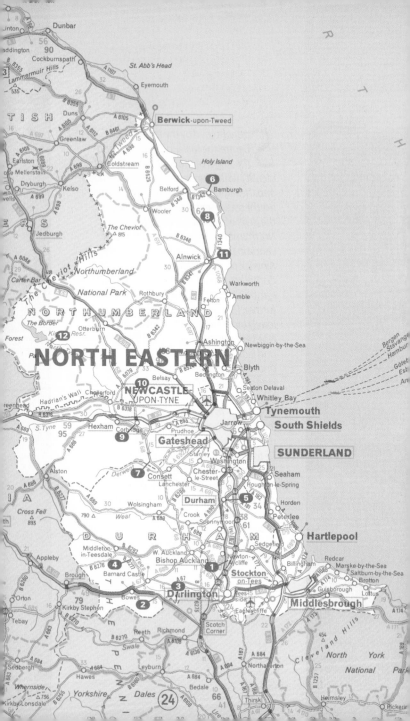

Aycliffe

001 **The County**

13 The Green, Aycliffe DL5 6LX

Tel.: (01325) 312273 - Fax: (01325) 308780
Website: www.the-county.co.uk

Greene King IPA, Charles Wells Bombardier, Northumberland Brewery Holy Island, Jennings Sneck Lifter

Attention to detail comes first in what must surely be one of Northumbria's most keenly run pubs: that's clear from the warm welcome and the pub itself – three neat, cheerfully coloured rooms with chairs and two-seater pews at polished pine tables. There's further proof in the seasonally changing cooking, as the landlord leads by example in the kitchen, producing piquant, balanced dishes like tomato cake with peppered goat's cheese and balsamic vinegar, fillets of sea bass with a tangy, sticky ratatouille chutney and vegetable spring rolls on sweet chilli noodles. Well-drilled staff with a spring in their step are always discreetly helpful, and make the whole thing seem even more of a bargain.

Food serving times:
Monday-Saturday:
12pm-2pm, 6pm-9.15pm
Sunday: 12pm-2pm
Closed 25-26 December and 1 January
(booking essential)
Prices:
Meals: a la carte 17.40/26.40

Typical Dishes

Haddock risotto

Pork belly with rosemary jus

Orange and almond tart

5.5mi North of Darlington on A167. Parking

Greta Bridge

002 Morritt Arms

Greta Bridge DL12 9SE

Tel.: (01833) 627232 - Fax: (01833) 627392
e-mail: relax@themorritt.co.uk - Website: www.themorrit.co.uk

VISA

Black Sheep ales, Timothy Taylor Landlord, Jennings Cumberland

Charles Dickens travelled across the land giving readings from his novels, and in 1839 he stopped off at Greta Bridge to stay at this stone-built inn of 18C origins. That's why you can cosy up to the locals for a drink at the Dickens bar, and admire its Dickensian style murals by John Gilroy, the Guinness firm's historian. The owners have named their restaurant after the latter, and created their own modern palette of dishes, typified by roast loin of fallow deer on a sage rosti with sweet black pepper and apple gravy, or roast corn-fed chicken with savoury bread pudding and tarragon. Bedrooms, like the novels of Dickens, come in various degrees of light and shade, shape and size; country house antiques are also prevalent.

Food serving times:
Monday-Sunday:
 12pm-3pm, 6pm-9.30pm
Prices:
Meals: 14.95/21.00 and a la carte 14.95/40.00
23 rooms: 59.50/166.50

Typical Dishes

Salmon, prawns and crab, lemon and dill

Honey glazed duck

Parkin, rhubarb ice cream

4.5mi South East of Barnard Castle by B6277 off A66. Parking

Hutton Magna

003 **Oak Tree Inn**

Hutton Magna DL11 7HH
Tel.: (01833) 627371

 Timothy Taylor Landlord, Black Sheep Best Bitter, Charles Wells Bombardier

Personally run by an amiable couple, this whitewashed part-18C inn fits in perfectly in this unpretentious little village on Hutton Beck. Its simple interior – beamed ceiling, leather-seated pews and food-themed pictures on the walls – gives it an intimate atmosphere, helped along by some keen and friendly service. The blackboard changes daily, with lunch a concise, 'best-of' version of the dinner menu, but there's a consistent theme to the robust cooking: cauliflower soup with Parma ham, garlic and thyme grilled chicken and strawberry and white chocolate trifle are among the British classics to be given an understated modern twist.

Food serving times:
Tuesday-Sunday:
  12.30pm-2pm, 6.30pm-9pm
Closed 26 December and 1 week January
Closed Tuesday lunch - booking essential Wednesday-Saturday
Prices:
Meals: a la carte 17.50/26.50

6.5mi Southeast of Barnard Castle by B6277 Off A66
Parking

Typical Dishes

Pork belly and black pudding salad

Seared wild salmon

Chocolate fondant, pistachio ice cream

Romaldkirk

004 **Rose and Crown**

Romaldkirk DL12 9EB

Tel.: (01833) 650213 - Fax: (01833) 650828
e-mail: hotel@rose-and-crown.co.uk - Website: www.rose-and-crown.co.uk

Theakson Best, Black Sheep

T his extremely fine inn was built in 1733 and bears its age with much dignity, and not a little ivy cladding. It's idyllically located in the heart of a charming village of stone cottages, and set back politely from the green; the church is across the way. Inside are all the best elements of a good English inn, with open fires, oak settles and cosy bar, adjoined to elegant lounge with grandfather clock tick-tocking gently. Food is a strong point here: a daily changing menu reflects the seasons, with local meat and game forming the core of English dishes cooked with culinary good sense. You can eat in the bar or dining room, which is decorated with curios and antique china. Characterful, well-thought-out bedrooms complete a picture of restful country living.

Food serving times:
Monday-Sunday:
12pm-1.30pm, 7.30pm-9pm
Closed 24-26 December
Prices:
Meals: 26.00 and a la carte 14.00/22.00
12 rooms: 75.00/110.00

Typical Dishes

Scallop, prawn and mascarpone risotto

Wood pigeon with vegetable rösti

Hot sticky walnut tart

3.5mi Southeast of Middleton-in-Teesdale on B6277
On the village green, next to the church. Parking

Shincliffe

005 **The Seven Stars Inn**

High Street North, Shincliffe DH1 2NU

Tel.: (0191) 384 8454 - Fax: (0191) 386 0640

e-mail: enquiries@sevenstarsinn.co.uk - Website: www.sevenstarsinn.co.uk

⟡ ⊱rest ✕ **VISA** ⓜ©

Black Sheep, Castle Eden, Theakstons, Courage Directors

Three connecting rooms make up the ground floor of this creeper-clad former coaching inn: a wood-fitted bar, a slightly smarter part-panelled lounge with banquettes and high-backed dining chairs and the formal dining room with its neatly laid tables. The same sound modern cuisine is served throughout: prompt and polite staff hurry to and fro with bold flavour combinations like black pudding and duck confit salad with balsamic dressing or sea bass on chorizo mash with asparagus. Comfortable, co-ordinated bedrooms in cosy shades of red offer useful mod cons.

Food serving times:
Monday-Sunday:
12pm-2.30pm, 6pm-9.30pm
Prices:
Meals: a la carte 14.50/27.50
⊨ **8 rooms:** 45.00/59.95

Typical Dishes

Soup of the day

Beef Wellington, spring onion mash

Sticky toffee pudding

2mi Southeast of Durham on A177
Parking on road

Bamburgh

006 Lord Crewe Arms

Front Street, Bamburgh NE69 7BL
Tel.: (01668) 214243 - Fax: (01668) 214273
e-mail: lordcrewebamburgh@tiscali.co.uk - Website: www.lordcrewe.co.uk

  rest *VISA* MC JCB

 Bass, Fuller's London Pride

In the shadow of Bamburgh's delightful Norman castle and close to the dramatic North Northumbrian heritage coast, stands this neat and traditional market town hotel, once a country inn. A privately owned collection of Grade II listed adjoining cottages, it boasts a nice, simple homely feel, typified by the traditional bar with its fine selection of real ales and wines. You can relax in wooden pews: the tapestry covers strike a sympathetic tone with the castle. Good pub food is served in the bar or the recently refurbished dining room, from where you can take in spectacular views. Afterwards, stroll to the magnificent beaches – only a few minutes' walk away – or head on up to Lindisfarne and the Farne Islands. After which a very comfortable bed at the Crewe Arms may be the most welcoming thought of the day.

Food serving times:
Monday-Sunday:
12pm-2.30pm, 6.30pm-9.30pm
Closed 1 December-31 January
Prices:
Meals: a la carte 17.20/30.70
18 rooms: 52.00/98.00

Typical Dishes

Crab meat, sweet pepper coulis

Halibut, fig and dill compote

Sticky toffee pudding

In the town centre.
Parking

Carterway Heads

007 **Manor House Inn**

Carterway Heads DH8 9LX
Tel.: (01207) 255268

Theakstons Best, Courage Directors, Charles Wells Bombardier and locally brewed guest ales

A personally owned and run pub with a growing reputation for good, honest homecooked food: a separate dining room overlooking the countryside allows you to forget the inn's on a busy road, but you'll find more of a local atmosphere in the trim little wood-fitted bar – good for a pint and a game of darts with the locals if you're feeling confident; a characterful lounge with comfy banquettes and views over the fields has the best of both worlds. Amiable staff serve an interesting, extensive menu: look out for medallions of pork with leek and Calvados and their nourishing ham broth, an ideal starter on a cold night. Pleasant, conveniently appointed bedrooms make a handy stopover if you're heading on north of the border, while a short drive west takes you to Derwent Reservoir, with lakeside walks through rolling moorland and pine forest.

Food serving times:
Monday-Sunday:
  12pm-2.30pm, 7pm-9.30pm
Closed dinner 25 December
Prices:
Meals: a la carte 18.00/25.00
4 rooms: 40.00/75.00

Typical Dishes

Chicken liver pâté, onion marmalade

Cajun blackened salmon, salsa

Sticky toffee pudding

3mi West of Consett at junction of B6278 and A68
Parking

Christon Bank

008 **Blink Bonny**

Christon Bank NE66 3ES

Tel.: (01665) 576595

Hadrian Brewery and guest ales offered

Named after the famous 19C racehorse which won the Derby and the Oaks, this 200 year-old, stone-built inn sits at the T-junction of a rural Northumbrian village by the main East Coast railway line. A passionately run place, it places a real emphasis on local produce throughout a varied menu: the owner's brother-in-law has a fishing boat and the pub's medley of fish and shellfish, including langoustines, mussels and crab, depends in part on his daily catch. The dining room is bright, colourful and modern, but elsewhere there's a stronger traditional air and a curious quirk of history: the wooden bar is from the second-class lounge of one of the Titanic's sister ships. The large fire roars here in winter – perfect for a cosy after-dinner drink.

Food serving times:
Monday-Friday:
6.30pm-9pm
Saturday: 6.30pm-9.30pm
Lunch served July-mid October
Prices:
Meals: a la carte 12.00/25.00

Typical Dishes

Maryland crab cakes

Seafood platter

Banana and amaretti cheesecake

8mi North of Alnwick on B1340
Parking

Corbridge

009 The Angel of Corbridge

Main St, Corbridge NE45 5LA

Tel.: (01434) 632119
Website: www.theangelofcorbridge.co.uk

   VISA AE ◎ ⓂⒸ

 Black Sheep and up to 3 guest ales

Personally owned and run for the first time in over 100 years, this renovated coaching inn now offers some of the best-value food for miles around, even if its friendly, unassuming bar isn't the first place you'd think of looking. Chalked up above the counter, the well-judged dishes are classically tasty: the tomato and pesto tart, double-baked cheese and spinach soufflé and bitter lemon tart combine lightness and delicacy with pronounced, balanced flavour, and for every more modern main – bream in saffron broth with fennel and pancetta – there's a traditional favourite like Corbridge sausage and mash. Quality and value qualify for Michelin Bib Gourmand recognition. Service is polite and well-meaning.

Food serving times:
Monday-Saturday:
 12pm-2.30pm, 6pm-9pm
Sunday: 12pm-2.30pm
Closed 25-26 December
Prices:
Meals: 13.50 and a la carte
11.50/27.50
🛏 **5 rooms:** 55.00/165.00

Typical Dishes

Trout, black pudding, nettle mustard

Red mullet, orange and fennel salad

Treacle tart

In the town centre
Parking

Great Whittington

010 ## Queens Head Inn

Great Whittington NE19 2HP
Tel.: (01434) 672267

 ✂ ✗ **VISA** **MC**

Queens Head Bitter, Hambleton Bitter

In the rolling wooded countryside near Hadrian's Wall lies this quiet village and its characterful pub, personally run for over 20 years. Exposed stone walls and old-English fixtures and fittings give the firelit bar a unpretentious, well-ordered atmosphere, and a neat dining room with a mix of banquettes, pews and old spokeback chairs has the same feeling of everything neatly in its place. Suitably traditional cooking has a real Northumbrian flavour to it – home-made pâtés, roast pork with caramelised apples, bread-and-butter pudding – and the service is as polite as you could wish.

Food serving times:
Tuesday-Saturday:
12pm-2pm, 6.30pm-9pm
Sunday: 12pm-2pm
Closed 1 week in Autumn
Prices:
Meals: a la carte 19.50/25.00

Typical Dishes

Avocado and prawn, apple dressing

Lamb with rosemary and redcurrant

Iced nougatine

6mi North of Corbridge by A68 off B6318
Parking

Newton on the Moor

011 Cook and Barker Inn

Newton on the Moor NE65 9JY

Tel.: (01665) 575234 - Fax: (01665) 575234
Website: www.cookandbarkerinn.co.uk

 Timothy Taylor Landlord, Black Sheep, Old Speckled Hen, Fuller's London Pride, Theakston's XB

To recommend the Cook and Barker simply as a useful stop for motorists ploughing up and down the A1 doesn't do justice to this big, friendly pub, which has been run by the same team for over 15 years. Traditional country style extends through a series of split-level rooms, main bar and a spacious restaurant, and onto an extensive menu. There's nothing revolutionary here and while a blackboard of daily specials rings the changes, most people seem happy with something classic: deep-fried Brie with apple and raisin chutney, a mixed grill and a slice of cappucino cheesecake, served by a considerate and friendly local team who are clearly used to being kept busy. Bedrooms vary in size and style, but all are comfy and dependable.

Food serving times:
Monday-Sunday:
    12pm-2pm, 6pm-9pm
Closed dinner 25 December
Prices:
Meals: 19.50 and a la carte 15.95/30.00
19 rooms: 45.00/65.00

Typical Dishes

Sea bass stir fry

Chicken supreme, warm potato salad

Blueberry crème brûlée

5mi South of Alnwick by A1. Parking

Stannersburn

012 ## Pheasant Inn

Falstone, Stannersburn NE48 1DD

Tel.: (01434) 240382 - Fax: (01434) 240382
e-mail: enquiries@thepheasantinn.com - Website: www.thepheasantinn.com

 VISA **MC** **JCB**

Timothy Taylor Landlord, Theakstons, Black Sheep, Wylam Brewery Bohemia and Gold Tankard

This impressive, ivy-clad inn boasts 17C origins; its neighbour can claim even earlier roots, but then that neighbour is the Northumberland National Park. Tradition is a byword at the Pheasant Inn: the owners have been here for nearly 20 years, and run it as keenly now as the day they arrived. There's a two-roomed bar with low beamed ceiling, polished wood tables, cluttered knick-knacks reflecting local history, and the glint of lovingly cared-for brass. The pine furnished dining room is the place for good, old fashioned, tried-and-tested cooking, where you can expect grand portions of popular favourites such as fish from North Shields quay or home-made game and mushroom pie. An old barn conversion next door has been turned into simply furnished, comfy bedrooms.

Food serving times:
Monday-Sunday:
    12pm-2pm, 7pm-8.30pm
**Closed 25 December,
Monday and Tuesday
November-March**
Closed Monday lunch
Prices:
Meals: a la carte 14.00/20.00
🛏 **8 rooms:** 45.00/75.00

Typical Dishes

Red onion and goat's cheese tartlet

Roast lamb, rosemary and redcurrant jus

Date, toffee pudding

0.5mi Northeast crossing North Tyne river
Parking

*S*tretching from the Cheshire plains to the Solway Firth, this region defies all easy definitions. Roman Chester, the busy Pennine market towns and the peaceful and scenic West Cumbrian coast are North-East England at its most traditionally picturesque, though there's a very different history to be traced in the decline and renewal of Liverpool's Albert Dock and in the shimmering modern metal of Salford Quays. Lancashire's towns, built for industry and "King Cotton", are now at least as well-known for their cross-Pennine rivalries in football, rugby and the Roses Match as for Lowry's busy cityscapes. Most famous by far, though, is Cumbria's Lake District which, at its best and quietest, remains both a challenging wilderness and a picture of serenity. Bikes, boats, trains, bridlepaths and hiking trails will all get you closer to the beauty of Derwentwater and Buttermere and the bleak grandeur of Striding Edge. Local specialities like hot pot, black pudding, Morecambe shrimps, Cumberland sausage, Cumberland sauce and air-dried ham, sticky toffee pudding and Cheshire cheese have all spread well beyond the bounds of the region, but taste as good as ever after all that fresh North Country air…

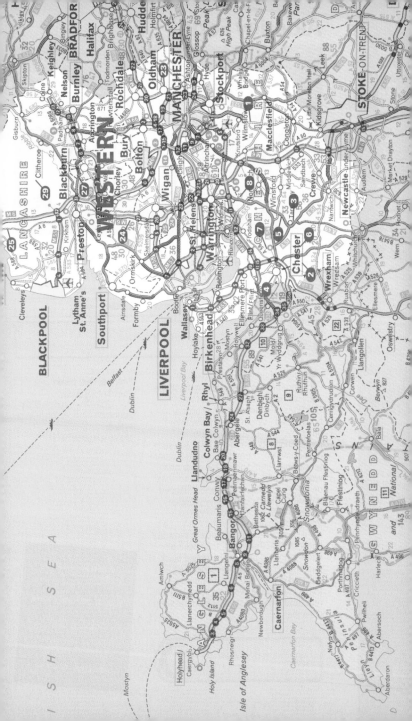

Alderley Edge

001 The Wizard

Macclesfield Rd, Alderley Edge SK10 4UB
Tel.: (01625) 584000 - Fax: (01625) 585105

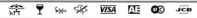

VISA **AE** **MC** **JCB**

No real ales offered

The National Trust has a good presence in these parts in the shape of Hare Hill and the local watermill. The Wizard – named after a children's book called "Wizard of Alderley Edge" – has proved an institution worth preserving in its own right. It's a 200 year-old pub which, these days, has restaurant sensibilities. Standing on the edge of a woodland park, it earns a tick in the box on most rustic counts: beamed, flagged and wood floors, with heavy wooden tables and chairs located everywhere. Very good value lunches and evening à la carte have deservedly earned the Wizard a Michelin Bib Gourmand; the cooking's interesting and precise. Try grilled black pudding on mash with poached egg and mustard cream, cod with buttered spinach and salsa verde, or sea bass with red chard, avocado salad, lemongrass and coriander.

Food serving times:
Tuesday-Saturday:
    12pm-2pm, 7pm-9.30pm
Sunday: 12pm-2pm
Prices:
Meals: a la carte 35.00

Typical Dishes

Tian of crab and prawns

Rack of lamb

Chocolate pudding, honeycomb ice cream

1.25mi Southeast on B5087.
Parking

Aldford

 **002** **The Grosvenor Arms**

Chester Rd, Aldford CH3 6HJ

Tel.: (01244) 620228 - Fax: (01224) 620247
e-mail: grosvenor.arms@brunningandprice.co.uk - Website: www.grosvenorarms-aldford.co.uk

VISA *AE* *M/C*

Flowers IPA, Weetwood, Deuchars IPA, Cotleigh 25, Robinsons

Victorian visitors to the then recently built Grosvenor Arms would find it hard to relate their experience with a modern day excursion. They might recognise the lawned gardens of this spacious, red brick establishment, set in a rural village close to the River Dee, but the bustling, wood-furnished outside dining terrace and conservatory extension would be an eye-opener, to say nothing of the huge, modern interior and busy comings-and-goings of the ever-friendly staff. The Grosvenor owes much of its recent reputation to interesting menus, which combine contemporary and rustic cooking, as typified by butterbean, bacon and watercress soup, duck breast with herb potato cake and sweet and sour beetroot, or parsnip, red onion and goats' cheese tart. What would the Victorians have made of all that?

Food serving times:
Monday-Saturday:
12pm-10pm
Sunday: 12pm-9pm
Closed for dinner 25-26 December and 1 January
Prices:
Meals: a la carte 14.25/28.40

Typical Dishes

Black pudding and red onion tart

Braised lamb, rosemary and garlic sauce

Strawberry Pavlova

3.5mi South of Chester by B5130
On the main village road. Parking

Bunbury

003 Dysart Arms

Bowes Gate Rd, Bunbury CW6 9PH

Tel.: (01829) 260183 - Fax: (01829) 261286
e-mail: dysart.arms@brunningandprice.co.uk - Website: www.dysartarms-bunbury.co.uk

Thwaites, Timothy Taylor Landlord, Weetwood Eastgate, Phoenix Arizona, Roosters Yankee

Next to the impressive part-14C parish church, this trim, redbrick house, standing four-square by a little lane, is handsome enough in itself, particularly when floodlit at night. Away from the central bar, Victorian portraits, engravings and memorabilia line the white walls and polished wood, Persian rugs and floor-to-ceiling bookshelves give the place a spacious, country feel: broad French windows flood the back room with sunlight on bright days and lead out to benches and tables on the lawn. Fresh, tasty cooking ranges from pie and ploughmans to dishes with a more modern edge, including sweet potato and pepper tarte Tatin and seafood casserole. Though busy with eaters and drinkers in the early evening, it's usually a little quieter after 8.30.

Food serving times:
Monday-Friday:
   12pm-2.15pm, 6pm-9.30pm
Saturday: 12pm-9.30pm
Sunday: 12pm-9pm
Closed 25 December
Prices:
Meals: a la carte 14.75/27.50

Typical Dishes

Satay prawns, crispy rice noodles

Monkfish wrapped in Parma ham

British cheeses

3.25mi South by A49 then take Bunbury Mill rd.
Parking

Chester

004 Old Harkers Arms

1 Russell St, Chester CH3 5AL

Tel.: (01244) 344525 - Fax: (01244) 344812
e-mail: harkers.arms@brunningandprice.co.uk

 VISA **AE** **MC**

Flowers IPA, Thwaites Best, Ossett, Harkers Silver Pale Ale and up to 7 guest ales

Especially on busy Saturday nights, it's hard to believe that this big, friendly canalside bar was half-derelict not so many years ago. Steel beams, brick pillars and tall sash windows hint at its past as a Victorian warehouse and the heavy restoration, from the ground up, kept the long, open-plan interior, adding hundreds upon hundreds of old framed cuttings, period prints, cover pages and photographs. It's got the right atmosphere for just meeting up for drinks, though a large blackboard menu covers lunchtime sandwiches, snacks and tasty, modern gastropub standards including chicken stuffed with spinach and ricotta and seared salmon on chive and yoghurt mash.

Food serving times:
Monday-Friday:
12pm-2.30pm, 5.30pm-9.30pm
Saturday: 12pm-9.30pm
Sunday: 12pm-9pm
Prices:
Meals: a la carte 16.00/20.00

Typical Dishes

Grilled goat's cheese, rocket salad

Beer battered salmon

White chocolate truffle torte

Between A51 and the canal

Cotebrook

005 Fox and Barrel

Forest Road, Cotebrook CW6 9DZ

Tel.: (01829) 760529 - Fax: (01829) 760529
e-mail: martin@thefoxandbarrel.com - Website: www.thefoxandbarrel.com

John Smiths Cask, Marstons Pedigree, Jennings Cumberland, Bass

It may look pretty ordinary on the outside, but step into the neat front bar and you'll recognise the atmosphere of a personally run pub with a friendly husband and wife team keeping things ticking over, pulling pints and pointing out any daily specials to the diners. They certainly know what their regulars like: as well as light meals and sandwiches, there's a traditional menu built around sound, substantial English dishes, and while this still offers decent variety, you can't go far wrong with braised beef on horseradish mash, followed by a trifle. The panelled, open-plan dining room can feel a bit less intimate than the lounge, but there's plenty of likeable neighbourhood spirit here too, especially when the local jazz quintet play New Orleans classics on Monday nights.

Food serving times:
Monday-Sunday:
  12pm-3pm, 6.30pm-9.30pm
Closed 25 December
Prices:
Meals: a la carte 12.50/20.00

Typical Dishes

Black pudding, feta and pear salad

Duck breast, spiced noodles

Rich chocolate torte

1.5mi Northeast of Tarporley by A49
Parking

Higher Burwardsley

006 **The Pheasant**

Higher Burwardsley CH3 9PF

Tel.: (01829) 770434 - Fax: (01829) 771097

e-mail: reception@thepheasant-burwardsley.com - Website: www.thepheasant-burwardsley.com

VISA AE D MC JCB

Weetwood ales

There's been an inn on this elevated site since the 17C; certainly, few pubs can enjoy such enviable views as those afforded from The Pheasant. Its appealing sandstone and timber frame sits atop the Peckforton Hills, giving it astonishing vistas over the Cheshire Plain to Liverpool and the Welsh Hills. Whilst beamed and open-fired, it also boasts a smart, modern feel after refurbishment a few years ago; everyone's made to feel welcome, particularly the many walkers who pass this way. Food is hearty and nourishing, ideal if you've been working up a hiker's hunger. Sandwiches get a modern twist; more accomplished dishes boast interesting and original combinations. An adjacent sandstone barn now houses attractively furnished bedrooms, and, yes, they all have the excellent view.

Food serving times:
Monday-Sunday:
12pm-2.30pm,
6.30pm-9.30pm

Prices:
Meals: a la carte 22.00/35.00
10 rooms: 65.00/90.00

Typical Dishes

Black pudding tarte Tatin

Fillet steak

Chocolate pudding, sweetcorn ice cream

2.5mi Southeast of Tattenhall
Parking

Little Barrow

007 The Foxcote Inn

Station Lane, Little Barrow CH3 7JN

Tel.: (01244) 301343 - Fax: (01244) 303287
e-mail: thefoxcote@hotmail.com - Website: www.thefoxcote.com

♛ ✗ ✗ **VISA** ⓂⒸ

No real ales offered

From the outside, this traditional looking inn certainly gives the impression of being somewhere to sink a pint. Wrong! This is now a dining pub, pure and simple, though the courteous, friendly staff and relaxed atmosphere certainly create a very gentle, local feel. The Foxcote is in a tiny Cheshire village off the beaten track, its interior given over to dining tables with gingham cloths; seafood and country prints line the walls. A vast number of blackboards greet you upon arrival: they mostly list seafood dishes featuring a broad variety of ingredients prepared in an accomplished, modern manner. Vegetarians and meat eaters are not forgotten, though, and are well catered for on the blackboards.

Food serving times:
Monday-Saturday:
  12pm-2.30pm, 6pm-9.30pm
Sunday: 12pm-2.30pm
- Seafood -
Prices:
Meals: 9.95/20.00 and a la carte 15.00/25.00

Typical Dishes

Tower of avocado crab and brown shrimp

Lobster thermidor

Chocolate and pear Bakewell tart

6.5mi Northeast of Chester by A56 on B5132
Parking

Lower Whitley

008 **Chetwode Arms**

Street Lane, Lower Whitley WA4 4EN

Tel.: (01925) 730203

 Jennings Cumberland, Charles Wells Bombardier, Marstons Pedigree, Cains Bitter

Popularity is clearly nothing new to this neighbourhood favourite, where a brisk, personally led team are well used to a full house of contented diners. The brick-built former coaching inn still welcomes its regulars for a pint, and there are few better places for it than the inviting front bar: old framed prints, real fires, even the Victorian style tiled floor all add a bit of unassuming charm. Find a simply set table in one of the three former bar-parlours and choose from a blackboard menu that might list Bury black pudding with mustard mash or liver and onions: honest, unfussy and full of appetising Northern flavour, if ever there was cooking tailor-made for a decent local ale, this is it.

Food serving times:
Monday-Sunday:
12pm-3pm, 6pm-9pm

Prices:
Meals: a la carte 16.95/30.00

Typical Dishes

Loch Fyne smoked salmon

Marinated pork chop, baked feta cheese

Eton Mess

6.5mi Northwest of Northwich by A533 off A49
Parking

Ambleside

009 **Drunken Duck Inn**

Barngates, Ambleside LA22 0NG

Tel.: (01539) 436347 - Fax: (01539) 436781
e-mail: info@drunkenduckinn.co.uk - Website: www.drunkenduckinn.co.uk

🍷 ✕rest 🚭 **VISA** **AE** **MC** **JCB**

Barngates Catnap, Cracker, Tag Lag, Chesters Strong and Ugly

A handsome inn that takes its name from a story involving a 19C landlady, a leaky barrel and a gaggle of unsteady ducks: true local history or an old taproom canard? Either way, this trusty Lakeland landmark still marks the old crossroads, in the midst of stunning fell and high peak scenery. Its lovely rustic bar with open fire is a haven for walkers, particularly those who like real ale, as The Duck has an on-site micro-brewery producing four beers on handpump, and local waterfowl are kept well away these days. The beers can be enjoyed in one of the cosy, beamed rooms which radiate from the bar, while meals are served in two pleasant dining rooms with polished wooden tables: a modern style menu has a seasonal base and an elaborate, eclectic range. Bedrooms are snug and of fine quality; importantly, they all boast the excellent view.

Food serving times:
Monday-Sunday:
12pm-2.30pm, 6pm-9pm
Closed 25 December
Prices:
Meals: a la carte 25.00/35.00
🛏 **16 rooms:** 67.25/190.00

Typical Dishes

Pigeon with liquorice

Lamb cutlets with rosemary jus

Green tea and vanilla panna cotta

3mi Southwest of Ambleside by A593 and B5286 on Tarn Hows road
By the crossroads at the top of Duck Hill

Beetham

010 **Wheatsheaf Inn**

Beetham LA7 7AL

Tel.: (015395) 62123 - Fax: (015395) 64840
e-mail: wheatbeeth@aol.com - Website: www.wheatsheafbeetham.com

Jennings Cumberland, Heysham Brysons, Shifting Sands and alternating guest ales

Stained glass windows, old prints of country life and prize sportfish from the Cumbrian rivers and lakes, mounted in glass cases, all add to the genuine charm of this part-16C inn, its beamed bar set with polished tables and spokeback chairs and filled with a warm and bustling atmosphere. An extensive menu – served downstairs and in the quieter first floor dining room – begins with reliable pub standards and interesting sandwiches, but also finds room for a few more dishes with a modern edge. Pastel-toned bedrooms with neat fittings and tapestry-style fabrics are all named after nearby areas: you should find them homely and practical, even if local geography isn't your strong point.

Food serving times:
Monday-Saturday:
12pm-2pm, 6pm-9pm
Sunday: 12pm-2pm,
6.30pm-8.30pm
Closed 25 December
(fixed price meal 6pm-7pm)
Prices:
Meals: 11.95 and a la carte
16.85/26.00
🛏 **6 rooms:** 40.00/80.00

Typical Dishes

Scallops, rhubarb and pepper compote

Wood pigeon tartlet

Pear and butterscotch parcel

Off the A6, 1mi south of Milnthorpe.
Parking

Cartmel Fell

011 Masons Arms

Strawberry Bank, Cartmel Fell LA11 6NW

Tel.: (015395) 68486 - Fax: (015395) 68780
e-mail: info@strawberrybank.com - Website: www.strawberrybank.com

 Hawkshead bitter, Black Sheep, Timothy Taylor Landlord, Jennings Cumberland

The characterful downstairs bar and its layout of little snugs, parlours and open fires in the old ranges are all clues to the history of the Masons Arms, originally built as a cottage and converted in the 1800s. This smaller, family scale can make it feel a little crowded at the busiest times, so head upstairs to the restaurant if you want a touch more comfort and formality, or take a seat outside. From the heights of Strawberry Hill there are charming views to be had from the rear garden or the front terrace, handsomely equipped with broad canopy parasols, lights and heaters to bring a hint of café culture to the Lakes. A popular menu – the same at lunch and dinner – combines British standards like Stilton mousse and chutney or chicken, leek and ham pie with international favourites like Caesar salad, lasagne and barbecue ribs.

Food serving times:
Monday-Sunday:
        12pm-2pm, 6pm-9pm
Prices:
Meals: a la carte 15.00/25.00
3 rooms: 125.00

Typical Dishes

Warm duck salad

Shoulder of lamb, honey and garlic

Cheesecake with Drambuie fruits

3.75mi North East of Newby Bridge by A590 off A592. Parking

Casterton

012 Pheasant Inn

Casterton LA6 2RX

Tel.: (015242) 71230
e-mail: pheasantinn@fsbdial.co.uk - Website: www.pheasantinn.co.uk

    rest *VISA* **MC**

Theakston Best Bitter, Black Sheep, Dent Aviator

Halfway between the Lake District and the Dales lies the agreeable little village of Casterton and, at its centre, this traditional 18C inn at the foot of the fell. With its easy pace and a very open and natural warm welcome, it seems to draw on the best of the village's character, and its collection of local artefacts and farming prints are reminders that this part of Cumbria still earns part of its living from the land. There's a room set aside for dining, but you can also choose from a full menu - with surprisingly varied daily specials – in the three traditionally appointed bars and lounges: very comfortable, especially when they stoke up the fires. Tasty, homely dishes, from sandwiches, grills and filling stews to baked crab and honey-roast ham, seem entirely in keeping here. Inviting, good-sized bedrooms.

Food serving times:
Monday-Sunday:
12pm-2pm, 6pm-9pm
Closed dinner 25 December and 2 weeks January
Prices:
Meals: a la carte 14.90/27.00
10 rooms: 35.00/84.00

In the centre of the village. Parking >

Typical Dishes

Egg mayonnaise, fresh asparagus

Topside beef and Yorkshire pudding

Sticky toffee pudding

Castle Carrock

013 The Weary Sportsman

Castle Carrock CA8 9LU

Tel.: (01228) 670230 - Fax: (01228) 670089
e-mail: relax@theweary.com - Website: www.theweary.com

  VISA **MC**

  Occassionally one local guest ale

Two minutes' drive from the beauty spot of Talkin Tarn, this white-painted pub looks the picture of pretty Lake District gentility – until you open the front door. Striking modern lighting, chic wood and slate and dashes of zingy modern colour make the restyled front bar look anything but weary: you can take a seat on the sofa and dine here, or head through to the conservatory and a smart walled terrace. With a nod to local tradition, a sizeable modern menu finds room for toffee pudding or a starter of black pudding and apple mash with whisky sauce, but also takes in vegetable tempura, chilli and garlic sea bass and a Pernod parfait with cassis pear. Fine new bedrooms certainly don't let the side down, with more bold colourways plus stylish bathrooms and flat-screen televisions.

Food serving times:
Monday-Sunday:
12pm-2pm, 6pm-7pm
Closed 25-26 December and
1 January
Closed Monday lunch
Prices:
Meals: a la carte 18.00/32.00
🛏 **5 rooms:** 70.00/125.00

4mi south of Brampton on B6413.
Parking

Typical Dishes

Scallops, ginger and spring
onion sauce

Lamb fillet in Parma ham,
mushroom jus

Assiette of desserts

Coniston

014 **The Black Bull Inn**

1 Yewdale Rd, Coniston LA21 8DU

Tel.: (015394) 41335 - Fax: (015394) 41168

e-mail: theblackbullconiston@easicom.com

 VISA **MC**

 Coniston Bluebird, Old Man Ale, Opium, Blacksmiths Ale from own microbrewery, Belgian bottled beers

There's no mistaking this sizeable 16C coaching inn at the foot of the Old Man, not with the sign of a hefty-looking bull hanging below the eaves. From blackened timbers to stone floor, it's a decent, personally run inn of the old school, though with far more depth of character than most. The pleasant dining room is neatly kept, but the bar itself just edges it for warmth and personality, and beer experts will waste no time in pulling up a stool and ordering its great speciality. Of the pints produced on-site, none is more renowned than Bluebird: it shares its name with Duncan Campbell's record breaking hydroplane and a memento recalls the triumph and loss of the speed-king on nearby Coniston Water. With its true local flavours, honest and homely Lakeland cooking makes a fine accompaniment to an ale; try local beef followed by apple pie.

Food serving times:
Monday-Sunday:
12pm-9pm
Closed 25 December
Prices:
Meals: a la carte 12.00/20.00
15 rooms: 35.00/90.00

On A593
Parking

Typical Dishes

Soup of the Day

Trout with almonds

Plum pudding

Crosthwaite

015 Punch Bowl Inn

Crosthwaite LA8 8HR

Tel.: (015395) 68237 - Fax: (015395) 68875
e-mail: enquiries@punchbowl.fsnet.co.uk - Website: www.punchbowl.fsnet.co.uk

Black Sheep, Coniston Bluebird, XB

Seasonal ingredients and a traditional base define the menu in this part 17C Cumbrian inn. The fine balanced cuisine draws out robust, pronounced flavours from classic combinations - at prices in the Bib Gourmand range - and among the best are a satisfyingly meaty pea and ham soup, crisp, juicy beetroot tart with goat's cheese, honey and mustard chicken and chocolate and ginger tart served with honey ice cream. Framed menus from around the world decorate three dining areas, including a raised gallery, and the friendly, efficient service would be worthy of a restaurant, but the Punch Bowl is still recognisibly a neighbourhood pub, with locals propping up the front bar. In the fells and banks of the Lake District, there's no shortage of after-lunch walks in the area, and the road running west leads on to Windermere. Simple, rustic rooms.

Food serving times:
Tuesday-Saturday:
12pm-2pm, 6pm-9pm
Sunday: 12pm-2pm
Closed 25 December and 2 weeks November-December

Prices:
Meals: 14.95 and a la carte 20.00/30.00
⊨ **3 rooms:** 37.50/65.00

5.25mi West of Kendal by All Hallows Lane
Next to the church. Parking

Typical Dishes

Cullen skink

Rolled saddle of rabbit, parsnip mash

Honey and Drambuie brûlée

Great Salkeld

016 **Highland Drove Inn**

Great Salkeld CA11 9NA

Tel.: (01768) 898349 - Fax: (01768) 898708
e-mail: highlanddrove@btinternet.com - Website: www.highland-drove.co.uk

Theakstons Black Bull, John Smiths Cask and various guest ales

Approaching the Lake District from the north, this is an ideal stop-off point before the inevitable encounter with the tourist masses. It's a pleasant whitewashed pub in a tiny village in the heart of the Eden valley, and dates back hundreds of years. There are beams and a good selection of cask ales, but what really catches the eye is the content of the menus. Dishes are changed on a daily basis and revolve around local meat, game and fish. Sea bass, salmon fillet and brill regularly share the honours with mallard duck, rack of lamb and spiced Elizabethan pork; look out too for the steaks from herds reared in Cumbria. Suitably replenished, you'll need no reminding that you're in first-class walking country. Comfy bedrooms await those staying on.

Food serving times:
Monday-Sunday:
12pm-2pm, 6.30pm-9pm
Closed 25 December
Closed Monday lunch
except Bank Holidays
Prices:
Meals: 13.50 and a la carte
17.50/28.95
5 rooms: 35.00/65.00

Typical Dishes
Seafood plate
Beef fillet, Stilton butter, port sauce
Raspberry and hazelnut meringue

6.75mi North of Penrith by A686.
Parking

Loweswater

017 Kirkstile Inn

Loweswater CA13 0RU

Tel.: (01900) 85219 · Fax: (01900) 85239
e-mail: info@kirkstile.com · Website: www.kirkstile.com

Jennings, Coniston Bluebird, Yates and Melbreak and Grasmoor brewed on site

A part-16C inn in a picture-perfect setting: an isolated and beautiful valley between Loweswater and Crummock Water. If you can tear yourself away from the view, head inside to the welcoming beamed bar or a more formal dining room and choose a lighter lunch – from sandwiches upwards – or more substantial cooking at dinner. Fresh Cumbrian produce, organic where possible, is the cornerstone of their traditional cooking: decent, substantial dishes like Lakeland rump steak or beef and ale pie – plus a couple of specials – find favour with locals and visitors and certainly suit the home-brewed beers. Simple tidy accommodation with lovely hill views; two rooms suitable for families. Needless to say, there's good climbing and walking nearby.

Food serving times:
Monday-Sunday:
12pm-2pm, 6pm-9pm
Closed 25 December
Prices:
Meals: a la carte 12.00/17.00
🛏 **9 rooms:** 45.00/90.00

Typical Dishes

Black pudding, Kirkstile's beer batter

Lamb, honey and mint

Cumberland rum Nicky

Located between Loweswater and Crummock Water. Parking

Portinscale

018 The Farmers

Portinscale CA12 5RN

Tel.: (017687) 73442
e-mail: lynne@irowe.fsnet.co.uk

  VISA

Jennings Bitter, Cumberland Ale

On the face of it, this slate-built village pub looks much the same as it ever was: a few tables out front, a tiny beer garden behind and a neat, stone-flagged bar with stools and tables occupied by the regulars, who make up the backbone of the pub's darts and quiz teams and sup their pints to the quiet click of dominoes. But the remainder of the pub, decorated in bright Mediterranean tones, is given over to dining; besides the lunchtime ciabattas, galettes, ploughmans and homemade breads, a more adventurous main menu offers pancetta wrapped salmon on olive ratatouille, and rhubarb and white chocolate fool. Very helpful service binds together this deserving combination of the modern and the traditional.

Food serving times:
Monday-Sunday:
12pm-2pm, 6pm-9pm
Prices:
Meals: a la carte 18.00/25.00

Typical Dishes

Potato and haggis hash brown

Honey and mustard baked salmon

Chocolate brownie

1.5 miles West of Keswick by A66. Limited parking in the village

Tirril

019 Queens Head Inn

Tirril CA10 2JF
Tel.: (01768) 863219 - Fax: (01768) 863243
e-mail: info@queensheadinn.co.uk - Website: www.queensheadinn.co.uk

Up to 4 ales from Tirril brewery, plus 1 guest Cumbrian ale

W hen not wandering lonely as a cloud, the great William Wordsworth also dabbled in the more profitable world of property management. God's gift to the Lakes Tourist Board signed away the family's stake in this charming 18C inn in 1836 and the contract still hangs in the atmospheric bar, along with such un-Wordsworthian curios as a hunting horn, a First World War shell and a diving helmet. Ullswater trout and local lamb feature on a hearty but carefully prepared menu which works much better on the plate than on the page: lamb and rosemary pie and steak and ale pudding show the same full-flavoured style. The pub also hosts a Cumbrian Beer and Sausage weekend every August. Four rooms for dining include a pleasant conservatory, ideal in summer.

Food serving times:
Monday-Sunday:
    12pm-2pm, 6pm-9.30pm
Closed dinner 25 December
Prices:
Meals: a la carte 14.00/24.00
🛏 **7 rooms:** 40.00/70.00

Typical Dishes

Penrith sausage salad

Lamb in redcurrant jus

White chocolate brûlée, shortbread

3mi South West of Penrith by A6 on B5320. Parking

Troutbeck

020 Queens Head

Troutbeck LA23 1PW

Tel.: (015394) 32174 - Fax: (015394) 31938
e-mail: enquiries@queensheadhotel.com - Website: www.queensheadhotel.com

🍷 ✕ room   *VISA* **M**©

Coniston Old Man, Hawkshead Red, Barngates Tag Lag, Tirrel Old Faithful

N ot many pub bars are built around superbly carved Elizabethan four-poster beds. In fact, this 400 year old posting inn boasts probably the only one in the country. The place has charm and character to spare. You might get lost in the warren of beamed and panelled rooms, in which cobwebbed musical instruments hang, and beribboned stuffed beasts gaze. You'll come across old cushioned settles, stone walls and a roaring open fireplace. The upstairs dining room has capacious windows for even bigger views over valley and moor. Settle down at scrubbed oak tables and extinguish countryside appetites with imaginative, well-cooked, tasty Northern food with traditional and modern options, served by staff eager to please. You might want to stay the night: bedrooms boast antique furnishings and terrific views.

Food serving times:
Monday-Sunday:
12pm-2pm, 6.30pm-9pm
Closed 25 December
Prices:
Meals: 15.50 and a la carte 15.00/25.00
🛏 **14 rooms:** 65.00/105.00

Typical Dishes

Duck breast with smoked chicken mousse

Lamb shank, wine jus

Bread and butter pudding

4mi North of Ambleside by A592
Parking

Ulverston

021 **Bay Horse**

Canal Foot, Ulverston LA12 9EL

Tel.: (01229) 583972 - Fax: (01229) 580502
e-mail: reservations@bayhorsehotel.co.uk - Website: www.thebayhorsehotel.co.uk

 rest **VISA** **AE** **MC**

 Old Speckled Hen, Thwaites, Jennings, Marston

Commanding views of the Lancashire and Cumbria Fells are just one reason to recommend this well-established little inn by Ulverston Sands. The bar area, well known for its capacious horse's head of stone, has a smart ambience, afforded by plush built-in wall banquettes, stylish wooden armchairs, beams and open fire. An adjacent conservatory houses a more formal linen-clad restaurant, which boasts fine views over Morecambe Bay. Tasty, effectively prepared cooking finds favour with appreciative diners, who have long admired the flavourful, seasonal menus, typified by roast fillet of halibut, or Cumberland sausage with date chutney, cranberry and apple sauce. Bedrooms - snug and with a host of extras - have the enviable coastal view.

Food serving times:
Monday-Sunday:
12pm-2pm, 7.30pm
Closed Monday lunch. One sitting for dinner 7.30pm for 8pm
Prices:
Meals: 18.95/28.50 and a la carte 30.00/35.00
🛏 **9 rooms:** 80.00/150.00

Typical Dishes

Potted Morecambe Bay shrimps

Salt marsh lamb cutlets

Sticky toffee pudding

2.25mi East of Ulverston by A5087, turning left at Morecambe Tavern B&B and beyond industrial area, on the coast. Parking

Watermillock

022 **Brackenrigg Inn**

Watermillock CA11 0LP

Tel.: (017684) 86206 - Fax: (017684) 86945
e-mail: enquiries@brackenrigginn.co.uk - Website: www.brackenrigginn.co.uk

   rest   **VISA** MC

Coniston Bluebird, Jennings Cocker Hoop, Cumberland Ale, Theakstons, Black Sheep, Tirril Old Faithful

Commanding fine views of the lakes and mountains, the Brackenrigg Inn is sure to appeal to Lakeland pub lovers, for many reasons. Its open main bar has changed a little since it welcomed the post coach in the 18C, but its comfy seats, dartboard and promising line of bar taps still sends the right message to the tired traveller. Meals are also served in two more formal adjoining rooms and the appealing, full-flavoured cooking casts its net surprisingly wide. They aim to offer something for everyone, serving potato, chorizo and trout salad or salmon with basil and asparagus alongside well-known favourites, snacks and daily specials. Well marshalled service directed by the experienced patrons – still as keen and amiable as ever – binds the whole place together.

Food serving times:
Monday-Sunday:
  12pm-2.30pm, 6.30pm-9pm
Prices:
Meals: 18.95 and a la carte
17.95
17 rooms: 32.00/87.00

Typical Dishes

Mussels, wine, dill and salmon sauce

Cumberland sausage, apple mash

Stickly toffee pudding

On A592 besides Ullswater
Parking

Oldham

023 The White Hart Inn (Brasserie)

51 Stockport Rd., Lydgate, Oldham OL4 4JJ

Tel.: (01457) 872566 - Fax: (01457) 875190
e-mail: bookings@thewhitehart.co.uk - Website: www.thewhitehart.co.uk

VISA AE MC

Timothy Taylor Landlord, JW Lees, Tetleys and a selection of guest ales

Between the town centre and Saddleworth Moor, this great local favourite remains ever-popular; in part a tribute to the attentive staff who provide a pleasant but quite formal style of service. Two rooms off the main bar – one larger and slightly more comfortable – are set aside for lunch and dinner, but share the same likeably no-frills décor of bricks, beams and open fires: overall there's a friendly mix of drinkers and diners, although the focus is very definitely on the owner's locally renowned cooking. On an expanding menu you'll find full-flavoured cooking in the Modern British vein including goat's cheese ravioli with tomato concassé, sea trout on lightly curried spinach or lemon tart and raspberry sorbet. It's Bib Gourmand value, but they occasionally offer a special set-price lunch and early evening menu.

Food serving times:
Monday-Saturday:
12pm-2.30pm, 6pm-9.30pm
(booking essential)
Prices:
Meals: 14.50 and a la carte 21.00/31.75
12 rooms: 80.00/110.00

Typical Dishes

Grilled Saddleworth
sausage, mash

Beer-battered haddock

Carrot and marzipan sponge

3mi East of Oldham by A669 on A6050. Parking

Wrightington Bar

024 **The Mulberry Tree**
Wrightington Bar WN6 9SE
Tel.: (01257) 451400 - Fax: (01257) 451400

VISA **MC**

 Flowers IPA

Not a pub for the traditionally-minded lover of beams and foaming ale. Nevertheless, what it lacks in traditional character, it makes up for in ample size and ultimately in the quality of the food. The rather cavernous open plan interior has a spacious bar with simple tables and chairs occupying one end, and a large, more formal linen-clad restaurant at the other. Both share a warm, buzzy atmosphere as well as the same range of specials, and this is where the pub comes into its own: the satisfying modern cooking demonstrates sound experience and culinary know-how and portions are, by any standards, generous. Local, seasonal ingredients are to the fore in cuisine which pays due homage to global influences and earns a Bib Gourmand for its quality and keen pricing

Food serving times:
Monday-Sunday:
12pm-2pm, 6pm-9.30pm
Closed 26 December and 1 January
Prices:
Meals: 19.50 and a la carte 22.50/35.00

Typical Dishes
Black pudding on an English muffin
Lamb shank, basil and tomato jus
Chocolate pudding

3.5mi Northwest of Standish by A5209 on B5250
Parking

Forton

025 ## Bay Horse Inn

Forton LA2 0HR

Tel.: (01524) 791204 - Fax: 01524 791204
e-mail: wilkicraig@aol.com - Website: www.bayhorseinn.com

 VISA *AE* *MC* *JCB*

Pendle Witches Brew, Lancaster Bomber, Everards Tiger, Boddingtons

With service from a cheery local team, enthusiastic, all-action management from the chef, well-chosen regional produce and big helpings of homemade everything, this hidden 18C inn has personality in abundance. A lovely rustic bar, filled with framed menus and sporting memorabilia and warmed by an open fire, leads into a smart, airy dining room. Pick whichever suits you best and choose from a quarterly menu, a list of chalkboard specials or the daily-changing sandwich board: Lancashire hot pot terrine, Morecambe Bay shrimps and Cumbrian roast beef sum up an appealing modern-rustic range with a forthright Lancastrian flavour.

Food serving times:
Tuesday-Saturday:
    12pm-2pm, 7pm-9.30pm
Sunday: 12pm-2pm
Closed 25 December, 1 week January and 1 week August
Prices:
Meals: a la carte 25.00/35.00

Typical Dishes

Langoustines

Beef, mushroom and truffle sauce

Cheesecake, apple and vanilla ice cream

1.25mi North by A6 on Quernmore rd
Parking

Hornby

026 The Barns Brasserie

Main St, Hornby LA2 8JT

Tel.: (015242) 21204 - Fax: (015242) 22258
e-mail: information@diningroomhornby.co.uk - Website: www.thecastlehotel.net

   VISA **M©**

Black Sheep Bitter, Copper Dragon, Brysons Castle Bitter, Jennings Cumberland

This spacious, simply styled dining room began life as a stable block, serving the ivy-twined coaching inn at the front, and still has the exposed brick and flagged floor to prove it. A large, traditional lounge bar is fine for a drink, but there's far more emphasis on food. A broad but familiar choice of tried-and-tested English cooking incorporates some popular international dishes for good measure: don't be surprised to find Caesar salad and smoked salmon pasta alongside kidney and bacon or fish and chips. Though on the road to Lancaster, a short drive takes you up the Vale of Lune or off towards the Forest of Bowland.

Food serving times:
Monday-Sunday:
12pm-10pm

Prices:
Meals: 9.95 and a la carte 14.95/39.99
10 rooms: 50.00/90.00

Typical Dishes

Black pudding, bacon, bitter leaves

Pork, apple and onion mash

Local cheeseboard

9mi Northwest of Lancaster on A683
Parking

Mellor Brook

027 ## The Feilden's Arms

Branch Rd, Mellor Brook BB2 7PR
Tel.: (01254) 812219 - Fax: (01254) 769011

🍴 🍷 room *VISA* ⓜⓒ

 No real ales offered

Though neatly refurbished, this well-run village pub still does right by its regulars. It's centred on a big main bar and feels best when there's a good local turn-out for a couple of pints, the best-of-three at the dartboard or a game of pool. Though most of the eating actually goes on in the snug towards the back or in the slightly smarter conservatory, the careful cooking is anything but an afterthought. An enjoyable bar menu offers precisely prepared classics like shepherds pie, goat's cheese salad with walnut dressing and a rich, smooth chocolate marquise, never over-complicating something that's best done simply and offering very good value for money. The more formal dining room is matched by more elaborate cuisine, which remains well-judged and presented; an efficient team provide composed but cheery service.

Food serving times:
Monday-Saturday:
12pm-2.30pm,
6.30pm-9.30pm
Sunday: 12pm-9pm
Closed 25 December
(bar meals Sunday-Tuesday)
Prices:
Meals: a la carte 11.00/24.00
🛏 **4 rooms:** 70.00/96.00

Typical Dishes

Veloute of smoked salmon

Belly of pork, grain mustard jus

Sable of strawberries

3.5mi Northwest of Blackburn by A677
Parking

Tunstall

028 Lunesdale Arms

Tunstall LA6 2QN

Tel.: (015242) 74203 - Fax: (015242) 74229
e-mail: info@thelonesdale.com - Website: www.thelunesdale.com

Black Sheep and weekly changing guest ales

This rural dining pub with Cumbria to the north and Yorkshire to the west is making friends across the board, and across the borders. What was probably once a licensed room of the old village hall now feels pleasantly, deliberately modern; uncluttered and bright with chunky tables and chairs dotted around, squashy sofas facing a vast fireplace and a combined family and games room for post-lunch pool or table football. Eat – or drink – where you like: a blackboard menu changes as seasons and local suppliers dictate, but sharp, simple, flavourful dishes like spinach, pea and mint soup with homemade bread, goujons of cod, or broccoli, mustard and cheese tart make good, nourishing lunches, while a larger dinner selection could take in chicken with pesto or herb-crusted fennel with garlic butter.

Food serving times:
Tuesday-Friday:
 12pm-2pm, 6pm-9pm
Saturday-Sunday:
 12pm-2.30pm, 6pm-9pm
Closed 25-26 December.
Open Bank Holiday Mondays
Prices:
Meals: a la carte 15.00/22.00

Typical Dishes

Deep fried Brie, tomato chilli relish

Duck breast, ginger and almond couscous

Honey cheesecake

4mi South of Kirkby Lonsdale on A683
Parking

Whitewell

029 Inn at Whitewell
Forest of Bowland, Whitewell BB7 3AT
Tel.: (01200) 448222 - Fax: (01200) 448298

  VISA *MC* *JCB*

 Marstons Pedigree, Timothy Taylor Landlord

A delightful location in a river valley in the Forest of Bowland means that a visit is always going to be special. The pub itself is an extended 14C cottage which once served as a coaching inn; nowadays it's very personally run with a endearing eccentricity which surfaces at the unlikeliest moments! It has considerable charm downstairs with a lovely faded bar full of eyecatching curios, a reception-cum-shop and an intimate restaurant overlooking the River Hodder and Trough of Bowland. Dishes have a traditional base and make good use of sound Lancastrian produce: ask for a table in the restaurant or just pull up a chair in the bar. The large, comfortable bedrooms really are the pick of the place - they boast plenty of style, and some have real peat fires. All have CD players and fittings that touch on the highest inn standards.

Food serving times:
Monday-Sunday:
    12pm-2pm, 7pm-9.30pm
Prices:
Meals: a la carte 15.00/35.00
🛏 **24 rooms:** 69.00/140.00

Typical Dishes

Roast pigeon breast

Fillet of beef with horseradish mash

Toffee and banana brûlée

6mi Northwest of Clitheroe by B6243
Parking

☐ a. *Hollywood Studios (California)?*
☐ b. *Tabernas Mini Hollywood (Spain)?*
☐ c. *Atlas Film Studio (Morocco)?*

**Can't decide?
Then immerse yourself in
the Michelin Green Guide!**

- Everything to do and see
- The best driving tours
- Practical information
- Where to stay and eat

The Michelin Green Guide:
the spirit of discovery.

*N*ot content with seven historic counties, the South East has always looked further for inspiration. This, after all, is the region that gave the world a prince's Indian pavillion facing the Brighton seafront, the pretty redbrick streets of Sandwich, bridging the Channel to Holland and Germany, and Waddesdon Manor, a perfect Loire Chateau just off the A41. Yet these are as much images of "Englishness" as the domes and spires of Oxford or Kent's white-capped oasthouses amid the hop-poles and apple orchards of the Weald. Here in the South East you'll find the start of the Cotswolds and the freedom of the South Downs Path, the ancient vantage of White Horse Hill and the rural calm of Royal Berkshire's riverside villages, while Canterbury and Winchester, Blenheim, Chartwell and Windsor all have their special place in British history. For a change of pace, fast or slow, the quiet countryside or the colourful cultural life of Brighton are both within an hour of the capital. The South East is also a place to dine well: Whitstable oysters, delicately flavoured Romney Marsh lamb and Aylesbury duck, not to mention a long brewing tradition, are just some of its specialities.

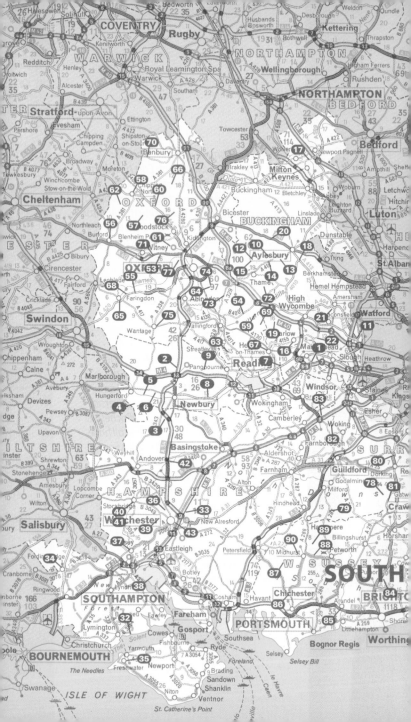

Bray-on-Thames

001 Royal Oak

Paley St, Bray-on-Thames SL6 3JN

Tel.: (01628) 620541
e-mail: parkinson2002uk@yahoo.co.uk

VISA *MC*

 Fuller's London Pride

A pleasant, proudly preserved village pub, but with a difference: framed photos of the owner's father, chatshow legend Michael Parkinson, and his showbiz friends beam affably from the wattle and timber walls. Attentive staff share Parky's talent for putting guests at their ease and serve up classically tasty, no-nonsense cooking with proper seasonal character: dishes could include chicken parfait and grilled sole with asparagus, followed by a lemon tart. A smart yet cosy bar, complete with dedicated regulars, offers a fine selection of wines and real ales and a quietly convivial atmosphere.

Food serving times:
Monday-Saturday:
12pm-2.30pm,
6.30pm-10.30pm
Sunday: 12pm-2.30pm
Prices:
Meals: 19.50 and a la carte
20.00/35.00

3.5mi Southwest by A308, A330 on B3024
Parking

Typical Dishes

Warm crab, prawn and cheese tart

Duck, fried noodles

Apple, raisin and cinnamon crumble

Chieveley

002 The Crab at Chieveley

Wantage Rd, Chieveley RE20 8UE

Tel.: (01635) 247550 - Fax: (01635) 248440
e-mail: info@crabatchieveley.com - Website: www.crabatchieveley.com

 London Pride, Timothy Taylor

Down a country road, surrounded by waving fields of wheat and well-ordered countryside, The Crab doesn't look like the kind of place to rock the boat, but country pub preconceptions are best forgotten here. The old fishing nets give you a clue to the menu – an extensive choice of seafood served in the more casual Fish Bar and a surprisingly formal dining room. The real surprise, though, is reserved for diners who decide to stay the night. Ten bedrooms in the modern annex eclipse the average inn for originality and luxury. Decorated in the style of famous hotels from Raffles to Sandy Lane in Barbados and La Mamounia in Marrakesh, each one is equipped with DVD players and other delightful extras: ground floor rooms have their own private terrace with a hot tub!

Food serving times:
Monday-Sunday:
  12pm-2.30pm, 6pm-10pm
- seafood -
Prices:
Meals: 14.50 (fixed price lunch) and a la carte 20.00/40.00
10 rooms: 120.00/140.00

Typical Dishes

Scallops and bacon salad

Paella

Lemongrass crème brûlée

2.5mi West of Chieveley by School Road on B4494. Parking

Highclere

003 **The Yew Tree**

Hollington Cross, Andover road, Highclere RG20 9SE
Tel.: (01635) 253360 - Fax: (01635) 255035
e-mail: eric.norberg@theyewtree.net

 Fuller's London Pride and regularly changing guest ales

The rustic black and white pub outside Highclere looks the very picture of an English country inn, but it's carved out more than just a traditional role in village life. As well as its blackboard menus and dishes of the day, the well-restored part-17C bar still offers full measure to its drinkers, but the four classically elegant dining rooms at the back add candlelight and white linen to the same handsome period décor. Though a clear split between the two helps each keep their true atmosphere, the lunch and dinner menus are the same in both halves: a typical selection might take in lamb with champ and red onion marmalade, chicken en papillote and gravadlax - a taste of home for the amiable owner.

Food serving times:
Monday-Sunday:
    12pm-3pm, 6pm-10pm
Closed dinner 25 December
Prices:
Meals: a la carte 15.90/35.95
🛏 **6 rooms:** 60.00

Typical Dishes

Pigeon in port and tarragon jus

Salmon in wine sauce

Chocolate and hazelnut semifreddo

1mi South of Highclere by A343
Parking

Inkpen

004 Swan Inn

Craven Rd, Lower Green, Inkpen RG17 9DX
Tel.: (01488) 668326 - Fax: (01488) 668306
e-mail: enquiries@theswaninn-organics.co.uk - Website: www.theswaninn-organics.co.uk

    VISA MC JCB

 Butts Jester, Traditional, Maggs Magnificent Mild

This enthusiastic husband and wife team don't do things by halves, managing a likeably down-to-earth community pub – with darts or quiz night on Thursdays – as well as running the 100% organic farm just down the road in this pretty corner of Berkshire. It supplies home-made sausages and tender sirloins, as well as the nicely matured steak for their locally renowned beef and ale pies. Next door is their farm shop, stocking more home-reared meats and much else besides. A small, neatly set restaurant to the rear is traditional in style with a menu of familiar favourites to match; simple bedrooms in pine and patchwork overlook the fields.

Food serving times:
Monday-Sunday:
12pm-2pm, 7pm-9.30pm
Closed 25-26 December
Prices:
Meals: a la carte 16.00/29.00
10 rooms: 40.00/90.00

Typical Dishes

Prawns in Pernod

Sirloin steak, mustard and red wine jus

Strawberry millefeuille

3.5 mi Southeast of Hungerford by Inkpen rd.
Parking

Kintbury

005 The Dundas Arms

Station Rd, Kintbury RG17 9UT

Tel.: (01488) 658263 - Fax: (01488) 658568
e-mail: info@dundasarms.co.uk - Website: www.dundasarms.co.uk

Butts Barbus Barbus, Adnams, West Berks Good Old Boy, Mr Chubb's Lunchtime Bitter

After supplying Kintbury with sustaining dinners and its daily pint for over three decades, the long-standing landlord knows he's among friends in the bar. Never ones to pass up a good thing, the locals arrive on the dot for filling dishes like fried skate with capers and jacket wedges or roast duck with apple and cider sauce, and a friendly, familiar atmosphere prevails. It can get just a little too busy and smoky for some tastes, in which case the trick is to ask if they're opening the rear restaurant, usually reserved for more formal dinners. But on a summer afternoon, there's only one place to be. A lovely double terrace borders the edge of the Kennet and the canal: watch the narrowboats passing the lock as the stopping trains roll away to Bedwyn and the Wessex Downs. Five neat, light bedrooms face the river.

Food serving times:
Tuesday-Saturday:
    12pm-2pm, 7pm-9pm
Sunday: 12pm-2pm
Closed 25 December-
1 January
Prices:
Meals: a la carte 16.00/25.00
🛏 **5 rooms:** 75.00/85.00

Typical Dishes

Leek and potato soup

Duck, cider and apple sauce

Assiette of desserts

3.5mi East of Hungerford by A4
Parking

Marsh Benham

006 **The Red House**
Marsh Benham RG20 8LY
Tel.: (01635) 582017 - Fax: (01635) 581621

No real ales offered

Once inside this well cared-for thatched inn, there's a choice to be made. To the front, the more casual bar: grab one of several tables by the old mullioned windows, if you can. To the back, pleasant countryside views, courteous, attentive service, smartly set dining tables polished to a high sheen and the option of an à la carte or prix-fixe bistro menu. A classical French influence comes through in rather delicate, carefully presented dishes like chicken and wild mushroom terrine with brioche or a buttery asparagus risotto; they're also very proud of their banoffee pie with cinnamon and nut crumble.

Food serving times:
Tuesday-Saturday:
    12pm-2pm, 7pm-9.30pm
Sunday: 12pm-2pm
Closed 25-26 December and 1 January
Prices:
Meals: 16.95 and a la carte 30.00/36.00

Typical Dishes
Foie gras terrine
Fillet of beef with tarragon jus
Chilled poached peach, syrup glaze

Off the A4 between Newbury and Hungerford. Parking

Wargrave

007 ## St George & Dragon

High Street, Wargrave RG10 8HY

Tel.: (01189) 405021 - Fax: (01189) 405024
e-mail: stgeorgeanddragon@hotmail.com - Website: www.stgeorgeanddragon.co.uk

 VISA **AE** **MC** **JCB**

 Fuller's London Pride, Bass, Tetley

Summer visitors to this delightfully modern and relaxed pub should make sure they arrive early: the enviably located raised deck terrace is a perfect spot to watch life go by on the neighbouring River Thames, but a place here is at a premium. Don't worry if your best bet is to stay inside – this is a textbook contemporary pub with a central bar, copper topped tables, tub chairs and several inviting log fires on colder days. To make the most of the river views, the main restaurant with open kitchen is around the side: heavy wood tables, fine glassware and interesting, modern specialities from the wood-fired oven and spit roast, alongside other up-to-date, globally inspired dishes at a keen price.

Food serving times:
Monday-Saturday:
12pm-2.30pm, 6pm-9.30pm
Sunday: 12pm-2.30pm
Closed 25-26 December
Prices:
Meals: a la carte 16.40/30.00

Typical Dishes

Foie gras, chicken liver parfait

Fillet steak, creamed potatoes

Sticky toffee pudding

Moorings on the River Thames, at the end of the garden. Parking

Woolhampton

008 ## The Angel

Bath Rd, Woolhampton RG7 5RT

Tel.: (0118) 971 3307
e-mail: mail@a4angel.com - Website: www.a4angel.com

No real ales offered

A first impression of the Angel – green window frames in a curtain of ivy – offers no hint of the highly personalised design inside. Tropical plants, flowers, hops and yet more ivy set off some eye-catching modern art and photographs in a series of intimate, candlelit rooms: burgundy, green and ochre, with rows of wine bottles glinting between the beams. Fish and chips aside, much of an ambitious modern repertoire takes French culinary style as its starting point, and delicately presented starters and mains might include tuna on salad niçoise or prawns in lobster broth. Compiling the wine list is clearly a labour of love: some rare vintages – like the empties on the ceiling – may be out of reach to most of us, but the selection includes a more accessible range by the glass and even a homemade sloe gin.

Food serving times:
Tuesday-Saturday:
12pm-3pm, 6pm-10pm
(booking essential)
Prices:
Meals: a la carte 16.00/20.00

Typical Dishes

Cream of fresh pea with
fried gnocchi

Confit of duck, chorizo and
cassoulet

Tarte Tatin

Located on the A4 between Reading and Newbury. Parking

Yattendon

009 Royal Oak

The Square, Yattendon RG18 0UG

Tel.: (01635) 201325 - Fax: (01635) 201926
e-mail: oakyattendon@aol.com

🍷 ✂ **VISA** **AE** **◐** **Ⓜ©**

Wadworth 6X, West Berkshire Good Old Boy

Though not a million miles from the roaring intensity of the M4, this very pleasant redbrick former coaching inn could inhabit another age. Sympathetically set in a picture postcard village, its well-appointed lounge with real fire sets the scene, evoking English country house style at its more comfortable and unassuming. Choose from two dining rooms, one in smart, classic style with cloth-clad tables and fine quality cover, the other more pubby and relaxed. Menus, invariably with plenty of choice, change every two and a half months but never stray far from a confidently executed classic base with distinctly modern overtones, their influences stretching globally. Comfortable, pretty bedrooms, with a rather chintzy quality, beckon upstairs.

Food serving times:
Monday-Sunday:
    12pm-2pm, 7pm-9.30pm
Closed 1 January
Prices:
Meals: a la carte 26.00/35.00
🛏 **5 rooms:** 105.00/130.00
🍽 8.00

Typical Dishes

Home-cured salmon, soft
baked egg

Rabbit with liver and
mushroom mousse

Vanilla cheesecake

In the village centre
Parking

Cuddington

010 Crown

Aylesbury Rd, Cuddington HP18 0BB

Tel.: (01844) 292222

e-mail: david@thecrowncuddington.co.uk - Website: www.thecrowncuddington.co.uk

Fuller's London Pride, Adnams

Locals swarm to this highly renowned village pub, and not just because it's 16C, Grade II listed, and thatched to boot. The interior is a most welcoming place to be, with subdued lighting, small windows and several period fireplaces, though the collection of Victorian prints reveal a lightly quirky side, too. There are four areas in which to relax and mingle; the two most sought-after being around the bar, near the fires, though you can eat wherever you like. Menus mix pub staples, like steaks and lamb casserole, with more contemporary dishes, such as scallops and chilli jus, or chicken saltimbocca with sweet potato mash, while puddings come under the heading 'heart-warming'. Enthusiastic, down-to-earth service is entirely in keeping for a pub with the true "local" ambience.

Food serving times:
Monday-Saturday:
    12pm-2pm, 6.30pm-9pm
Sunday: 12pm-9pm
Prices:
Meals: a la carte 20.00/25.00

Typical Dishes

Scallops, chilli jam

Haddock on bubble and squeak

Tarte au citron, raspberry coulis

West of Aylesbury by A418. Some parking spaces available

Denham

011 The Swan Inn

Village Rd, Denham UB9 5BH

Tel.: (01895) 832085 - Fax: (01895) 835516
e-mail: info@swaninndenham.co.uk

Courage Best, Directors, Morrell's Oxford Blue

Very much at the heart of one of the loveliest villages in Buckinghamshire, the pretty, ivy-clad Swan Inn is half bar, half restaurant, but it's run in such a pleasant, accommodating spirit that everyone feels welcome; drinkers and diners mingle under the broad umbrellas on the terrace, which leads into a spacious garden. Choose from a menu with a modern edge or daily changing blackboard specials which reflect the season; typical of these are tasty black and white puddings with crispy pancetta, halloumi with saffron vegetables and couscous and a subtly flavoured elderflower and lavender crème brulée.

Food serving times:
Monday-Saturday:
   12pm-2.30pm, 7pm-10pm
Sunday: 12pm-3pm,
                7pm-10pm

Closed 25-26 December
(booking essential)

Prices:
Meals: a la carte 17.50/25.50

Typical Dishes

Roquefort souffle, salad

Roast cod, spinach and chorizo

Plum frangipane tart

Pass through the centre of the village and over the bridge, follow the road and the pub is on the left. Parking

Easington

012 **Mole & Chicken**

The Terrace, Easington HP18 9EY

Tel.: (01844) 208387 - Fax: (01844) 208250
e-mail: shanepellis@hotmail.com - Website: www.moleandchicken.co.uk

Y ✆room 🚭 *VISA* AE M©

Greene King IPA, Old Speckled Hen, Fuller's London Pride

The bend in the road of a tiny Buckinghamshire hamlet provides the cosy backdrop to this attractive, wisteria clad country pub. There's a really comfortable ambience here, highlighted by the carefully chosen fabrics in pretty country pub style, roaring fires, beams, decorative candles and scrubbed pine tables and chairs: it's a cosy and intimate place. Menus are changed regularly (apart from the well-established favourites the regulars won't allow to go!). Good modern dishes are served in hearty sized portions: originality is the keyword. Service is locally renowned: staff are known for their enthusiasm. Adjacent cottages provide bright, modern bedrooms, some with countryside views.

Food serving times:
Monday-Sunday:
    12pm-2pm, 7pm-9.30pm
Closed 25 December
(booking essential)
Prices:
Meals: 20.00 (fixed price dinner) and a la carte 20.00/ 25.00
🛏 **5 rooms:** 50.00/65.00

Typical Dishes

Creamed chilli mussels

Pan-fried red snapper, Thai noodles

2.5mi Northwest of Thame by B4011
Parking

Ford

013 ## Dinton Hermit

Water Lane, Ford HP17 8XH

Tel.: (01296) 747473 - Fax: (01296) 748819
e-mail: colinswooddeb@aol.com - Website: www.dinton-hermit.com

 VISA AE M⊙

 Fuller's London Pride, Adnams, Youngs Special

Although it's much less secluded than the name suggests – surely the only hermit with an extensive car park – the gently firelit bar of this listed pub does provide a lovely, if temporary, retreat from the world. Burnished benches, cane-backed chairs, whitewashed walls with bricks and beams make it recognisably traditional in spirit, but there's also a modern sense of clutter-free space about the place. Neatly set dining rooms are in similar style, and the upfront country flavours in a modern pub menu seem to go down well: try braised ham with tarragon and Cheddar sauce or pot-roast guinea fowl with a nutty, zesty sauce. The restored outbuilding now houses the inn's bedrooms: two have Jacobean style four-posters, the others have a pleasing modern look: bright, tidy and individual.

Food serving times:
Monday-Saturday:
12pm-2pm, 7pm-9pm
Sunday: 12pm-2pm
Closed 25 December
Prices:
Meals: a la carte 20.00/25.30
🛏 **12 rooms:** 65.00

5.5mi Southwest of Aylesbury by A418. Parking

Typical Dishes

Grilled asparagus, cherry tomatoes

Herb crusted lamb

Warm chocolate brownie

Haddenham

014 **Green Dragon**

8 Churchway, Haddenham HP17 8AA

Tel.: (01844) 291403 - Fax: (01844) 299532
Website: www.eatatthedragon.co.uk

Notley Wytchert and 2 guest ales

ersonally run with an affable ease which seems to spread through the place, the well looked-after Green Dragon has a reputation for good food, one which now reaches far beyond the picturesque village it still serves so well. An extensive menu – with a few unexpected combinations – ranges from partridge with parsnips and pear sauce or scallops with white wine and vanilla dressing to a few simple but carefully sourced pub classics like chicken and wild mushroom pie and steak and kidney pudding with local ale. Haddenham was once as famous for its ducks as nearby Aylesbury and they still have quite a taste for them here, so look out for confits or roasts among the specials. Light lunches and dinners are served at the same neatly set tables, laid out all around the central bar.

Food serving times:
Monday-Saturday:
  12pm-2pm, 6.30pm-9.30pm
Sunday: 12pm-3pm
Closed 25-26 December and
1 January
(booking essential)
Prices:
Meals: 11.95/17.95 and a la
carte 20.00/30.95

Typical Dishes

Salmon and crab fishcakes

Halibut in pancetta

*Lemon and lime tart,
raspberry sorbet*

By the Green and St Mary's Church.
Parking

Long Crendon

015 Angel

47 Bicester Rd, Long Crendon HP18 9EE
Tel.: (01844) 208268 - Fax: (01844) 202497

  room   VISA

Hook Norton, Brakspear, Bass

This attractive part-16C inn is now most assuredly in the quality restaurant-with-rooms category, but qualifies in the pub league due to its bright and cheery bar area with leather sofas. This is where the regulars gather to pay homage to the local beer on draught. Characterful dining areas lead off from here, defined by tiled flooring, bare wood tables and crisp linen napkins. To the rear an air-conditioned conservatory adds another enticing option. Seasonally changing, modern, creative menus have assured the Angel of a grand reputation, enhanced by daily changing fish specials. The word has spread, too, about the bedrooms here. They've been refurbished on a lavish scale with rich fabrics and wrought iron beds. One even allows you the luxury of a roll-top bath.

Food serving times:
Monday-Saturday:
  12pm-2.30pm, 7pm-9.30pm
Sunday: 12pm-2.30pm
Prices:
Meals: 19.95 and a la carte 13.50/25.50
🛏 **3 rooms:** 65.00/75.00

Typical Dishes

Salad of roast pigeon

Smoked haddock, leek and cheese mash

Crème brûlée

1.5mi Northwest of Thame by B4011
Parking

Marlow

016 Royal Oak

Frieth Rd, Bovingdon Green, Marlow SL7 2JF

Tel.: (01628) 488611 - Fax: (01628) 478680
e-mail: info@royaloakpub.co.uk

Marlow Rebellion IPA, Brakspear, Fuller's London Pride

Though it remains every inch the rural pub, from the old beams to the logs stacked by the wood burners, plenty of well thought-out details lend the Royal Oak an eclectic, but well-adapted, modern atmosphere. A bright conservatory bar feels clean and airy: barmen, spotting the regulars arriving, can get pouring before they've even walked through the door! Beyond, salvaged antique chairs and tables and fine tableware invite an easygoing attitude to good eating, and the charming staff do the same, carrying off what's actually very efficient, personalised service with breezy friendliness. Offering great value for this part of the world, ably judged dishes share a fresh, seasonal, classically balanced taste.

Food serving times:
Monday-Saturday:
 12pm-2.30pm, 7pm-10pm
Sunday: 12pm-3pm,
 7pm-10pm

Closed 25-26 December
Prices:
Meals: a la carte 17.50/27.00

Typical Dishes

Smoked bacon, bubble and squeak

Tiger prawn spaghetti

Tonka bean crème brûlée

From the town centre, head towards Bovingdon Green, pub is on the left as you leave the woods. Parking

Newton Longville

017 Crooked Billet

Newton Longville MK17 0DF

Tel.: (01908) 373936 - Fax: (01908) 631979
e-mail: john@thebillet.co.uk - Website: www.thebillet.co.uk

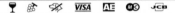

Old Speckled Hen, Wadworth 6X, Greene King Triumph, Hobgoblin, Batemans XXXB

The Crooked Billet's phenomenal wine list, chosen with passionate connoisseurship to include over 300 wines by the glass, makes remarkable reading and very enjoyable drinking. With their typically helpful friendliness, the owner and his staff are happy to recommend a good match for lunch or dinner, and the well-judged modern cooking does it justice. In fact, it's hard to fault this smoothly run, ever welcoming pub with its thatched roof and pretty gardens: a spacious firelit bar still attracts its locals – you're welcome for a pint or a lunchtime sandwich if that's all you feel like – while the comfortable dining room with a hint of 16C character is a lovely setting for a dinner at leisurely pace.

Food serving times:
Monday-Saturday:
12pm-2.30pm, 7pm-10pm
Sunday: 12pm-3pm
Closed 25-26 December and 1 January
Closed Monday lunch
Prices:
Meals: a la carte 20.00/40.00

Typical Dishes

Pan fried corned beef hash

Pork loin, black pudding stuffing

Selection of cheeses

6mi Southwest of Milton Keynes by A421
Parking

Stoke Mandeville

018 **The Wool Pack**

21 Risborough Road, Stoke Mandeville HP22 5UP

Tel.: (01296) 615970 - Fax: (01296) 615971

Greene King IPA, Fuller's London Pride

An object lesson in how to bring an old pub up to date, the low-ceilinged but now very contemporary bar of this part-thatched pub seems to get more cosy as the night draws in, especially if you've bagged one of the leather tub chairs and copper topped tables, or a spot near the fire. At the back is a sizeable dining room with French doors leading out onto the terrace, and this is where the contemporary influence is really brought to bear. Dishes like duck confit with pak choi and chilli are the exceptions in a repertoire which is more likely to turn to Italian cuisine for its subtle fusion twists: fresh, tasty stone-baked pizzas, grills and dessert treats like lemon polenta cake are all prepared with understanding and care and served by knowledgeable, spontaneous staff who seem genuinely happy to be there.

Food serving times:
Monday-Saturday:
   12pm-2.30pm, 6pm-9.30pm
Sunday: 12pm-2.30pm
Closed 26 December and 1 January
Prices:
Meals: a la carte 15.00/40.00

South of town on A413 close to the hospital. Parking

Typical Dishes

King prawns in butter and garlic

Ribeye steak with blue cheese

Toffee apple tart

Turville

019 **Bull & Butcher**

Turville RG9 6QU

Tel.: (01491) 638283 · Fax: (01491) 638836
e-mail: info@thebullandbutcher.com · Website: www.thebullandbutcher.com

 ✗ *VISA* Ⓜ️ⓒ

Brakspears Bitter, Hook Norton

B uilt in the mid-16C, this handsome, half-timbered pub served its first ales to the workmen restoring nearby St Mary's church. Tasty, tried-and-tested bar dishes can be as simple as ploughman's, fish and chips or a "Farmer's Supper and pint", while the table d'hôte might offer confit of duck or shellfish cakes with spicy lentils, unless it's time for a themed dinner: the "Bangers", "South Africa" and "Beaujolais" nights all went down well. Menus and specials are served in the restaurant and in the bar, where a semi-circular table centres on the rediscovered pub well. The charming village of Turville is worth an after-dinner stroll: fans of "The Vicar of Dibley" may find that it all looks strangely familiar…

Food serving times:
Monday-Friday:
  12pm-2.30pm, 7pm-9.45pm
Saturday: 12pm-9.45pm
Sunday: 12pm-4pm,
              7pm-9.45pm

Prices:
Meals: a la carte 22.00/29.00

Typical Dishes
Potted goose with gooseberry relish

Honey glazed chicken

Banana and strawberry sorbet

5mi North of Henley on Thames by A4130 off B480
Parking

Waddesdon

020 **Five Arrows**

High St, Waddesdon HP18 0JE

Tel.: (01296) 651727 - Fax: (01296) 658596

e-mail: bookings@thefivearrowshotel.fsnet.co.uk - Website: www.waddesdon.org.uk

  **VISA** **AE** **MC**

 Fuller's London Pride

Certainly not your everyday local, this delightful late 19C inn is part of a magnificent estate built by Baron Rothschild, complete with attractive gardens and courtyard terrace, and close to Waddesdon Manor, now a National Trust property. Numerous comfy dining rooms centre on a charming bar; they're undeniably characterful and period features like wood panelling and parquet floors fit the studied country-house style to the last detail. Extensive menus offer a mix of British classic and contemporary, and though the service has an element of restaurant smartness, this aristocrat among pubs wears its hint of formality with good grace. As might be expected, very spacious bedrooms offer some stylish touches, along with an almost de rigeur four-poster. It's all very impressive, though maybe not for those who want to "pop out for a swift half."

Food serving times:
Monday-Saturday:
  12pm-2.15pm, 7pm-9.15pm
Sunday: 12.30pm-2.30pm,
        7.30pm-8.30pm

Closed 25-26 December, dinner 31 December and 1 January

Prices:
Meals: a la carte 23.40/41.10
11 rooms: 70.00/160.00

Typical Dishes

Aubergine, feta and sundried tomatoes

Salmon confit, passion fruit, grapes

Honeycomb ice cream

On A41
Parking

Winchmore Hill

021 ## The Plough

The Hill, Winchmore Hill HP7 0PA
Tel.: (01494) 721001 - Fax: (01494) 728105

 VISA AE M©

No real ales offered

For all its rural setting, this converted pub sets itself cosmopolitan standards of style, and loses little by the comparison. Beyond an intimate bar, in the glow of church candles, is the split-level dining room: with discreetly spaced tables, sparkling silverware and a feeling of quietly confident chic, it's a careful study in modern refinement, and the deferential service seems calculated not to disrupt the mood. Seasonal modern cuisine catches the tone exactly: asparagus and sorrel risotto, chicken niçoise, salmon with fennel and crevettes; the lighter "Lawn Menu", served at the front of the pub, might include gazpacho, goat's cheese and pepper salad, 'nouveau' ploughman's and plates of charcuterie.

Food serving times:
Monday-Sunday:
    12pm-2.30pm, 6pm-10pm
Closed 25 December and
1 January
Prices:
Meals: 11.50 and a la carte
approx. 29.00

Typical Dishes

Ham hock terrine, scallop purée

Lamb with tomato and zucchini tartlet

Calvados tarte Tatin

2mi Southwest of Amersham by A416
off A404
Parking

Wooburn Common

022 Chequers Inn

Kiln Lane, Wooburn Common HP10 0JQ

Tel.: (01628) 529575 · Fax: (01628) 850124
e-mail: info@chequers-inn.com · Website: www.chequers-inn.com

Ruddles, Abbot, IPA and 1 guest ale

You're looking for a handsome redbrick inn, but alternatively you could just follow your nose: the famous garden barbecues at The Chequers do all their own advertising, and if you arrive on a sunny evening, your mouth may be watering by the time you reach the front door. Bring your elbows to make your way through a well-dressed knot of post-commute drinkers until around eight, but you should be able to grab a table for sandwiches or a full meal in the bar, or something a touch more adventurous in the restaurant at the back: favourites include ribeye and chips and almond and pear tart with crème anglaise. Bedrooms are perfect for anyone who wants pretty, cottage-style furnishings, but can't be without modems and satellite television. A well run place with real personality.

Food serving times:
Monday-Sunday:
12pm-2.30pm, 6pm-9pm
Prices:
Meals: 18.95/23.95 and a la carte 20.00/40.00
17 rooms: 99.50/107.50

Typical Dishes

Shellfish and red mullet, lime butter

Caramelised duck

Banana pancakes, toffee sauce

3.5mi Southwest of Beaconsfield by A40
Parking

Bodiam

023 The Curlew

Junction Rd, Bodiam TN32 5UY

Tel.: (01580) 861394 - Fax: (01580) 861396

e-mail: enquiries@thecurlewatbodiam.co.uk - Website: www.thecurlewatbodiam.co.uk

 🍷 🍇 **VISA** **MC**

 Harveys Sussex Best, Youngs Best Bitter

A pub of two halves, but a local favourite either way: choose from a good list of snacks and simpler meals in the main bar, its timbers edged with beardy fringes of Sussex hops, or a thoughtfully composed menu on a classic base which shows the owner-chef's decades of experience in France to better effect. Smooth-clothed tables, elegant china and glassware in the dining room suggest a rather formal approach, but it feels entirely appropriate for a tasty fish soup with all the accompaniments or a duck confit and frisée salad, not to mention the truly comprehensive selection of fine wines – there can't be many roadside stops with a cellar list like this. A short drive takes you to Bodiam Castle.

Food serving times:
Tuesday-Saturday:
12pm-2pm, 7pm-9.30pm
Sunday: 12pm-2pm
Closed 26 December,
1 January and Bank Holidays
Prices:
Meals: a la carte 25.30/40.00

Typical Dishes

Prawn, avocado and salmon, mango salsa

Salt-baked sea bass

Chocolate fondant, chocolate ice cream

On the B2244 Hawkhurst to Sedlescombe road, by the Bodiam Castle crossroads. Parking

Danehill

024 Coach & Horses

School Lane, Danehill RH17 7JF

Tel.: (01825) 740369 - Fax: (01825) 740369
e-mail: coachandhorses@danehill.biz

  VISA

Harveys Best, Horsham Best and a weekly changing guest ale

Rough-hewn stone gives this Sussex hostelry a solid presence, softened somewhat by the magical nearby presence of the Bluebell Railway. The locals love it here; they're still an important part of its character, despite its recent "conversion" into a destination dining pub, and can usually be found having an afternoon ale in the small bar as you enter, dogs at their side. There are two separate dining areas, a top one which enjoys the atmosphere created in the bar, and another in the converted stables, with well-spaced fables, beams adorned with dried hops, and walls decorated with modern art. Particularly welcoming service adds the final touch to seasonally changing modern menus that dance to a distinctly Gallic tune: dishes are robust, frill-free, and full of flavour.

Food serving times:
Monday-Saturday:
      12pm-2pm, 7pm-9pm
Sunday: 12pm-2pm
Closed 25-26 December
Prices:
Meals: a la carte 20.70/25.50

Typical Dishes

Scallops, pea and mint purée

Loin of pork, confit white cabbage

Rhubarb panna cotta

0.75mi North East on Chelwood Common Rd. Parking

East Chiltington

025 Jolly Sportsman

Chapel Lane, East Chiltington BN7 3BA
Tel.: (01273) 890400 - Fax: (01273) 890400
e-mail: jollysportsman@mistral.co.uk - Website: www.thejollysportsman.com

 VISA **MC**

Regularly changing ales, mainly from micro breweries

Once you know the right sequence of narrow country lanes, the trip to the Jolly Sportsman is half the fun; set in the lee of the South Downs, it's just secluded enough for driver and map reader to feel they've earned that first drink. Not that everyone comes from far afield; the enthusiastic team here certainly know the locals, and regulars are as likely to head for the cheerfully painted dining room as prop up the bar. As well they might: dishes from an appetising menu, with a sensible balance and extra variety from the specials list, prove to be well-presented and, as a rule, their clean-cut, direct flavours come over well – a plate of horseradish-dressed smoked fish might be followed by venison with juniper sauce. Should any of the local artwork on the walls catch your eye over coffee, ask at the bar: if the price is right, it's yours!

Food serving times:
Tuesday-Friday:
  12.30pm-2pm, 7pm-9.15pm
Saturday: 12.30pm-2pm,
                     7pm-10pm
Sunday: 12.30pm-3pm
Closed 24-27 December
Prices:
Meals: 14.75 and a la carte
19.85/27.50

Typical Dishes

Thai crab beignets

Marinated rump of lamb with mint

Chocolate tart, crème fraîche

5.5mi Northwest of Lewes by A275 and B2116 off Novington Lane. Parking

Fletching

026 The Griffin Inn

Fletching TN22 3SS
Tel.: (01825) 722890 - Fax: (01825) 722810
Website: www.thegriffininn.co.uk

 Harveys, King of Horsham, Tanglefoot, Woodhouse

Pubs are meant to lie at the heart of a community, and this one certainly fits the bill. Reassuringly situated in the middle of a smart village, and boasting huge views to Ashdown Forest, the Griffin dates back to the 16C, as witnessed by the open fires, beams and oak panelling. The feel of a local is enhanced by the pool table at the back and the informality when ordering food: no bookings taken, order directly from the bar. Go through to the restaurant and it's something else again: rafters, candlelight and linen-clad tables. Modern menus have pride of place here: many feature scallops on a Thai-inspired base, but Europan and local dishes are also prominent, such as fish risottos and roasted wood pigeon. Up-to-the-minute bedrooms – shared between the main house and garden annexe – are, quite simply, immaculate.

Food serving times:
Monday-Saturday:
  12pm-2.30pm, 7pm-9.30pm
Sunday: 12pm-2.30pm,
               7pm-9pm

Closed 25 December
Closed Sunday dinner in winter - (fixed price Sunday lunch)
Prices:
Meals: 25.00 and a la carte 17.00/30.00
8 rooms: 60.00/120.00

Typical Dishes

Scallops with pancetta
Rump of lamb, borlotti beans
Italian chocolate torte

Between Uckfield and Haywards Heath off A272
Parking

Heathfield

027 Star Inn

Church St, Old Heathfield, Heathfield TN21 9AH

Tel.: (01435) 863570 - Fax: (01435) 862020
e-mail: heathfieldstar@aol.com - Website: www.bestpubsinsussex.co.uk

  VISA **MC** JCB

 Harveys Best, Shepherd Neame Master Brew, Hopback Summer Lightning

Standing in the grounds of the village church, this ivy-clad 14C pub is particularly charming on fine afternoons, when drinkers and diners have the run of a lovely lawned garden with tree-trunk benches, but don't wait for the first summer sun. Two intimate and ultra-traditional bars, with silver tankards hanging from the beams, are made all the more cosy by a wood-burning stove and an open fire: a couple of tables are tucked into a big inglenook fireplace. One blackboard lists familiar pub meals alongside ploughmans and potatoes, others offer the season's specials; expect decent-sized helpings of robust cooking in either case. The Star is so well regarded in the neighbourhood that it's as well to book, even for a midweek lunch, but at busy times they open the upstairs restaurant; some tables to one side have views of the church.

Food serving times:
Monday-Thursday:
   12pm-2.15pm, 7pm-9.30pm
Friday-Saturday:
   12pm-2.15pm, 7pm-10pm
Sunday: 12pm-2.15pm,
                        7pm-9.30pm
Closed dinner 25-26 December
Prices:
Meals: a la carte 17.50/26.00

Typical Dishes

Anchovy fillets, onions

Duck breast, chocolate and chilli sauce

Black pepper meringue

South East 2 miles by A265, off B2096. Parking

Peacehaven

028 The Badger's Watch

South Coast Rd, Peacehaven BN10 7BE

Tel.: (01273) 579031

rest *VISA* **AE** **mc**

Harveys Best, Bass

Equally impressive under cloudless blue skies or in the face of a sea storm, the sweeping prospects of the Channel from the Badger's Watch once made this the perfect lifeboat lookout station. The picnic benches out in the fresh sea air are always popular if the weather is set fair, but the extended pub itself – all interconnecting lounges and stairways in a rustic décor of bricks and beams – has good views too, not to mention the easy, down-to-earth comfort of the best kind of local and the courtesy and obliging service to go with it. A straight choice of traditional pub meals holds few surprises, but there are no complaints from a happy local crowd of diners and drinkers, who get right into the spirit of things.

Food serving times:
Monday-Saturday:
12pm-10pm
Sunday: 12pm-9pm
Prices:
Meals: a la carte 12.75/23.00

Typical Dishes

Deep fried goat's cheese salad

Hunters chicken

Caramel apple pie

Follow A259 to the top of Telscombe Cliffs. Parking

Piltdown

029 **Peacock Inn**

Shortbridge, Piltdown TN22 3XA

Tel.: (01825) 762463 - Fax: (01825) 762463

  VISA

Harveys Best, Fuller's London Pride, Wadworth 6X

A quintessentially English pub in the heart of the Sussex countryside, its 16C black and white timbered exterior enhanced by two very neatly trimmed yew trees at the entrance. There are benches at the front, too, and a sign with a brightly painted peacock in full plumage. The rear has a children's play area and large paved terrace, where they sometimes host barbecues in summer. Inside are spacious bar rooms, full of character: log fire, dark beams, brass ornaments and an old framed peacock tapestry in pride of place. A variety of photos cover the walls: those of the owner with celebrity guests testify to the Peacock's enduring popularity and warm atmosphere. Menus are traditional and unpretentious, complemented by chef's blackboard specials, with fresh ingredients from mainly local suppliers. The home-made desserts are warmly recommended.

Food serving times:
Monday-Sunday:
12pm-2.30pm, 6pm-9.30pm
Closed 25-26 December
Booking advisable at weekends
Prices:
Meals: a la carte 14.50/28.00

Typical Dishes

Avocado, Stilton and bacon salad

Chicken with cashew nuts, garlic butter

Fruit crème brûlée

Between Uckfield and Haywards Heath off A272
Parking

Rushlake Green

030 ## The Horse and Groom

The Green, Rushlake Green TN21 9QE

Tel.: (01435) 830320

e-mail: chappellhatpeg@aol.com - Website: www.thebestpubsinsussex.com

 VISA **M©** **JCB**

 Harveys Local, Shepherd Neame Master Brew and 1 monthly changing guest ale

One for the traditionalist in all of us: horsebrasses twinkle, copper kettles gleam and ostlers and riders pose proudly with their glossy steeplechasers in the old prints above the fire. The two cosy, beamed rooms, their candles lit even at lunchtime, are at either end; although the Gun Room, its three fearsome-looking shotguns kept safely in the rack, is set slightly apart from the bar, the same menu is available throughout the pub. Using seasonal produce and market-fresh meat and fish, it's generous country cooking through and through. Full-flavoured roast lamb and other classics are served in good-sized portions, as you would expect, but even their orange brulée cheesecake and a tasty goat's cheese, aubergine and onion tart come in satisfyingly hearty wedges. With prompt and friendly staff into the bargain, it's no wonder they're busy.

Food serving times:
Monday-Sunday:
 12pm-2.15pm, 7pm-9.30pm
Closed dinner 25-26 December
Prices:
Meals: a la carte 20.00/30.00

Typical Dishes

Asparagus wrapped in salmon

Monkfish, duo of sweet pepper sauces

Chocolate meringue

3mi Southeast of Heathfield by B2096
Parking

Wartling

031 **Lamb Inn**
Wartling BN27 1RY
Tel.: (01323) 832116

Harveys, Horsham Best, Badger

On the edge of the Pevensey Levels, this part 16C pub is personally run and proudly traditional. Little black-framed windows give it the look of a country cottage from the outside, as do the dark beams and pretty chintz patterns in the little front bar, while the more spacious restaurant is decorated in shades of terracotta and dusky pink. The menu – served throughout – changes weekly, with plenty of thought going into the choice of ingredients and new season's produce, be it Devon Southdown lamb or additive-free beef from the farm right next door. The choice of sausages and pies varies every day, and there's a separate seafood menu. Chirpy and prompt staff serve their guests well.

Food serving times:
Monday-Sunday:
11.45am-2.15pm,
6.45pm-9pm
Prices:
Meals: a la carte 18.00/29.00

Typical Dishes

Scallops, brioche and chorizo

Steak with port and mushrooms

Raspberry brûlée

3.75miles South-East of Herstmonceux by A271 and Wartling Rd. Parking

East End

032 East End Arms

Main Rd, East End SO41 5SY

Tel.: (01590) 626223
e-mail: jennie@eastendarms.co.uk

  VISA MC JCB

 Ringwood Best, 49er and a selection of guest ales

After daydreams of speed, glamour and gleaming metal at Beaulieu's National Motor Museum, take a steady and responsible fifteen-minute drive down to the East End Arms for an enjoyable lunchtime pit-stop. The public bar is still a real locals' meeting-place, where real ale and sandwiches are the order of the day, but a larger, simply styled lounge, its walls covered with an absorbing and unexpected collection of photographs, serves something more substantial. A choice of filled baguettes and half a dozen generous main courses make up the midday menu, while in the evening they add both modern dishes and traditional favourites to the list, perhaps including black pudding fritters, whole Dover sole and chips or venison with a Calvados sauce.

Food serving times:
Tuesday-Saturday:
12pm-2pm, 7pm-9pm
Sunday: 12pm-2pm
Closed 25 December,
1 January, first 2 weeks
March and first 2 weeks
October
Closed Tuesdays after Bank
Holidays
Prices:
Meals: a la carte approx. 23.50

Typical Dishes

Black pudding fritters, beetroot salad

Dover sole, raspberry vinegar

Selection of cheeses

4.25mi Northeast of Lymington by B3054 off South Baddesley rd
Parking

Easton

033 **The Chestnut Horse**

Easton SO21 1EG

Tel.: (01962) 779257 - Fax: (01962) 779037

London Pride, Courage Best, Chestnut Horse Bitter

Just a short drive from the centre of Winchester, The Chestnut Horse is a real find, with individuality and charm written right through it. For a start, there's the bar, showing its age in the best sense. A log fire, beams and rows of pint pots and jugs bring out the building's 16C character, while two more formal rooms introduce subtle changes of style: "Green" makes a natural setting for lunch, "Red", with dark tones offset by candlelight, is better for intimate dinners, but the pretty rear terrace, with an abundance of plants and flowers, trumps them both on a hot summer's day – friendly staff are happy to guide you round them all before you decide! An extensive menu runs from pub favourites to more modern dishes and a big line-up of specials: crab and avocado salad, robust pork in mustard sauce and homemade treacle tart.

Food serving times:
Monday-Sunday:
12pm-2.30pm,
6.30pm-9.30pm

Prices:
Meals: a la carte 18.00/30.00

4mi North East of Winchester by A3090 off B3047. Parking

Typical Dishes

Avocado and warm bacon salad

Home-made steak and kidney pudding

Champagne jelly

Fordingbridge

034 **Three Lions**

Stuckton Rd, Stuckton, Fordingbridge SP6 2HF

Tel.: (01425) 652489 - Fax: (01425) 656144
Website: www.thethreelionsrestaurant.co.uk

  ≒room   **VISA** **MC** **JCB**

 Ringwood Best

Though not an everyday local, by any means, this redbrick converted farmhouse, owned by a husband and wife team, does have the kind of informal atmosphere you would hope to find in a good country inn. Certainly there's something relaxing about being able to peruse the menu – and blackboard - over a pre-dinner drink in the casual bar, and the rural feel of the area comes across in a menu featuring flavourful local loin of lamb, smoked haddock galette and a hearty treacle and hazelnut tart. Guests staying overnight should be pleased with the brightly decorated, pine-furnished rooms – although the sound insulation isn't the greatest, all are spacious and neatly fitted.

Food serving times:
Tuesday-Saturday:
        12pm-2pm, 7pm-9.30pm
Sunday: 12pm-2pm
Closed last 2 weeks January and first week February
Prices:
Meals: 15.75 and a la carte 24.00/32.00
🛏 **4 rooms:** 59.00/95.00

Typical Dishes

Mushroom ravioli

Sea bass, red wine, nutmeg sauce

Grand Marnier strawberries

1mi Southeast of Fordingbridge by B3078
Parking

Littleton

036 **The Running Horse**

88 Main Road, Littleton SO22 6QS

Tel.: (01962) 880218 - Fax: (01962) 886596

e-mail: runninghorse@btconnect.com - Website: www.therunninghorsepubrestaurant.co.uk

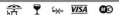
🏠 ♈ ⌿ *VISA* 💳

 Ringwood Best

Delightful service from a considerate and well-drilled young team is just one element in a winning formula for the Running Horse, which has changed almost out of recognition from the run-down village pub that finally closed its doors. They re-opened on a radical rehaul - an attractive modern bar and a cleanly styled restaurant, smart wicker-backed chairs, even trendy new cutlery – and the gamble is paying off, with a good many takers for lighter bar lunches and the sophisticated but well-priced evening menu. With an enjoyable balance of full, fresh flavours, the latter might cover foie gras, goat's cheese, tomato and rocket salad or braised beef with celeriac mash.

Food serving times:
Tuesday-Saturday:
12pm-2.30pm,
6.30pm-9.30pm
Sunday: 12pm-2.30pm
Closed 25-26 December and first 2 weeks January
(fixed price meal Sunday)
Prices:
Meals: 18.00 and a la carte 22.00/32.00

Typical Dishes

Risotto of confit pork, apple sauce

Shoulder of lamb

Lemon passett, cassis milkshake

2.5mi North West from Winchester by B3049. Parking

Romsey

037 Three Tuns

58 Middlebridge Street, Romsey SO51 8HL

Tel.: (01794) 512639 - Fax: (01794) 514524
e-mail: threetunsromsey@aol.com

   VISA ① ⓜⓒ JCB

 Ringwood Best Bitter, Gales HSB

Romsey town centre has seen various changes over the years, but The Three Tuns remains an engaging constant. It's been in Middlebridge Street for 300 years and the perennial log fire and timbers help it retain its period feel, much to the contentment of a large group of regulars. A facelift, though, is evident in the slate flooring and understated décor. The fairly large bar inhabits one side of the pub; a restaurant the other – this has a haphazard, rustic appeal with bare tables of various shapes and sizes alongside mismatched chairs. Relaxed but helpful service will ease you into a modern menu which you'll find characterised by capable, well-judged cooking using first-rate ingredients, not least game from the nearby Broadlands Estate.

Food serving times:
Monday-Saturday:
    12pm-2pm, 7pm-9.30pm
Sunday: 12pm-2pm
Closed 25 December and 1 January
Prices:
Meals: a la carte 21.00/33.00

Towards the western end of the town, off the by-pass. Parking

Typical Dishes

Scallops, celeriac purée, oxtail sauce

Trio of pork, parsnip purée

Mango mousse

Southampton

038 White Star Dining Rooms

28 Oxford Street, Southampton SO14 3DJ
Tel.: (023) 8082 1990
e-mail: manager@whitestartavern.co.uk - Website: www.whitestartavern.co.uk

🍷 🚫 **VISA** **AE** **MC**

Fuller's London Pride

aming their new venture after the Titanic's ill-fated shipping line was a brave move but, a few years on, it's full steam ahead for the team behind the White Star, who are making their London experience count in Southampton's wining and dining district. Neatly redesigned, the former chain pub is now split into an intimate lounge bar - complete with chill-out leather armchairs - and a comfortable dining room, spacious, understated and stylishly functional: all the old tables can be extended if a few more friends show up for dessert. A British/eclectic menu with a pleasantly familiar ring to it goes more free-form at lunch, with no distinction between "starters" and "mains".

Food serving times:
Monday-Sunday:
 12pm-3pm, 6pm-10pm
Closed 25-26 December and 1 January
Prices:
Meals: a la carte 15.00/30.00

Typical Dishes

Salad of curly endive, poached egg

Scallops with chicken wings

Honey almond tart

Parking meters directly outside ➤➤

Sparsholt

039 Plough Inn

Main Road, Sparsholt SO21 2NW
Tel.: (01962) 776353 - Fax: (01962) 776400

VISA MC JCB

Old Speckled Hen, Wadworth 6X, Henry's IPA, Summersault

Proving that people really will go the extra mile for a good pub lunch, the friendly Plough Inn is often packed, even in midweek, so booking is a must. Even at its busiest, though, the atmosphere in the softly lit bars and lounges remains relaxed and warm, and in fine weather, a good-hearted crowd from the village and beyond are only too happy to spread out onto the front terrace and cottage garden, or take a seat on the benches in the field at the back, where the pub's donkeys crop the pasture with Eeyore-ish reserve. Back inside, big blackboard menus of wholesome country cooking offer some subtle variation: after a range of tasty starters, the mains diverge, with lighter pub fare on the one hand and more elaborate entrées on the other: you might find anything from Thai curry and steaks to baked sea bass or scallops.

Food serving times:
Monday-Sunday:
     12pm-2pm, 6pm-9pm
Closed 25 December
(booking essential)
Prices:
Meals: a la carte 16.00/23.00

3.5mi Northwest of Winchester by B3049
Parking

Typical Dishes

Watercress and potato soup

Salmon and crab cake

Melon, mango and ginger parfait

Stockbridge

 040 Peat Spade Inn

Longstock, Stockbridge SO20 6DR

Tel.: (01264) 810612 - Fax: (01264) 810612
e-mail: peat.spade@virgin.net

Ringwood 49er, Hopback GFB, Hampshire Angry Trout

Even in a quintessentially pretty English village like Longstock, this 18C redbrick gem makes you stop specially and look. The name derives from the peat that was dug locally; these days, labour-induced thirst is hardly a pre-requisite for loyal regulars. Outside, chickens wander round a pleasant garden and terrace; visiting dogs are welcome, but only even-tempered ones! Behind the gabled entrance, the feeling is almost avuncular: the friendly and accommodating owner keeps a homely house. Neat dining areas fan out from the simple bar, with a mix of scrubbed wood tables and chairs and a large fireplace boasting a collection of Toby jugs. A small menu is changed regularly according to market produce available; seasonal, organic ingredients are guaranteed, with more than a token offering of vegetarian specials.

Food serving times:
Wednesday-Thursday:
    12pm-2pm, 7pm-9pm
Friday-Saturday:
    12pm-2pm, 7pm-9.30pm
Sunday: 12pm-2pm
Prices:
Meals: a la carte 18.50/25.00
⊨ **2 rooms:** 62.50

Typical Dishes

Salmon mousse

Lemon sole, cauliflower risotto

Belgian chocolate biscuit cake

1.5mi North of Stockbridge on A3057. Parking

Stockbridge

041 **The Greyhound**
31 High St, Stockbridge SO20 6EY
Tel.: (01264) 810833 - Fax: (01264) 811184

 VISA Ⓜⓒ

 Butcombe, Brakspear, Wychwood Hobgoblin

Standing snugly at one end of Stockbridge High Street since time immemorial, this honey-hued pub now tends to attract a rather "smartly casual" set after a 21C clean-up in which its 18C features were carefully restored and brought to prominence. Bend down, if needs be, to make progress through the characterful, low-beamed lounge, to arrive at the bare tables and wood flooring of the two dining areas where your rustic notions will be suitably enhanced. It feels like a pub but quite clearly has restaurant sensibilities, reflected in the chef's metropolitan background and Michelin star winning modern menus, prepared with skill and imagination: expect Gressingham duck with mixed bean hash and balsamic jus, foie gras with beef, or black bream with roasted salsify and artichoke, served by an enthusiastic brigade of young waiters.

Food serving times:
Monday-Saturday:
12pm-2.30pm, 7pm-9.30pm
Sunday: 12pm-2.30pm
Closed 25 December and
1 January
Prices:
Meals: a la carte 20.00/35.00
🛏 **8 rooms:** 95.00

On A30
Parking

Typical Dishes

Pigeon breast, raisins and mushrooms

Turbot, leek vinaigrette

Fried rice pudding

Whitchurch

042 Red House Inn

21 London St, Whitchurch RG28 7LH
Tel.: (01256) 895558 - Fax: (01256) 895966

 Cheriton Pots

To save any fruitless searches for red houses, what you're actually looking for is a row of 400 year-old whitewashed cottages: as you'll see inside, from the black and white photographs of the market town in bygone days, the conversion took place nearly a century ago. One door leads to the public bar, the other takes you into the restaurant: uncovered pine tables, a big mirror giving a pleasing sense of space and a large brick fireplace by the bar. Blackboard menus promise everything from lunchtime filled baguettes to scallops or shin of beef, and a more formal printed menu retains the same modern style. Weather permitting, tables are also available on the raised terrace outside.

Food serving times:
Monday-Sunday:
   12pm-2pm, 6.30pm-9.30pm
Prices:
Meals: a la carte 20.00/30.00

Typical Dishes

Salmon and chilli fishcakes

John Dory on crab and saffron risotto

Selection of cheeses

In the village. Parking

Winchester

043 Wykeham Arms

75 Kingsgate St, Winchester SO23 9PE

Tel.: (01962) 853834 - Fax: (01962) 854411
e-mail: wykehamarms@accommodating-inns.co.uk

 ⌂ 🍷 ⌁room *VISA* AE ⊙ MC

HSB, Gales Best Bitter, Butser, Bass and 1 guest ale

On a quiet street between the Cathedral and the College stands Winchester's third great institution, the Wykeham Arms. Founded back in the 1700s, it continues to draw a loyal local following but should be first on any visitor's itinerary too: intimate and charming, its comfortable snugs contain an intriguing collection of prints, flags, rackets, straw boaters and other sporting and school memorablia, as well as old oak desks from the nearby classrooms. Well-informed young staff serve with enthusiasm and a good sense of timing; fresh, appetising cuisine – a modern-classic blend with nicely weighted flavours – puts the region's seasonal produce at the top of the list. Bedrooms are split between the main house – rich colour scheme and historical prints – and the annex across the road; the oak-panelled breakfast room is on the first floor.

Food serving times:
Monday-Saturday:
        12pm-2.30pm,
        6.30pm-8.45pm
Sunday: 12pm-2.30pm
Closed 25 December
Prices:
Meals: a la carte 19.00/28.00
🛏 **14 rooms:** 55.00/120.00

Near (St Mary's) Winchester College. Access to the car park via Canon Street only

Typical Dishes

Salmon rillettes

Turbot fillet, lobster cream

White chocolate and Baileys torte

Freshwater (Isle of Wight)

035 **Red Lion**

Church Pl, Freshwater PO40 9BP

Tel.: (01983) 754925 - Fax: (01983) 754925

e-mail: info@redlion-wight.co.uk - Website: www.redlion-wight.co.uk

Wadworth 6X, Fuller's London Pride, Flowers Original, Goddards

A handsome, part 14C building with little bay windows, this is as traditionally English a pub as any you might find on the slightly larger island across the water, and the characterful country style continues in its rustic interior. Run with a mix of enthusiastic quirkiness and good old fashioned hard work, it continues to do a thriving trade, with the focus squarely on a blackboard menu with daily variations – mostly traditional in its essentials, the pub's cuisine makes good use of its fresh ingredients, including newly-landed Channel fish. On busy days, your best chance of a seat may be in the garden or under the mini-marquee: a fixture since 2000, "the Dome" gets rather more use than the Greenwich version, but is generally reserved for private parties.

Food serving times:
Monday-Sunday:
12pm-2pm, 6.30pm-9pm
Closed 25 December
Prices:
Meals: a la carte 18.00/23.00

Typical Dishes

Herring roe on toast

Scallops in bacon, bubble and squeak

Bread and butter pudding

By the saltings of the River Yar. Parking

Biddenden

044 Three Chimneys

Hareplain Road, Biddenden TN27 8LW

Tel.: (01580) 291472
Website: www.uk.travelguide.co.uk

 Adnams Best, Harveys Best, Shepherd Neame Spitfire, Fuller's London Pride

Here's a pub full of Kentish character: it's only down the road from Sissinghurst, so make a day of it and combine a visit to both. The Three Chimneys has been around since about 1420, and its lovely old exterior has a rough thick cream coat. The attractive terrace is packed in summer; at other times, don't miss the definitively rustic bar: yellowing walls, dried hops, absurdly characterful (and original) beams, little burner fire, lots of rough furniture. The restaurant, at the back, is smarter, in a palette of chocolate brown, with leather chairs, sealed wooden floors, painted wood-panelled walls and spacious tables; what's more, it faces the garden. Dishes change regularly, from substantial salads to fish and steaks. Puddings are all homemade, in keeping with the warm, genuine feel that pervades here.

Food serving times:
Monday-Sunday:
12pm-1.50pm,
6.30pm-9.45pm
Closed 25 December and 31 December
Prices:
Meals: a la carte 15.00/25.00

West 1.5mi off A262. Parking

Typical Dishes

Sauteed chicken liver, port jus

Sea bass, coconut and coriander chowder

Treacle tart

Bridge

045 **White Horse Inn**

53, High St., Bridge CT4 5LA

Tel.: (01227) 830249 - Fax: (01227) 832814
e-mail: whitehorsebridge@hotmail.com - Website: www.whitehorsebridge.co.uk

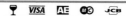

Up to 4 regularly changing ales

Particularly proud of their commitment to small local suppliers, not to mention their Kentish wines from Tenterden vineyards, the team at the White Horse have put together two menus with a common local and traditional theme. One, served in the classically styled dining room with more formal presentation and the little restaurant extras, has a touch more seasonality to it, while the bar menu combines long-standing pub favourites like fish and chips or sausage and mash with more modern or original dishes, including goat's cheese salad, Whitstable oysters and oxtail terrine with pickles and apple chutney. The British and Irish cheeseboard, with specialities from as close to home as Thanet and as far afield as Cork, deserves a menu in itself, and gets one, complete with tasting notes.

Food serving times:
Tuesday-Saturday:
    12pm-2pm, 6.30pm-9.30pm
Sunday: 12pm-2pm
Prices:
Meals: 12.95/23.50 and a la carte 12.95/35.00

Typical Dishes

Courgette and sweet cherry tomato tart

Lamb, caramelised vegetables

Hot raspberry soufflé

5 miles from Canterbury, off A2. Parking.

Dargate

046 **Dove Inn**

Plum Pudding Lane, Dargate ME13 9HB

Tel.: (01227) 751360

 Shepherd Neame Master Brew

Unremarkable on the outside, this Victorian redbrick pub feels much friendlier once you walk up to the bar: the smiling landlady is only to pleased to sort out drinks, talk you through the menu and find you a table. Three little pine-fitted bar-rooms are warmed by open fires and decorated with black and white photos – a real visual history of village, pub and landlords down the years. A surprisingly extensive menu balances classic and modern influences to good effect: well-judged and richly flavourful dishes include glazed goat's cheese with a ripe, moist tomato and red onion salad, a suitably robust and warming cassoulet and an old favourite, warm Bakewell-style tart with vanilla ice cream. Even with one or two slightly pricier dishes, this is excellent value for money, as shown by the Bib Gourmand award.

Food serving times:
Tuesday: 12pm-2pm
Wednesday-Saturday:
12pm-2pm, 7pm-9pm
Sunday: 12pm-2pm
(booking essential)
Prices:
Meals: a la carte 20.00/30.00

Just off the A299 between Faversham and Whitstable. Parking

Typical Dishes

Goat's cheese, tomato and onion salad

Cassoulet, herb crust

Apple and almond tart

Igtham Common

047 ## Harrow Inn

Common Rd, Igtham Common TN15 9EB
Tel.: (01732) 885912 - Fax: (01732) 885912

VISA ⓂⒸ

Greene King IPA, Abbot and 1 guest ale

Don't be misled by the Harrow Inn's location, down a sleepy little lane in a Kentish hamlet – you'll have to get here pretty early to be sure of securing a seat in this pretty, part 17C stone and brick pub. An open fire divides the lovely, pleasingly traditional bar, although you might also find a free table in the back dining room and conservatory extension, where a printed menu replicates the list on the blackboard. With its share of more inventive recipes, there's a little more to this good, honest country cooking than you might expect: smoked haddock rarebit followed by homemade lemon roulade makes a tasty light lunch before a trip to nearby Knowle or the Tudor castle at Ightham Mote. Cheerful service.

Food serving times:
Tuesday-Saturday:
  12pm-2pm, 6pm-9pm
Sunday: 12pm-2pm
Closed 1 January
(fixed price menu Sunday)
Prices:
Meals: 22.50 and a la carte approx. 25.00

Typical Dishes
Crab spring roll
Sea bass, spinach and lobster cream
Mango and passion fruit brûlée

5mi South East of Sevenoaks by A25 on Common Road. Parking

Langton Green

048 The Hare

Langton Rd, Langton Green TN3 0JA

Tel.: (01892) 862419 - Fax: (01892) 861275
e-mail: hare@bruningandprice.co.uk - Website: www.hare-tunbridgewells.co.uk

Greene King IPA, Abbot, Old Speckled Hen, Caledonian 80 Shilling

Just west of Tunbridge Wells on the outskirts of the town, stands this rather grand looking pub on a village green. The owners have created a kind of casual, modern-rustic interior, which has proved spot-on, judging by the bustling nature of the main bar - always busy but rarely overcrowded. Grab a drink here and move into one of the shiny rooms with well-spaced tables set around gleaming floorboards, above which chamber pots hang ominously over doorways. Or go into the more formal dining room, its walls filled with books, its tables and chairs in every assortment of style. Orders are taken at the bar from a blackboard menu, but take your time going through the list: there's everything from steaks to crab salads, assorted fish dishes to duck confit.

Food serving times:
Monday-Saturday:
          12pm-9.30pm
Sunday: 12pm-9pm
Prices:
Meals: a la carte 15.95/24.70

Typical Dishes

Tuna with lemon dressed salad

Pork with mustard and caper sauce

Apricot tart

2mi West of Royal Tunbridge Wells on A264
Parking

Pluckley

049 Dering Arms

Station Rd, Pluckley TN27 0RR
Tel.: (01233) 840371 - Fax: (01233) 840498
e-mail: info@deringarms.com - Website: www.deringarms.com

🍷 *VISA* AE ① M©

Geachers Dering

Step through the heavy, original doors of this mid-19C Dutch-gabled former hunting lodge and experience the genuine feel of a 'local'. A pleasant rural atmosphere is evoked from blazing log fires, reclaimed tables and chairs, farming implements and bars festooned with hops. Emphasis is on the hefty seafood menus. You might find salmon fishcakes with sorrel sauce; monkfish with bacon, orange and cream; or skate wing with capers and black butter. If you're not in the mood for fish, then opt for the likes of confit of duck or the pie of the day. Afterwards, order a pint of real farm cider – the Dering specialises in them - and flop into a leather armchair in the cosy lounge.

Food serving times:
Monday-Sunday:
12pm-2pm, 7pm-9.30pm
Closed 26-27 December
Prices:
Meals: a la carte 17.50/28.00
🛏 **3 rooms:** 35.00/45.00

1.5mi South on Bethersden rd
Parking

Typical Dishes
Crayfish tails, lime and chilli
Monkfish in bacon, orange and cream
Chocolate fudge cake

Sandwich

050 George & Dragon Inn

24 Fisher St, Sandwich CT13 9EJ
Tel.: (01304) 613106 - Fax: (01304) 621137

Shepherd Neame Master Brew and 2 guest ales

This rather ordinary looking little pub boasts never being closed since it acquired its name in 1615. From the street, the visitor to Sandwich might reasonably wonder what the locals find so special, but you'll soon see their point of view. Cosy and warm, with a detectably contemporary air, the front bar is where the locals gather for pints of local Kentish ale, and just beyond is a most welcoming dining room with warm yellow walls, scrubbed pine tables and chairs, and a serving hatch to kitchen. Service is noticeably bright, too, from staff kitted out in smart black and white outfits. An interesting menu ventures successfully down various modish gastronomic avenues: from local seafood to tasty Thai specialities. If you've got room, try the apple and coconut tart.

Food serving times:
Monday-Sunday:
    12pm-2.15pm, 6pm-9.30pm
Closed dinner 25 December,
26 December and dinner 1
January
Prices:
Meals: a la carte 17.00/27.50

Typical Dishes

Parma ham, rocket

Guinea fowl with shallots
and sherry

Vodka and rasberry crème
brûlée

In town centre
Parking on the town quay

Seasalter

051 **The Sportsman**

Faversham Rd, Seasalter CT5 4BP

Tel.: (01227) 273370 - Fax: (01227) 262314

 VISA **MC**

Shepherd Neame Master Brew, Porter, Late Red, Goldings, Bishops Finger

Sheltering in the lee of the sea wall, this rather ramshackle pub doesn't promise much; inside, though, it's a different story. The simple, modern styling in pale pine looks a little stark at first, but as the log fires get going, the front and back bars fill up with a good mix of weekenders and regulars, sheep huddle on the marshes and circling gulls are blown past the window, it starts to feel quite cosy. A chatty, knowledgeable team, led by brothers Phil and Steve, runs the place with real enthusiasm, preparing a good-value blackboard menu centred on well-chosen seafood. With such skillful combinations of flavours, it's hard to put a foot wrong, but favourites include cod and langoustines, monkfish in sauce vierge, confit of duck and, of course, the local oysters fresh from the quay. A Michelin Bib Gourmand winner for quality and value.

Food serving times:
Tuesday-Saturday:
12pm-2pm, 7pm-9pm
Sunday: 12pm-2pm
Closed 25-26 December
Prices:
Meals: a la carte 18.00/28.00

Typical Dishes

Oysters and hot chorizo

Turbot braised in vin jaune

Rhubarb sorbet

2mi Southwest of Whitstable by B2205
Parking

West Peckham

052 Swan on the Green

West Peckham ME18 5JW

Tel.: (01622) 812271 - Fax: (0870) 0560556
e-mail: info@swan-on-the-green.co.uk - Website: www.swan-on-the-green.co.uk

 On-site microbrews include Whooper, Trumpeter Best, Bewick Special, Mild, Ginger and Portside

Pub settings rarely come more attractively old English than this – the Swan's redbrick and ornate gabled exterior sits idyllically by the green, right next to the village's Saxon church. There's no pub garden, but benches perch along the terrace at the front. Inside, a framed history puts the inn's origins at 1526, but it's been given a pleasing modern makeover with pale wood throughout: the dried hops and real fire add a rustic twist. At the back is a micro-brewery, so a selection of unique ales are chalked up on the board behind the bar. There's a loyal local following and menus, featuring an interesting eclectic à la carte, change weekly. Try to visit in summer, when the owners provide blankets for you to eat on the green.

Food serving times:
Tuesday-Saturday:
12pm-2pm, 7pm-9pm
Sunday: 12pm-2pm
Prices:
Meals: a la carte 20.00/26.00

Typical Dishes

Prawns, vanilla and curry oil

Fillet steak, red wine

Honey and ginger cheesecake

7.75mi South West of Maidstone by A26 and B2016. Parking

Barnard Gate

053 The Boot Inn

Barnard Gate OX29 6XE

Tel.: (01865) 881231 - Fax: (01865) 882119
e-mail: info@theboot-inn.com - Website: www.theboot-inn.com

 Hook Norton Best and up to 4 guest ales

The Cotswold stone walls of this eclectic pub are covered with the footwear of the famous from Stanley Matthews to the Bee Gees, though it's not clear what drinks, if any, they ordered at the bar and whether a pint was paid for with a pair of old trainers. However, elsewhere at the Boot, tradition plays a stronger role: snug corners, welcoming fire, beams and flagstones. Tables are rustic to the core, and chairs clatter on bare boards. Eating at lunchtime can be a simple affair - thick cut sandwiches or a plate of gammon and chips - but things get a little more elaborate in the evenings, with a mixture of traditional and more inventive dishes to be enjoyed in the candlelight. Friendly, approachable service comes naturally here.

Food serving times:
Monday-Sunday:
12pm-2.30pm, 7pm-9.30pm
(booking essential)
Prices:
Meals: a la carte 20.00/28.00

Typical Dishes

Chicken, coriander, vegetable roulade

Chicken supreme

Rhubarb and vanilla fool

3.25mi East of Witney by B4022 off A40
Parking

Britwell Salome

054 **The Goose**

Britwell Salome OX49 5LG

Tel.: (01491) 612304 - Fax: (01491) 613945
e-mail: thegooseatbritwellsalome@fsmail.net

     VISA **AE** **MC**

 Hook Norton Best Bitter and occasional guest ales

The Goose's kitchen was once famously run by Prince Charles' personal chef, and the former gastronomer-royal has left this lovely period pub in good keeping, passing the spatula to his right-hand man. It remains a charming and astutely judged blend of pub and restaurant, its stylish bar - comfy sofas and a faint aroma of wood smoke - leading on to a dining room with blue glassware, white china and a easy air of good taste. If sparkling, attentive service from a team in Oxford-cloth shirts and aprons deserves a special mention, the food itself steals the show. Waitresses will talk you through an outstanding-value set lunch or introduce a more elaborate but still concise and balanced menu – confidently prepared, deliciously moreish dishes burst with seasonal flavour and show a trust in quality produce that would please HRH. A real delight.

Food serving times:
Monday-Saturday:
    12pm-2.30pm, 7pm-9pm
Sunday: 12pm-3pm
Closed 25 December
Prices:
Meals: 15.00 and a la carte
26.00/35.00

Typical Dishes

Salmon, scallops, lime
pickled beetroot

Braised lamb, creamed
spinach

Sticky toffee pudding

Between Watlington and Benson on B4009
Parking

Buckland

055 Lamb Inn

Lamb Lane, Buckland SN7 8QN

Tel.: (01367) 870484 - Fax: (01367) 870675

e-mail: enquiries@thelambatbuckland.co.uk - Website: www.thelambatbuckland.co.uk

 rest 🍷 **VISA** ⓪ ⓜⓒ JCB

Adnams Broadside

This charming 18C pub luxuriates in a quiet village of Cotswold stone. Family owned for a number of years, it boasts a well-established local reputation and an extremely comfy atmosphere prevails, suitably enhanced by soft lighting, real log fire, and sheep motifs which show up in paintings, curios and even the capet. Choose to eat in a characterful beamed room or more formal linen clad dining area. Either way, the same blackboard menus are served; these consist of accomplished, traditional dishes, typified by locally smoked prawns and salad, loin of pork with wild mushrooms, and raspberry brulée with raspberry sorbet.

Food serving times:
Tuesday-Saturday:
  12pm-2.30pm, 6pm-10pm
Sunday: 12pm-2.30pm
Closed 2 weeks Christmas-New Year
Prices:
Meals: a la carte 15.00/35.00

Typical Dishes

Scallops and bacon, salad

Rack of lamb, mint and sorrel

Orange crème caramel

Between Farington and Kingston Bagpuize off A420
Parking

Burford

056 Lamb Inn

Sheep St, Burford OX18 4LR

Tel.: (01993) 823155 - Fax: (01993) 822228
e-mail: info@lambinn-burford.co.uk - Website: www.lambinnburford.co.uk

 rest **VISA**

 Hook Norton, Wadworth 6X, Butcombe

Weathered local stone announces this strikingly relaxed part 14C inn, set prominently in a picture-postcard market town. The interior is as quietly charming as you would expect: flagstone floors and open log fires in three antique furnished lounges. Go through a separate entrance to a cosy bar where a good selection of real ales is enjoyed by the regulars. A classically formal restaurant reflects the age of the inn: appealing menus mix traditional and modern dishes which range from roast best end of lamb with sweetbreads and bubble and squeak, to smoked cod with cauliflower cheese and mustard potatoes. Bedrooms underwent a refurbishment early in 2004: now you can tumble blissfully into beds clothed in fine Egyptian linen and quality fabrics.

Food serving times:
Monday-Friday:
  12pm-2.30pm, 7pm-9.30pm
Saturday-Sunday:
  12pm-3pm, 7pm-9.30pm
Prices:
Meals: 29.50 and a la carte
25.00/35.00
15 rooms: 80.00/200.00

Typical Dishes

Smoked duck, spiced plums

Roast skate basquaise

Chocolate chip cookies,
panacotta

In town centre
Parking on the street

Charlbury

057 Bull Inn

Sheep St, Charlbury OX7 3RR
Tel.: (01608) 810689

🍷 🚭 *VISA* Ⓜ© JCB

Abbot, IPA, Hook Norton

This charming hostelry has been delighting the locals of Charlbury since the 16C, and in 500 years it hasn't compromised one jot on its traditional appeal. Creeper-clad in summer, it's the quintessential country pub right down to its flagstone floors and inglenook fires. You can whet your appetite before visiting with a stroll along the banks of the River Evenlode, just five minutes' walk away. The rustic bar is divided into three booths with wicker and pine chairs; the restaurant continues the rural theme with more hardy stone floors and rugged pine tables. Concise, fresh menus have earned the Bull a fine local reputation for its cooking: you might find braised lamb shank with a mint and redcurrant gravy; smoked haddock Florentine; or chicken, smoked ham and leek casserole.

Food serving times:
Monday-Sunday:
　　12pm-2pm, 7pm-9pm
Closed Monday lunch
Prices:
Meals: a la carte 15.00/25.00
🛏 **3 rooms:** 60.00/85.00
☕ 8.50

Typical Dishes

Home-made soup

Shank of lamb

Strawberry and Cointreau crush

In town centre
Parking

Chipping Norton

058 **The Masons Arms**

Banbury Rd, Swerford, Chipping Norton OX7 4AP

Tel.: (01608) 683212 - Fax: (01608) 683105
e-mail: themasonschef@hotmail.com

 VISA *AE* *D* *MC*

 Hook Norton Best, Wadworth 6X, Marstons Pedigree

A roadside Cotswold inn, raised above the norm by the keenness of a husband and wife team, whose hospitable approach seems to have spread to the rest of the helpful young staff. Dating back to the 1800s, its origins are rather mysterious – quite appropriate for a former Freemason's lodge – but apart from a nod to its Masonic past near the entrance, the interior resonates with bright, 21C country style: more rattan chairs and polished floors than horse brasses and swirly carpets. In contrast, the owner is a great advocate of culinary tradition. For the most part, only local produce makes it into the kitchen, and many methods and recipes described on the blackboard owe as much to the Victorian cookbook as to contemporary cuisine. Robust, flavourful food might include braised oxtail or sea bass in gazpacho sauce. Lovely views from the garden.

Food serving times:
Monday-Sunday:
   12pm-2.30pm, 7pm-9.30pm
Closed 25-26 December
Prices:
Meals: a la carte 16.00/23.00

Typical Dishes

Red mullet, lemon and mint couscous

Lamb in rosemary jus

Raspberry, honey and Drambuie brûlée

On A361, North East of the town. Parking

Christmas Common

059 The Fox & Hounds

Christmas Common OX49 5HL

Tel.: (01491) 612599

 🍷 *VISA* Ⓜ©

Brakspear, Special, Seasonal, Hook Norton Mild

Ideally set for walkers, with the Chilterns and the Ridgeway Path to hand, the pub's been here in the hills, in what's now rare red kite territory, since the 15C; recent years have seen a bit of updating, including the new restaurant, which has metamorphosed from the old barn. The pub proper retains its tiled and beamed interior, the gentle crackle in the inglenook on all but the hottest days, a delightful, laid-back atmosphere and plenty of quirky appeal. Savoury bar dishes of a traditional stamp cry out for a good ale, organic juice or wine, so try one with your Welsh rarebit or roast ham hock; if you fancy a full meal, blackboards list a mix of modern, traditional and Mediterranean dishes. Local suppliers stock the kitchen and produce for sale here includes everything from pickled onions to beeswax and eggs from 'the man up the road'.

Food serving times:
Monday-Saturday:
12pm-2.30pm, 7pm-9.30pm
Sunday: 12pm-3pm,
7pm-9pm

Prices:
Meals: a la carte 18.00/28.00

South East of Watlington, near Shotridge Wood. Parking

Typical Dishes
Asparagus in Parma ham
Rump of lamb, thyme rösti potato
Panettone bread and butter pudding

Church Enstone

060 The Crown Inn

Mill Lane, Church Enstone OX7 4NN

Tel.: (01608) 677262 - Fax: (01608) 677394
e-mail: tcwarburton@btopenworld.com - Website: www.crowninnenstone.co.uk

VISA MC

Hook Norton Best Bitter, Timothy Taylor Landlord, Shepherd Neame Spitfire

Close to the gurgling River Glyme, this 17C pub of Cotswold stone is one of the highlights of a charming little village. It's a well-kept establishment, personally run by a husband and wife team: she keeps things ticking over in the main bar while he does the cooking. Recent refurbishment has added a modish seagrass carpet across the floor, but other features have stayed reassuringly traditional: a cottagey bar, log fire in stone fireplace, beams and exposed stone. You can eat in two areas: a bright dining room with red hued walls and uncovered pine tables, or a conservatory extension. The lunchtime blackboard menu gives way to a more expansive repertoire in the evening, while charming, attentive service adds an extra dimension to the invariably pleasant atmosphere.

Food serving times:
Monday-Saturday:
12pm-2pm, 7pm-9pm
Sunday: 12pm-2pm
Closed 25-26 December and 1 January. Open Bank Holiday Mondays
Prices:
Meals: 16.50 and a la carte 16.25/27.95

Typical Dishes

Scallops and bacon salad

Roast duck leg, rocket

Poached peaches, amaretti biscuit

3.5mi Southeast of Chipping Norton by A44
Parking

Church Hanborough

061 **Hand & Shears**

Church Hanborough OX29 8AB

Tel.: (01993) 883337

 🍷 ✗ **VISA** **MC**

🍺 *Hook Norton Best, Old Hooky*

A handsome 17C inn in mellow Oxfordshire sandstone, the Hand and Shears is just the sort of place you hope you'll find in such a pretty village. It looks quite small opposite the parish church, but once inside feels positively spacious. Two richly decorated parlours off the main bar have big scrubbed pine tables for eating or drinking, while to the back an inviting lounge with leather sofas connects to an airy restaurant, its high, beamed ceiling making it look more like a converted barn than a pub. The balanced menu presents re-invented classics and Modern British dishes in equal measure, plus a very affordable set-menu lunch deal and four children's choices.

Food serving times:
Monday-Saturday:
12pm-3pm, 6.30pm-10pm
Sunday: 12pm-3pm
Prices:
Meals: a la carte 20.00/30.00

Typical Dishes

Smoked salmon risotto

Fish pie with mussels, hake and prawns

Peaches on brioche, vanilla custard

4.25mi South West of Woodstock by A44 off A4095. Opposite the church. Parking

Churchill

062 **The Chequers**

Church Rd, Churchill OX7 6NJ
Tel.: (01608) 659393

 VISA **MC**

 Hook Norton Best, Old Speckled Hen, Timothy Taylor Landlord, Adnams

Set on the main road of a delightful Cotswold village, this charming hostelry is idyllically placed opposite All Saints Church. It's been creating quite a buzz since it opened its doors in the spring of 2004, after nine months of refurbishment, having lain idle for five years. An 18C inn lurks in there somewhere; the owners have added in a sympathetic and careful way using honey coloured Cotswold stone. The bustling atmosphere is testament to good local opinion. You can dine in two areas: downstairs – a combination of beams, high arched ceiling and exposed stone; or upstairs, where a cosy lounge is ideal for pre- or post-prandial drinks. Well-balanced menus might include pan fried swordfish with olive beurre blanc, or tenderloin of pork with grilled black pudding.

Food serving times:
Monday-Saturday:
    12pm-2pm, 7pm-9.30pm
Sunday: 12pm-3pm,
                         7pm-9.30pm
Closed 25 December
Prices:
Meals: a la carte 17.00/22.50

Typical Dishes

Goat's cheese pastry, mango chutney

Tenderloin of pork, rosemary sauce

Lemon cheesecake

South West of Chipping Norton by B4450. Parking.

Crays Pond

063 **The White Lion**

Goring Rd, Goring Heath, Crays Pond RG8 7SH
Tel.: (01491) 680471 - Fax: (01491) 681654
e-mail: reservations@innastew.com - Website: www.innastew.com

 Greene King IPA, Abbot

A stylish mix of old and new has earned this village pub outside Goring a strong local reputation. Part built in 1756, its wooden window shutters and paved terrace give it a modern veneer, but old beams and low ceilings have been retained from a refurbishment in 2003, which now sees smart oak floors combined with burgundy and sage green walls. These are adorned by framed menus from Gordon Ramsay, Le Manoir and the like, some of which were obtained from patrons' visits, others from auction. Soft wall lighting enhances a couple of roaring log fires. Eclectic dishes and good British staples dominate menus which offer a robust, hearty choice and plentiful portions. Everything is cooked freshly to order, from the homemade chips to puddings. This is a busy, popular destination: it could be worth booking at weekends.

Food serving times:
Tuesday-Saturday:
    12pm-2pm, 6pm-9.30pm
Sunday: 12pm-2.30pm
Closed 25-26 December
(fixed price lunch Sunday)
Prices:
Meals: 16.95 and a la carte
20.00/30.00

Typical Dishes

Devilled kidneys

Cod with chorizo and pickled mushrooms

Roast fig tart, goat's cheese ice cream

2mi East of Goring on B4526. Parking

Cuddesdon

064 ## The Bat & Ball Inn

High St, Cuddesdon OX44 9HJ

Tel.: (01865) 874379 - Fax: (01865) 873363
e-mail: bb@traditionalvillageinns.co.uk - Website: www.traditionalvillageinns.co.uk

  room

 Marston Pedigree, House LBW and 1 guest ale

Cricket lovers will be in their element here, with enough conversation pieces to see them through lunch – and the tea interval. Scorebooks, trophies and old cigarette cards are proudly displayed and batting gloves hang above the window in the flag-floored bar, while the very rafters of the new dining room are braced with ancient stumps and well knocked-in bats: some, with a blackboard slab set into the willow, list the chef's daily specials. British cooking, hearty and plentiful, runs from venison in red wine to cod and chips, by way of salads and lunchtime baguettes or panini, all served at big pine tables by a young team who are casual, friendly and far too modest to mention Australia's defence of The Ashes. For the full Test Match Special experience, they also serve decent slabs of chocolate cake.

Food serving times:
Monday-Friday:
12pm-2.45pm, 6pm-9.45pm
Saturday-Sunday:
12pm-9.45pm
Closed 26 December
Prices:
Meals: 12.50 and a la carte 16.00/30.00
7 rooms: 53.00/65.00

Typical Dishes

Garlic mushroom soup

Herb crusted cod, red pepper cream

Chocolate and strawberry shortcake

6mi East of Oxford city centre. Parking

Faringdon

065 ## The Trout at Tadpole Bridge

Buckland Marsh, Faringdon SN7 8RF

Tel.: (01367) 870382

e-mail: info@trout-inn.co.uk - Website: www.trout-inn.co.uk

   ⌘room *VISA*

Youngs PA, Archers Village, Brakspear and several guest ales

This attractive old inn stands next to a pretty bridge by the Thames and is locally renowned by the anglers who gather along the riverbanks. You can watch them in action - or inaction - from the Trout's relaxing terrace: on the menus, the eponymous fish itself is caught by a local fisherman. The rustic interior has a number of charming, recently refurbished rooms, boasting a mix of old pine and polished tables, assorted chairs, and newspapers and magazines lying invitingly to one side. It's most certainly a pub to stretch out in. Cooking is satisfying and reliable: game and meat come from local estates and farms, with some vegetables picked fresh from the back garden. Tasty, accomplished dishes, including seafood specials on the blackboard, are the result. Smart bedrooms may entice weary rod danglers.

Food serving times:
Monday-Saturday:
12pm-2pm, 7pm-9pm
Sunday: 12pm-2pm
Closed 25-26 December, 31 December, 1 January and 1st week February

Prices:
Meals: a la carte 16.85/29.85
6 rooms: 55.00/110.00

4.5mi Northeast of Faringdon by A417, A420 on Brampton road
Parking

Typical Dishes

Scallops with veal sweetbreads

Halibut with haddock and leek tart

Lemon passet

Great Tew

066 Falkland Arms

Great Tew OX7 4DB

Tel.: (01608) 683653 - Fax: (01608) 683656
e-mail: sjcourage@btconnect.com - Website: www.falklandarms.org.uk

 Wadworth IPA, 6X and seasonal guest ales

A picture-perfect village inn without a scrap of preciousness or pretension. Its 17C Cotswold stone is wreathed in ivy and climbing roses; in the cosy, flag-floored bar, orderly rows of crocks and mugs hang from the beams and polished pint-pot tankards glint in the lamplight. Chalked up on the board are six classic dishes, tasty and fortifying, plus potatoes and baguettes, but plenty of the locals are happy enough with the friendly welcome, a seat on the old settles and benches, a well-kept beer and a bit of old-English aromatherapy: tins of snuff and clay pipes are sold behid the bar. The spiral staircase leads up to six charming, period styled rooms in country patterns.

Food serving times:
Monday-Saturday:
12pm-2pm, 7pm-8pm
Sunday: 12pm-2pm
Restricted opening at Christmas
(booking essential)
Prices:
Meals: a la carte 13.75/24.45
5 rooms: 50.00/100.00

Typical Dishes

Thai crab cake salad

Slow cooked lamb shank

Warm banana tart

6.5mi East of Chipping Norton by A361 and B4022
Parking in village car park

267

Henley-on-Thames

067 ## The Three Tuns Foodhouse

5 The Market Pl, Henley-on-Thames RG9 2AA

Tel.: (01491) 573260
e-mail: thefoodhouse@aol.com

VISA **MC**

 Brakspear

Henley isn't all about the river and the regatta. There's a smart, buzzing town beyond the bridge, and right in the heart of the market place is this little pub sandwiched between the shops. It's an early 16C hostelry with a traditional appearance: 'foodhouse' has been added to the frontage to denote its recent change of tack. There's a distinct gastro-pub style here. The front bar is quirkily fashionable, while the back has been transformed into a cosy, dining area with rough ceiling beams, a mix of oak tables and old school style chairs and an offbeat clutch of collectables and curios: many of the furnishings are supplied by a local antiques shop. Menu ingredients are also locally sourced. Much market-fresh produce goes into the interesting British and Mediterranean dishes.

Food serving times:
Monday-Sunday:
  12pm-2.30pm, 7pm-9.30pm
Closed 25-26 December
Prices:
Meals: a la carte 20.00/30.00

In the town centre. Public parking off Greys Rd. and at National Rail station

Typical Dishes

Squash, rocket and cheese tart

Sea bass, pea and broad bean salad

Chocolate cherry cake

Littleworth

068 The Snooty Fox Inn

Littleworth SN7 8PW
Tel.: (01367) 240549 - Fax: (01367) 240549

VISA M©

Wadworth 6X, IPA, Fuller's London Pride

To the south: the Vale of White Horse. To the north: the Thames Path. Slap bang in the middle: this yellow-painted roadside pub with gardens and a welcoming, if somewhat minimalist, ambience for visitors to this pleasant part of Oxfordshire. The spacious interior fans out into a coterie of private dining areas supported by oak beams, with wooden flooring and polished tables. Further in you can choose a nice, comfy sofa to loll around in as you peruse the huge wine rack beside a modern bar. A blazing, brick-built fireplace adorns the main dining room, where an extensive menu takes a bit of investigating. In the end, you might decide on slow-roasted half-shoulder of lamb glazed with honey, or lamb kidneys turbigo; an interesting range of fish and pasta dishes waits temptingly in the wings.

Food serving times:
Monday-Sunday:
12pm-10pm

Prices:
Meals: a la carte 15.00/25.00

3mi Northeast of Faringdon by A417
off A420
Parking

Typical Dishes

Scallops in bacon, garlic butter

Fillet steak Rossini

Sticky toffee pudding

Maidensgrove

069 The Five Horseshoes

Maidensgrove RG9 6EX
Tel.: (01491) 641282 - Fax: (01491) 641086

 Brakspear, Special, Mild, Seasonal

Halfway between the Ridgeway and the upper Thames, this pleasantly down-to-earth pub in 17C redbrick looks out over wooded hills. In summer, you'll want to make straight for the tables in the conservatory, but the same menu is served in the cosy main bar; its low, black-beamed ceiling is papered with old banknotes, some in currencies which haven't aged nearly as well. Tasty dishes might include smoked trout and salmon salad, or pork with Stilton, mango and ginger or scampi and chips: it's substantial cooking on a traditional base and there's always a good turnout for summer barbecues in the garden. The Oxfordshire Way skirts the village, and there are plenty of shorter rambles around the woods, but walkers should make sure they have somewhere to stow their muddy boots. Stonor Park, a part-Tudor manor house, is a few minutes' drive away.

Food serving times:
Monday-Sunday:
 12pm-2pm, 6.30pm-9.30pm
Closed Sunday dinner in autumn and winter
Prices:
Meals: a la carte 16.00/27.50

Typical Dishes
Goat's cheese filo parcels, onion jam
Lambs liver with bacon and onions
Mars bar cheesecake

Near Stonor Park. North of Henley by A4130 on B480, then 0.75mi West. Parking

Sibford Gower

070 Inn at Sibford Gower

Temple Mill Road, Sibford Gower OX15 5RX

Tel.: (01295) 788808 - Fax: (01295) 788806

e-mail: enquiries@innatsibfordgower.co.uk

Greene King Abbot, Fuller's London Pride, Charles Wells Bombardier, The Inns Best

The Inn at Sibford Gower opened its characterful doors in May 2004 and became an instant hit with Oxfordshire locals and Cotswold tourists. This was a farmhouse 400 years ago. Since then, it's been added to but the thatched roof and hanging baskets mean it's still very pretty and charming. There's a bright interior, accentuated by wood flooring, original inglenook fireplace in the bar, low beamed ceiling and dining areas spread between the bar and a second room adjacent to it. A separate spacious garden or the terrace is an ideal spot to pop a champagne cork on a summer's day. Dine on inventive, modern fare, with set price menus at lunchtime and a la carte later in the day, local ingredients always being a priority here.

Food serving times:
Monday-Sunday:
    12pm-3pm, 6pm-10pm

Prices:
Meals: 11.95 and a la carte
22.00/34.00

Typical Dishes

Baked tart of Devonshire shellfish

Ribeye steak, red wine sauce

Toffee pudding

8mi West of Banbury by B4035.
Parking

South Leigh

071 # Mason Arms

South Leigh OX29 6XN
Tel.: (01993) 702485

 🚭 **AE**

Telfords Burton Ale

Sensitive vegetarians and critics beware: this may not be the place for you! It's run in highly 'individualistic' style by the owner who keeps a tight reign on what he serves, and whom he serves it to! The pub itself is a charming 15C thatched inn with pleasant gardens in a tranquil village. Inside, much of the interior is given over to the restaurant: antiques are set on both solid wood and linen-clad tables. Three fascinating rooms have dark walls enhanced by paintings, and cigar boxes mingling with old wine bottles: fine vintages and cigars are evidently a personal passion, and appreciation of both is encouraged. Food is quite classically based, on both menu and blackboard specials, and ranges from cottage pie to caviar. If you're staying overnight, two clean, functional bedrooms await.

Food serving times:
Tuesday-Saturday:
12.30pm-2.30pm,
7.30pm-10.45pm
Sunday: 12.30pm-2.30pm
Closed 25 December and 1 January
Prices:
Meals: a la carte 30.00/50.00
🛏 **2 rooms:** 35.00/65.00

Typical Dishes

Mr Baxters potted shrimps
Beef and venison casserole
Queen of puddings

3mi Southeast of Whitney by B4022
Parking

Sprig's Alley

072 ## Sir Charles Napier

Sprig's Alley OX39 4BX
Tel.: (01494) 483011 - Fax: (01494) 485311
Website: www.sircharlesnapier.co.uk

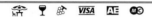 VISA AE MC

 Wadworth 6X, Summer Ale

The big draw of this attractive flint-built pub-restaurant regularly turns the sleepy Oxfordshire hamlet of Sprigg's Alley into a vibrant, buzzy location. Very much a dining destination, it nevertheless retains a pubby feel with beer from the wood and roaring fires in the low-beamed bar. Individuality is writ large, particularly the elegant restaurant – where most people head – which has commissioned marble sculptures, antique silver and smart linen napkins. It opens onto pleasant gardens, a further attraction for diners once summer's here. Interesting menus showcase game and local produce in a seasonal menu that's prepared with care to a most agreeable standard. Service is never less than engaging, which is one reason why those visitors keep coming back.

Food serving times:
Tuesday-Saturday:
  12pm-2.30pm, 7pm-9.30pm
Sunday: 12pm-2.30pm
Prices:
Meals: a la carte 28.00/33.75

2.5mi Southeast of Chinnor by Bledlow Ridge road
Parking

Typical Dishes

Cornish crab salad

Rump of lamb, aubergine and squash

English cheeseboard

Stadhampton

073 Crazy Bear

Bear Lane, Stadhampton OX44 7UR
Tel.: (01865) 890714 - Fax: (01865) 400481
e-mail: sales@crazybearhotel.co.uk - Website: www.crazybearhotel.co.uk

Greene King Ruddles County, Old Speckled Hen

A traditional and rather understated pub appearance belies what's going on here. The Crazy Bear has a modern English restaurant upstairs, a Thai restaurant in the basement, a bar with a stuffed "crazy bear" where you can order cocktails, oysters and frozen vodkas (preferably not at the same time) on the ground floor, and bedrooms with zebra striped carpets and walls of peacock blue and purple, not to mention Philippe Starck inspired bathrooms. Of main interest for foodies is the Thai half of the eating equation: prawn in filo pastry with dipping sauce; duck with tamarind crust and Asian greens; and coconut parfait to round things off – good quality, accomplished and tasty dishes.

Food serving times:
Monday-Sunday:
    12pm-3pm, 6pm-10pm
Prices:
Meals: 15.00 and a la carte
24.50/35.00
 12 rooms: 65.00/290.00

Typical Dishes
Scallops with chorizo
Beef fillet, wild mushroom risotto
Chocolate fondant, pistachio ice cream

Off Wallingford road
Parking

Toot Baldon

074 **The Mole Inn**

Toot Baldon OX44 9NG

Tel.: (01865) 340001 - Fax: (01865) 343011
e-mail: info@themoleinn.com - Website: www.themoleinn.com

VISA *AE* *MC*

Hook Norton, Courage Directors

The sleepy hamlet of Toot Baldon, just outside Oxford, has had a serious wake-up call with the renaissance of this attractive old stalwart as a real top-notch dining pub heavyweight. Huge amounts have been invested in The Mole's stylish refurbishment and it shows. Impressive features include stone tiled flooring, beams galore, cosy lounge area with leather sofas leading into a series of four dining areas, roaring log fires, pine and oak tables, crisp napkins and fine glassware: it's no less than immaculate. Though virtually everything is angled towards eating, drinkers are nevertheless welcomed. Interesting, well-priced cuisine – running from rustic, earthy pub classics to more modern, globally influenced dishes – is prepared with assurance and care. Add light and personable service and the whole experience is positively charming.

Food serving times:
Monday-Saturday:
   12pm-2.30pm, 7pm-9.30pm
Sunday: 12pm-9.30pm
Closed for food 25
December and 1 January
Prices:
Meals: a la carte 20.00/26.00

Typical Dishes
Carpaccio of beef
Cod, fettuccine, seafood
vinaigrette
Frozen chocolate and
amaretto mousse

Located a short distance from both the B480 and A4074. Parking

Wantage

075 Boar's Head

Church St, Ardington, Wantage OX12 8QA

Tel.: (01235) 833254 - Fax: (01235) 833254
e-mail: info@boarsheadardington.co.uk - Website: www.boarsheadardington.co.uk

  room *VISA* *AE* *MC* *JCB*

Hook Norton, Butts Barbus Barbus, West Berkshire Dr Hexter's Wedding Ale

S tunning scenery, in the stirring shape of the Vale of White Horse and Lambourn Downs, is tantalisingly close to this pretty little pub in Ardington, an attractive downland village that's just outside Wantage. From the look of the interior, there's nowhere it would rather be: hunting curios and country magazines appear at every turn, pints of Berkshire ale sit on rough pine tables and a good mix of locals at the bar and chattering diners creates a warm, relaxed atmosphere. The menus come from a modern British direction, featuring some well-balanced combinations like entrecôte of Angus beef with corned beef hash, or stuffed fillet of sea bass with scallop mousse. One further recommendation remains: the bedrooms, which are particularly strong for a pub, in bright, breezy colours and no little style.

Food serving times:
Monday-Thursday:
    12pm-2pm, 7pm-9.30pm
Friday-Saturday:
    12pm-2pm, 7pm-10pm
Sunday: 12pm-2pm
(fixed price meal Sunday)
Prices:
Meals: 18.50 and a la carte 18.00/35.00
🛏 **3 rooms:** 65.00/120.00

Typical Dishes

Foie gras terrine, grapes in Sauternes

Sea bass, girolles and tomato butter

Grand Marnier soufflé

2.25mi East of Wantage by A417
Next to the church. Parking

Wootton

076 **Kings Head**

Chapel Hill, Wootton OX20 1DX

Tel.: (01993) 811340

e-mail: t.fay@kings-head.co.uk - Website: www.kings-head.co.uk

Ruddles County, Wadworth 6X, Old Hooky

Located in a pretty village just outside handsome Woodstock, this attractive 17C Cotswold stone house has a fair degree of charm. Whilst originally an inn, it cottoned on to the possibilities of pub dining in the 1980s and 90s, earning itself a headstart in the gastropub stakes. There's a delightful bar area at the front with roaring fire, where you can eat from a blackboard menu, which might include oriental dishes and fish specials. Cooking is tasty, wholesome and well executed with a smattering of the ambitious. To the rear is a rather stark but still comfortable restaurant with quality napkins. As in the bar, the cooking is impressive, and includes homemade breads and ice creams. The overall feeling of quality and freshness continues to the bedrooms, which are simple but spotless.

Food serving times:
Tuesday-Saturday:
    12pm-2pm, 7pm-9.30pm
Sunday: 12pm-2pm
Closed 25 December. Open
Bank Holiday Monday
Prices:
Meals: a la carte 18.00/27.65
3 rooms: 65.00/100.00

Typical Dishes

Pigeon, black bean and oyster sauce

Steak, potato rösti, pepper dressing

Citrus tart

2.5mi North of Woodstock by A44
Parking

Wytham

077 White Hart

Wytham OX2 8QA
Tel.: (01865) 244372 - Fax: (01865) 812950
e-mail: whitehartwytham@yahoo.co.uk

 🍷 *VISA* Ⓜ©

 Hook Norton, Fuller's London Pride

Offering a perfect change of pace from Oxford, the White Hart is the pretty 18C village pub we would all love to have nearby: a relaxing atmosphere and an archetypal interior, right down to the fire in the hearth and the flagstone floor. Ask for a table in the front dining room, or a place on the attractive courtyard terrace warmed by heaters and tall clay ovens when the evening chill sets in. A laid-back but efficient young team provides attentive service of a carefully prepared menu, offsetting restyled classics with more inventive Modern British cooking: you might find a mustard-dressed salad of Stilton, bacon and black pudding, bream with tabbouleh and rocket pesto or fishcakes and mango salsa among the choices. Filled foccacias are a lighter lunchtime option.

Food serving times:
Monday-Sunday:
12pm-3pm, 6.30pm-10pm
Prices:
Meals: a la carte 18.00/32.00

Typical Dishes
Smoked haddock and spinach risotto
Lamb steak ratatouille
Chocolate fondant, amaretto biscuits

3.25mi North West of Oxford by A420 off A 34 (northbound). Parking

Abinger Common

078 ## The Stephan Langton Inn

Friday Street, Abinger Common RH5 6JR
Tel.: (01306) 730775

 VISA **MC**

 Adnams, Fuller's London Pride, Honey Dew

This bustling, inviting local favourite owes its name to a 13C Archbishop of Canterbury and its popularity to a heartily satisfying style of country cooking. Regulars and walkers to local landmark Leith Hill gather at the Langton, despite – or because of – its isolation and position at the end of a particularly elongated Surrey lane. Choose between two areas: a wood fitted pub or a dining room where modern art peers down on equally creative gastronomic delights. Typically, as a starter, you might try potato pancake with smoked salmon and pickled cucumber, followed by roast rump of lamb, boulangere potatoes and cabbage. If you've room, have a stab at the mouth-watering buttermilk pudding with poached rhubarb and ginger. Fine cooking in the Bib Gourmand price range.

Food serving times:
Tuesday-Saturday:
    12.30pm-3pm, 7pm-10pm
Sunday: 12.30pm-3pm
Closed 25 December and 1 week January
Prices:
Meals: a la carte 19.00/24.00

Typical Dishes

Chicken liver, pigeon and bacon terrine

Roast pork, bubble and squeak

Raspberry almond tart

4.5mi Southwest of Dorking by A25
Parking

Chiddingfold

079 The Swan Inn
Petworth Rd, Chiddingfold GU8 4TY
Tel.: (01428) 682073 - Fax: (01428) 683259

 ✗rest *VISA* **AE** ⓘ ⓜⓒ

Fuller's London Pride, Timothy Taylor Landlord, Hogback TEA

The handsomely mature exterior of this 14C Surrey redbrick village pub belies the extensive and stylish refurbishment which took place here in 2004. Despite the modern makeover, there remains a determinedly rustic atmosphere in most of the dining areas, with their bare wood tables. However, a formal dining room is available with white linen and elegant porcelain, while expansive terraced gardens beckon the summer visitor. Dishes remain constant to all eating areas: solidly grounded in a wide range of global favourites like snails with garlic, partridge with pasta or crab and saffron risotto. Smart, recently completed bedrooms await those staying overnight.

Food serving times:
Monday-Sunday:
 12pm-2.30pm, 6.30pm-10pm
Prices:
Meals: a la carte 16.00/29.00
⊨ **11 rooms:** 70.00/160.00

Typical Dishes

Seared scallops and crab salad

Barbary duck breast

Raspberry crème brûlée

On the right hand side of the A283, approaching from the South.
Parking opposite

Mickleham

080　The King William IV

Byttom Hill, Mickleham RH5 6EL

Tel.: (01372) 372590

Website: www.king-williamiv.com

  VISA

 Adnams, Badger Best, Hogsback TEA and 1 monthly changing guest ale

O verhung with trailing creepers, this very traditional, part-tiled pub stands a little way above the hamlet itself, its pretty terrace commanding views of the gentle hills. Where the workers from Lord Beaverbrook's estate once propped up the little taproom bar, you're now more likely to find weekend walkers and locals from round about, drawn by the promise of wholesome, dependable English cooking – tender steak and kidney pie in a rich stout sauce or fruit crumble and ice cream. They serve a selection of modern seafood dishes too: look for the list up on a large blackboard. Personally run by a good-natured team, this is just the kind of unfussy place that would have got the approval of the bluff Sailor King, or his contemporary, the cleric and wit Sidney Smith, nicknamed "The Bishop of Mickleham" for his many visits of the village.

Food serving times:
Monday-Sunday:
　12pm-3pm, 7pm-10.30pm
closed 25 December and
Sunday dinner
Prices:
Meals: a la carte 16.40/22.75

0.5mi North of Mickleham by A24. Difficult off-road parking nearby - allow time and patience!

Typical Dishes

Chicken liver pâte

Steak, kidney and mushroom pie

Bread and butter pudding

Ockley

081 **Bryce's**

The Old School House, Stane Str, Ockley RH5 5TH

Tel.: (01306) 627430 - Fax: (01306) 628274
e-mail: bryces.fish@virgin.net - Website: www.bryces.co.uk

 VISA

 | *Fuller's London Pride, Gales Best, Butser*

Just a short walk from the lovely green stands the former village school, now a traditional, personally run pub with a sound reputation in this quietly well-to-do part of Surrey. The spacious if low-beamed bar is the place to go for fresh fish and chips, langoustines and lighter meals, though for something closer to restaurant dining, the more formal room to one side is the better bet. Besides a few meat dishes, it concentrates on fresh seafood, introducing some more adventurous choices on the specials board, like red mullet with spinach and pesto or a puff pastry galette of devilled crab, without dispensing with the classics: there would be an outcry if they tried, albeit a very polite one. As it is, a rather reserved regular clientele soon warm to the friendly and attentive service from a smartly dressed team.

Food serving times:
Monday-Sunday:
12pm-2.30pm,
6.30pm-9.30pm
Closed 25 December, 1 January, Sunday dinner in November, January and February
- Seafood -
Prices:
Meals: 27.50 and a la carte 15.70/21.25

Typical Dishes
Bryce's Gravadlax
Deep fried skate, sweet and sour sauce
Panna cotta with summer berries

On A29
Parking

West End

082 ## The Inn @ West End

42 Guildford Road, West End GU24 9PW

Tel.: (01276) 858652 - Fax: (01276) 485842

e-mail: greatfood@the-inn.co.uk - Website: www.the-inn.co.uk

🍷 *VISA* AE M©

Fuller's London Pride, Courage Best

A busy roadside pub where the personable owners really lead from the front, energetically organising everything from themed suppers and wine tastings to just-for-fun boules tournaments in the pleasant garden out back. Even on an ordinary day you're likely to find the place busy, with a few knots of chatting regulars in the neatly overhauled modern bar and most of the diners in the conservatory or the dining room to the left; it's smarter than you might expect from the easy, informal tone of the place. A carefully prepared Modern British menu includes dishes like mussels in a cream sauce or roast pork on apple and celeriac mash, and their two or three-course lunch menus stand out as particularly good value: it's worth double-checking first, all the same.

Food serving times:
Monday-Sunday:
  12pm-2.30pm, 6pm-9.30pm
Prices:
Meals: 12.50/18.50 and a la carte 23.00/30.00

Typical Dishes

Scallops, grain mustard vinaigrette

Turbot and sea bass in saffron broth

Lemon tart

2.5mi from M3 on A322. Parking

Windlesham

083 The Brickmakers

Chertsey Rd, Windlesham GU20 6HT

Tel.: (01276) 472267 - Fax: (01276) 451014
e-mail: thebrickmakers@4cinns.co.uk - Website: www.4cinns.co.uk

 🍷 **VISA** **AE** **MC**

 Brakspears, Ruddles, London Pride and one guest ale

The very picture of a trim, Home Counties pub, built in Southern brick – naturally – and hung with baskets of flowers in summer. A simply styled room at the front, dominated by its big bar island, leads into a formal but still relaxed restaurant and adjoining conservatory. Sound, well-prepared cuisine weighs modern and traditional approaches to British cuisine and seems to have struck the right balance for its affluent clientele: a typical spring menu might include asparagus with lemon and garlic dressing, chargrilled steaks and any number of heartwarming "comfort" puddings, trifles and sponges. A polite young team approach the job in hand with cheery enthusiasm. A short drive away is Chobham Common, a rolling heathland nature reserve; sometimes bleak, but a rare piece of quiet wilderness so close to the capital.

Food serving times:
Monday-Sunday:
   12pm-3pm, 6.30pm-10pm
Prices:
Meals: 26.95 and a la carte 35.00

Typical Dishes

Smoked haddock rarebit

Chicken tagliatelle, mustard sauce

Selection of desserts

East 1mi on B386
Parking

Ashurst

084 **Fountain Inn**

Ashurst BN44 3AP
Tel.: (01403) 710219

Y   *VISA*   M©

Horsham Best, Harvey's Sussex

This whitewashed, tiled former farmhouse, dating from 1572, draws in locals like flies to a trap: Paul McCartney's even been in. It's not hard to see what attracts so many here, apart from the obvious charms of the South Downs. An alluring garden and decked area by a pond is instantly relaxing, a skittle alley at the front fosters a bit of healthy local competition and the scents of the pleasant kitchen garden carry gently on the breeze. It's no less charming inside: the low-ceilinged bar has beams galore and leads into a series of characterful rooms where fires and flagged floors set the tone. Flavourful traditional cooking take in char-grilled pigeon breast with sapphire plums, followed by moist treacle tart.

Food serving times:
Monday-Friday:
    12pm-2.30pm, 6pm-10pm
Saturday: 12pm-10pm
Sunday: 12pm-3pm,
                    7pm-10pm

Prices:
Meals: a la carte 12.75/17.20

Typical Dishes

Smoked haddock and prawns, cheese sauce

Sticky toffee pudding

3.5mi North of Steyning on B2135
Parking

Burpham

085 ## George and Dragon

Burpham BN18 9RR
Tel.: (01903) 883131

Dark Star, Arundel King

The his splendid old pub of mellow stone is set in a South Downs valley with sweeping views across to Arundel Castle on the skyline. Not surprisingly, it's prime walking country, so be prepared to share a pint with someone wearing big muddy boots. There's a large area at the front for outside dining in the sunny months, but at other times you'll want to get inside to sample the beamed bar, scrubbed pine tables and frothing real ale. It's where the regulars like to eat: steaks, pies and the like are on offer. To the left more diners settle into the small but irresistibly formed restaurant, which features an inglenook, full linen on antique tables and appealing mix of polished wood chairs. Menus are balanced, interesting and contemporary, using local produce and prepared with care and no little skill.

Food serving times:
Monday-Saturday:
     12pm-2pm, 7pm-9.30pm
Sunday: 12pm-2pm
Prices:
Meals: a la carte 22.00/32.00

Typical Dishes
Scallops and crevette, lemon risotto

Lemon sole, prawn and salmon farce

Crème brûlée

3mi Northeast of Arundel by A27
Parking

East Lavant

086 The Royal Oak Inn

Pook Lane, East Lavant PO18 0AX

Tel.: (01243) 527434 - Fax: (01243) 775062
e-mail: nickroyaloak@aol.com - Website: www.sussexlive.co.uk/royaloakinn

Up to 4 local ales

This elegant Georgian pub, within a turbo blast of Goodwood Motor Circuit and close to the Channel and the South Downs, adds up to more than the sum of its parts. It contains not just an inn with rustic walls of red brick and rafters, but also a barn and cottage - all with tastefully decorated and well-equipped bedrooms - set cosily round a charming courtyard. The pub cuisine is well-renowned in the Chichester area. There's an interesting à la carte choice with south European influence, as typified by red snapper with tomato linguini and black olives, and the specials board features perennial country pub favourites alongside modern dishes such as monkfish and scallop kebabs and beetroot risotto. Crème brûlée with rhubarb and raisin compote also comes highly recommended.

Food serving times:
Monday-Sunday:
    12pm-2pm, 6pm-9pm
Closed 25 December
Prices:
Meals: a la carte 15.00/30.00
7 rooms: 55.00/90.00

Typical Dishes

Warm smoked chicken and avocado salad

Lamb cutlets, rosemary roasted potatoes

Tarte Tatin

Off A286 after the hump-back bridge. Parking

Elsted

087 **Three Horseshoes**

Elsted GU29 0JY

Tel.: (01730) 825746

Cheriton Pots, Ballards Best, Timothy Taylor Landlord, Hopback Summer Lightning

From Uppark House to the Iron Age trails around Beacon Hill, the high, open downlands of East Sussex can make for exhilarating walking, and there are few more satisfying feelings than the stroll down from the scarp path to this welcoming 16C former drovers' inn, where you can enjoy more far-reaching countryside views from the garden or clink well-earned pints by the warmth of the wood burners. A delightful beamed bar fills up quickly at the weekend, when it's as well to get your reservation in early; locals and even one or two escaping Londoners enjoy modern dishes from the blackboard or tuck into homemade pies, puddings and other hearty British favourites. Cordial and kindly service.

Food serving times:
Monday-Saturday:
12pm-2pm, 7pm-9pm
Sunday: 12pm-2pm,
7pm-8.30pm

Prices:
Meals: a la carte 20.00/27.00

Typical Dishes

Mozzarella and bacon salad

Steak and kidney pie

Raspberry and hazelnut meringue

5mi Southwest of Midhurst by A272
on Elsted road
Parking

Halfway Bridge

088 The Halfway Bridge Inn

Halfway Bridge GU28 9BP

Tel.: (01798) 861281 - Fax: (01798) 861878
e-mail: mail@thesussexpub.co.uk - Website: www.thesussexpub.co.uk

 room **VISA** **M©**

Cheriton Pots Ale, Gales HSB, Harveys Sussex Best and one local guest ale

An easy-going, eat-where-you-like policy makes it all the more tempting to drop in and grab a table, but you may not always find your favourite corner free. A bustling crowd know a good thing when they see one, and come in numbers for seasonal cooking at a competitive price: winter dishes, for instance, could include black pudding salad with bacon and mushrooms or duck confit with honey and thyme, but tasty fish and game also make the specials board. To the back of the 17C pub itself – cosy and rustic with its stripped pine floors and log fires – you'll find the old barn, a reminder of the days when this was a coaching halt. Now smartly converted and facing a courtyard garden, it's split into thoughtfully appointed rooms, with vaulted ceilings, a few pieces of antique pine furniture and particularly impressive bathrooms.

Food serving times:
Monday-Sunday:
12pm-2pm, 7pm-10pm
Closed 25 December
Prices:
Meals: a la carte 18.95/27.50
8 rooms: 45.00/100.00

Halfway between Midhurst and Petworth on the A272. Parking

Typical Dishes

Steamed Thai mussels

Lamb, garlic and rosemary sauce

Mango rice pudding brûlée

Lickfold

089 Lickfold Inn

Lickfold GU28 9EY
Tel.: (01798) 861285 - Fax: (01798) 861342

Hair of the Hoy, TEK

Follow the narrow country road as it winds through the gentle Sussex countryside and eventually you'll catch a glimpse of the Lickfold Inn, a pretty, tile-hung pub dating back to the 1400s. The smart rear terrace, backing on to a mature garden, and the trimly kept bar, with its stone floor, open fires and scrubbed pine tables, are rather less formal than the dining room upstairs, but the same enjoyable modern cooking is available everywhere. Even on a weekday lunchtime you may find the place busy, but it doesn't dilute the informal charm and service is only a little stretched. Past favorites from a concise menu and specials board have included seared tuna with tangy mango salsa and roast new potatoes and, among the desserts, chargrilled bananas with ice cream and homemade toffee sauce. Ask about their popular summer barbecues.

Food serving times:
Monday-Sunday:
  12pm-2.30pm, 7pm-9.30pm
Closed 25 December and dinner 1 January
Prices:
Meals: a la carte 15.00/25.00

Typical Dishes

Foie gras boudin

Fillet steak, confit tomatoes

Chocolate torte, praline cream

6mi Northwest of Petworth by A272
Parking

Stedham

090 **Nava Thai at Hamilton Arms**

School Lane, Stedham GU29 0NZ

Tel.: (01730) 812555 - Fax: (01730) 817459

e-mail: hamiltonarms@hotmail.com - Website: www.thehamiltonarms.co.uk

   VISA **MC** **JCB**

 Fuller's London Pride, Young's Best, Ballard's Best

Happily situated in the rolling South Downs, this whitewashed inn boasts an authentic Asian ambience barely a couple of miles from the attractive and quintessentially homespun appeals of Midhurst. The bar area at the front is brimming with Thai artefacts set around polished tables – during the week, this is where lunch is usually served. Adjacent: a homely, comfortable restaurant with a similar interior gets you in the mood for excellently prepared, tasty Thai dishes, monosodium glutamate and additive free. For starters, try, perhaps, light, crisp sesame prawn toasts with a sweet and tangy cucumber dip, followed by fresh, moist fried rice with tender chicken breast, soy, egg and a series of chilli based dressings. Enjoyment is enhanced by polite service from traditionally attired Thai waiters.

Food serving times:
Tuesday-Saturday:
 12pm-2.30pm, 6pm-10.15pm
Sunday: 12pm-2.30pm,
                7pm-9.30pm
Closed 1 week January.
Open Bank Holiday Mondays
- Thai -
Prices:
Meals: 19.50 and a la carte
15.00/22.00

Typical Dishes

Prawns in filo pastry, chilli sauce

Green chicken curry

Thai egg custard, coconut ice cream

2mi West of Midhurst by A272
Parking

*A*s anyone west of the Avon will tell you, the historic West Country has been many countries in its time: the ancient land of Celtic saints and Arthurian legend, Drake's home port and the Old England of Hardy's Wessex are rediscovered every year by countless visitors, drawn by sun and surf and the West's astonishing variety. Where else can you find untamed moorland next to semi-tropical fantasy gardens? Which other region combines the magnificent Elizabethan Longleat House with the mysterious standing sarsens at Stonehenge, the genius of Brunel's grand designs and the exquisite style of Georgian Bath, not to mention the ultra-modern Eden Project? Add to this the seaside villages, sandy beaches and hundreds of miles of breathtaking clifftop trails and you have a glimpse of this amazing region, but for a real flavour of the place, get down to the dairy, the quay and the orchard.

Come harvest time, Pippins, Dabinetts and Somerset Redstreaks are ripened for slow-matured dry ciders, "real" Cheddar and Blue Vinney cheeses are in every farmers' market and Brixham and Newlyn's fresh and cured seafood appear on the specials boards. But there's much more to West Country cooking than these three famous exports, as you'll soon discover…

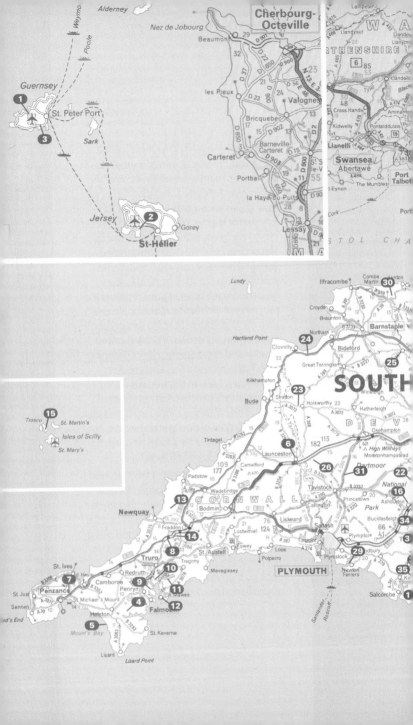

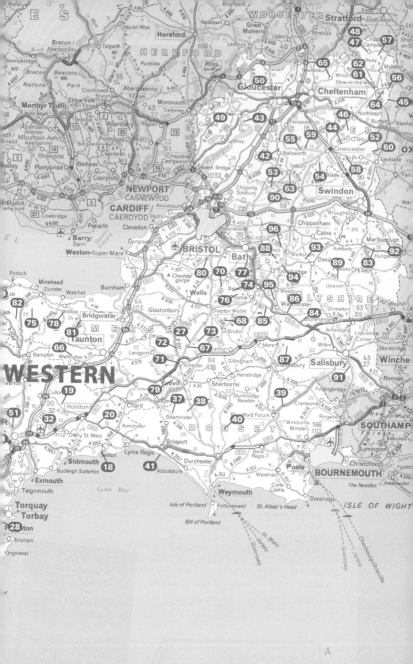

Kings Mills (Guernsey)

001 ## Fleur du Jardin

Kings Mills, Castel GY5 7JT
Tel.: (01481) 257996 - Fax: (01481) 256834
e-mail: info@fleurdujardin.guernsey.net - Website: www.fleurdujardin.guernsey.net

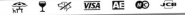

Guernsey Sunbeam and 1 guest ale

Couldn't be more aptly named: this welcoming old inn has good-sized gardens, colourful borders, shrubs, bright hanging baskets and flower barrels. Inside, the laid-back bar and adjacent alcoves sport low beams and thick granite walls confirming their 15C origins: there's well tended Guernsey real ale on draught. But it's the daily menus of local seafood which give the Fleur its standing of quiet renown. The beamed restaurant, with its reassuringly ancient granite fireplace, mixes these with a more eclectic, traditional range of dishes including pork and apple Cumberland sausage ring and mash, or lambs liver with balsamic jus. After eating, swim off delightful, nearby beaches, and sleep deeply in one of the pub's smart, sizable bedrooms.

Food serving times:
Monday-Sunday:
  12pm-2pm, 6.30pm-9.30pm
Closed dinner 25-26 December
(fixed lunch Sunday)
Prices:
Meals: 14.50 and a la carte 16.00/25.00
🛏 **17 rooms:** 55.00/110.00

Typical Dishes
Sauteed scallops, grilled black pudding
Monkfish in prosciutto
Strawberry risotto, basil ice cream

3mi West of St. Peter Port. Parking

Saint Aubin (Jersey)

002 **Old Court House Inn**

St Aubin's Harbour, Saint Aubin JE3 8AB

Tel.: (01534) 746433 - Fax: (01534) 745103
e-mail: ochstaubins@jerseymail.co.uk - Website: www.oldcourthousejersey.com

VISA · AE · D · M©

Marston Pedigree

This atmospheric 15C quayside inn has had a colourful history as a courthouse, merchant's house, and, more recently, bit-part player in the TV series Bergerac. Its traditional whitewashed façade looks beyond the harbour to St Helier. The main hub of activity is the Westward bar, built from the gig of a schooner scuttled off the Hurd Deep. Two areas are kept for dining: a characterful, Georgian glass-paned front room, or a courtyard restaurant at the back. Menus are the same throughout, and are rooted in the popular, tried-and-tested category: the highlight is the local seafood, in simple platters or elaborate specials, but the Old Court House is also good for the likes of vegetable lasagne or wild mushroom and asparagus risotto. Individually decorated bedrooms are colourful, countrified and most have harbour views.

Food serving times:
Monday-Sunday:
12.30pm-2.30pm,
7.30pm-10pm

Prices:
Meals: 12.95/21.00 and a la carte 25.00/60.00
9 rooms: 40.00/120.00

Typical Dishes

Moules marinière

Fillet of sea bass, sweet potato mash

Jersey ice cream

4mi West of St. Helier.
Parking opposite

St Martin (Guernsey)

003 **The Auberge**

Jerbourg Rd, St Martin GY4 6BH
Tel.: (01481) 238485 - Fax: (01481) 710936
e-mail: theauberge@cwgsy.net - Website: www.theauberge.gg

 No real ales offered

It's almost worth coming here for the views alone. The Auberge luxuriates in its attractive location on an elevated headland with superb vistas out to sea to the neighbouring islands: take it all in from the pleasant decked terrace or gardens. This is a stylish and modern establishment, formerly a private house, with wood floors and floor to ceiling glass. Have a drink at the modish bar, before taking a seat in the separate, rather classy restaurant, where large wooden tables and chairs are fitted with loose covers. Menus provide lots of choice, and good use is made of ingredients from the islands. This is a splendid spot to sample enjoyable flavours in brasserie-style dishes. The menu has a seafood slant, naturally, but offers some appetising game and meat options too.

Food serving times:
Monday-Sunday:
12pm-2pm, 7pm-9.30pm
Closed 25-26 December and 1 January
Prices:
Meals: a la carte 20.00/32.00

2mi Southwest of St. Peter Port. Parking

Typical Dishes

Duck breast, hazelnut and spring onion

Sea bass, chorizo mash

Lemongrass ice cream, summer fruit

Constantine

004 Trengilly Wartha Inn

Nancenoy, Constantine TR11 5RP

Tel.: (01326) 340332 - Fax: (01326) 340332
e-mail: reception@trengilly.co.uk - Website: www.trengilly.co.uk

VISA AE ① MC JCB

Sharps Cornish Coaster, Skinners Betty Stogs and 1 local beer

A good place to learn Cornish – that's the Trengilly Wartha (translation: settlement above the trees), because the locals throng here. It's not the easiest place to get to, being at the tail end of some notorious near vertical lanes, but the end product's worth it. This former crofter's abode has been enlarged over the years, but everyone spills out into the garden in summer. The interior is dominated by the airy main bar, which, apart from serving fine ales, also boasts a terrific selection of wines. The scrubbed wood tables and old Cornish settles almost invite you to sit, sup and relax. Dine in a formal restaurant or conservatory where the hearty pub grub is enlivened by daily changing specials boards. Menus are richly influenced by the seasons, and cooking is well honed and solidly skilful.

Food serving times:
Monday-Saturday:
12pm-2.15pm,
6.30pm-9.30pm
Sunday:
12pm-2pm,
7.15pm-9.30pm

Prices:
Meals: 27.00 and a la carte 15.00/24.00
8 rooms: 49.00/96.00

Typical Dishes

Potato, asparagus and Yarg cheese salad

Confit of chicken, parsnip purée

Nine maidens parfait

1.5mi South by Fore St off Port Navas road.
Parking

Gunwalloe

005 ## The Halzephron Inn

Gunwalloe TR12 7QB

Tel.: (01326) 240406 - Fax: (01326) 241442
e-mail: halzephroninn@gunwalloe1.fsnet.co.uk

 ⚐ ✗=rest ✗ *VISA* AE MC

Sharps Doom Bar, Halzephron Gold, St Austell Tribute

A visit to this extreme south-westerly corner of Cornwall wouldn't be complete without a visit to the Halzephron, staring out imperturbably across Mount's Bay. It knows its place: it's been here 500 years, and is wonderfully snug and rustic. The low ceiling boasts fine old timbers; gleaming copper and original paintings adorn the walls. Knickknacks, curios and higgledy-piggledy décor enrich four adjoining dining rooms: food's a serious business here, and wide-ranging menus are fiercely Cornish in produce and style. Portions are of the hearty variety; an impressive selection of local real ales is an ideal way to wash down lunch or dinner, followed by a walk on the nearby South West Coast Path. Two neat, cosy bedrooms await.

Food serving times:
Monday-Sunday:
12pm-2pm, 7pm-9pm
Closed 25 December
Prices:
Meals: a la carte 18.00/30.00
🛏 **2 rooms:** 48.00/85.00

Typical Dishes

Scallops, chilli, ginger and bacon

John Dory on pasta

Mascarpone panna cotta

3.5mi South of Helston by A3083.
Easter to end of September parking
in the field adjacent to the inn

Launceston

006 Springer Spaniel

Treburley, Launceston PL15 9NS

Tel.: (01579) 370424

e-mail: thespringer@wagtailinns.com - Website: www.thespringerspaniel.co.uk

Sharps Cornish Coaster, Doom Bar, Springer

A place as relaxed as this puts its guests at their ease without even having to try; everyone's helpful from the moment you walk in, but the watchword here is "simple is best", and it's hard to argue. The main bar is perfectly unfussy – flag floors, gently crackling fire, nice pub dog, local beers on tap and locals to drink them – and the same traditional approach holds good for lunch and dinner, served in a little snug to one side. By now, you'll be hoping for a sustaining, tasty meal, something with a hint of home cooking to it, and that's just what you'll get, the only surprise being the modest price. Enjoy creamed mushroom pots and pheasant and red wine casserole, then linger over coffee or another pint; nothing showy here, but then, at heart, The Spaniel is just happy to be a good, everyday pub – of the sort you don't find every day.

Food serving times:
Monday-Sunday:
12pm-2pm, 6pm-9pm
Prices:
Meals: a la carte 18.00/28.00

Typical Dishes
Smoked duck and melon salad

Chicken, red onion and balsamic sauce

Fruit panna cotta

4.5mi South on A388.
Parking

Ludgvan

007 ## The Old Inn

Ludgvan TR20 8EG
Tel.: (01736) 740419 - Fax: (01736) 740419
e-mail: samuel.page@tesco.net - Website: www.theoldinn-ludgvan.com

✸rest **VISA**

 St Austells Tunners, Tribute

L ooking like a run-of-the-mill village bar, the Old Inn is actually anything but, especially if you choose the door marked 'Pages Restaurant'. Neat and comfortable with its modern paintings, sprays of fresh flowers, neat linen and fine glassware, this firelit dining room says a lot about the attitude to food here: serious, but not off-puttingly so, relaxed, but with a tidy attention to detail. Classic dishes like chicken Marengo and tasty chicken liver pâté are set against others with a light, creative touch, like a creamy banana posset. Afterwards, you can always head through to the pine-fitted bar; you'll find service on this side has the touch of same warmth and helpfulness to it.

Food serving times:
Tuesday-Saturday:
    12pm-2pm, 7pm-9pm
Sunday: 12pm-2pm
Closed 25 December
Prices:
Meals: a la carte 17.00/28.00
🛏 **3 rooms:** 25.00/50.00

Typical Dishes
Home-smoked salmon
Lamb cutlets, thyme, red wine jus
Raspberry crème brûlee

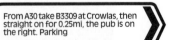
From A30 take B3309 at Crowlas, then straight on for 0.25mi, the pub is on the right. Parking

Mitchell

008 The Plume of Feathers

Mitchell TR8 5AX

Tel.: (01872) 510387 - Fax: (01872) 511124
e-mail: enquiries@theplume.info

   VISA **M©**

 Up to 6 guest ales offered

As good a break as you'll find from the drone of the A30, this smartly refurbished part 16C dining pub, away from the visitors' hotspots, comes into its own as an escape from the tourist influx of a Cornish summer, but you'll find a reassuringly good turnout - families and couples, groups of friends - on most days of the year. Set aside from an airy, sympathetically restored bar, several connecting lounges serve as the restaurant, although service is just as alert and organised at the bar. The cooking itself is steady as she goes, a sound, classic menu might include potato and mushroom soup or red snapper on lemongrass risotto, but the real draw is the relaxed, everyday atmosphere of the place: they have plenty of regulars, but are always happy to take on a few more. Large, bright bedrooms in the restored barns and stable.

Food serving times:
Monday-Sunday:
12pm-10pm
Closed dinner 25 December
Prices:
Meals: a la carte 12.00/26.00
⊨ **5 rooms:** 63.75/95.00

Typical Dishes

Scallops, orange and vanilla

Fillet of beef, chips

Honey and lavender panna cotta

Near the junction of A30 and A3076.
Parking

South West - Cornwall

Mylor Bridge

009 Pandora Inn

Restronguet Creek, Mylor Bridge TR11 5ST
Tel.: (01326) 372678 - Fax: (01326) 378958

VISA

 St Austel HSD, Tribute Tinners, Bass

S ail up Mylor Creek, moor at the pontoon, and you'll have taken the scenic route to this stunningly located pub, which dates back to the 13C. Its charming interior comes courtesy of timbered ceilings for the vertically challenged, shiny stone floors, cosy corners, open fire and seaside pot pourri. Food can be eaten at the bar or at a slightly more formal first-floor area: hearty pub menus take in a wide range of favourites, but are quite rightly dominated by fresh seafood off the blackboard, which you'll probably receive in double-quick time: the speedy, effective service has obviously evolved from being madly busy in the summer. A relaxed walk along creekside paths is a recommended way to work off your meal.

Food serving times:
Monday-Sunday:
12pm-6pm, 6.30pm-9.30pm
(bar lunch)
Prices:
Meals: a la carte 15.00/28.00

Typical Dishes

Scallop and bacon salad

Sea bass, creamed spinach risotto

Hazelnut meringue

1mi Northeast.
Parking

Penelewey

010 **Punchbowl and Ladle**

Penelewey TR3 6QY

Tel.: (01872) 862237 - Fax: (01872) 870401
Website: www.staustellbrewery.co.uk

St Austell Tribute, Hicks Special Draft

 erving ferrymen and travellers across this lonely reach of the Fal since the 1600s, the Punchbowl and Ladle can seldom have known popularity like this. The old thatched cottages have long since become two characterful bars and a lounge, with decorative plates and copper on the wooden walls; but all three fill quickly, eager regulars making a beeline for a comfortable bar sofa or a prettily set candlelit table in the restaurant. An extensive menu has it all covered, from lunchtime sandwiches and pasties, crab salad, lasagne and IPA-battered cod and chips, not to mention the catch of the day, right through to a more elaborate evening selection, perhaps including mussels in Pernod butter or duck in peach and brandy sauce. Welcoming and very professionally run.

Food serving times:
Monday-Sunday:
 12pm-2.30pm, 6pm-9.30pm
Prices:
Meals: a la carte 16.20/24.85

Typical Dishes

Mussels in pastis

Braised lamb with red wine and rosemary

Cornish cheeses

On B3289, leading to the King Harry Ferry across the Fal. Parking

Philleigh

011 Roseland Inn

Philleigh TR2 5NB

Tel.: (01872) 580254 - Fax: (01872) 272557
e-mail: info@roseland-inn.co.uk - Website: www.roseland-inn.co.uk

🍷 *VISA* M© JCB

Sharps Doom Bar, Cornish Coaster, Ringwood

You know you're edging into rural heaven when you come by ferry to this out-of-the-way Cornish pub - the chuch's next-door neighbour for the last 500 years - and step inside from the rose-covered courtyard. Making sure you don't tread on one of the ubiquitous cats, just look around and admire the charming rustic surrounds: exposed black beams, open fires, rugged stone floors and scattered knickknacks. A fine selection of real ales is on hand – a pint or two will go down exceptionally well with a dish or two from the wide-ranging menus, which owe much of their hearty character to Cornish produce. Recent recommendations include breast of chicken with bacon and mushrooms, venison with sweet potato mash, and a gloriously fruity poached pear for dessert.

Food serving times:
Monday-Sunday:
     12pm-2.30pm, 6pm-9pm
Prices:
Meals: a la carte 15.00/25.00

Typical Dishes

Gravadlax

Rack of lamb with liver dumplings

Pear and apple crumble

Situated between King Harry ferry and Ruan High Lanes.
Parking

St Mawes

012 **The Victory Inn**

Victory Hill, St Mawes TR2 5DQ

Tel.: (01326) 270324 - Fax: (01326) 270238
e-mail: info@roseland-inn.co.uk - Website: www.victory-stmawes.co.uk

Sharps Eden, Doom Bar, Cornish Coaster, Old Speckled Hen

There are various splendid ways of getting to the Victory Inn. You can reach it by ferry, road or on foot along the harbour; whichever alternative presents itself, the delights of the Roseland and Falmouth Bay are ever-present. This professionally run pub delights in a cosy interior with some charm, not a little enhanced by its enviable position on the Victory Steps next to the harbour. The real ale selection is broad; wander across to the open fire and mingle with the locals over a pint. The dining room is upstairs, a spacious area, with a more formal, contemporary feel. As you might expect, seafood figures strongly on the menu, aided and abetted by organic Cornish ingredients, all very simple, fresh and unfussy. Tuck into moules marinière, followed by roast sea bass with rocket and Parmesan.

Food serving times:
Monday-Sunday:
  12pm-3pm, 6pm-9.30pm
- Seafood specialities -
Prices:
Meals: a la carte 17.50/25.00
1 room: 35.00/70.00

Next to St Mawes harbour. Parking at the harbour car park

Typical Dishes
Terrine of venison, beetroot salad

Duo of fish

Almond and coconut panna cotta

St Mawgan

013 The Falcon Inn

St Mawgan TR8 4EP

Tel.: (01637) 860225 - Fax: (01637) 860884
e-mail: enquiries@falconinn.net - Website: www.falconinn.net

 𝓕𝓗𝓣 ✂️ *VISA* ① Ⓜ️Ⓒ 𝗝𝗖𝗕

 Tribute, HSD, Tinners

Set just inland from the delights of Newquay, in the splendid Vale of Mawgan, this 16C wisteria-clad hostelry rejoices in a totally unspoilt character and a quaint surrounding of antique shops. The bar is cosiness itself: roaring log fire, comfy settles, large antique prints and, naturally enough, pictures of falcons on the walls; you can sit at homely farmhouse tables and chairs. Eat either here, in the French-windowed restaurant, or at a delicious cobbled courtyard in the front. Dishes are based around freshly-caught seafood which arrives on the plate from the nearby beaches at Newlyn; classic dishes also make a solid appearance.

Food serving times:
Monday-Sunday:
12pm-2pm, 6.30pm-9.30pm
Prices:
Meals: a la carte 13.00/24.00
🛏 **3 rooms:** 27.00/75.00

Typical Dishes

Parma ham and pink grapefruit salad

Scallops with raspberry and chorizo

Passion fruit sorbet

Follow signs for the airport on A3059 between Newquay and St Colomb Major; the pub is down the hill. Parking

Summercourt

014 Viners

Carvynick, Summercourt TR8 5AF
Tel.: (01872) 510544 - Fax: (01872) 510468

   VISA   MC

   Sharps Doom Bar

This charming stone-built cottage, with origins stretching back to the 17C, can claim to have been here long before the landscaped encampments of mobile homes or the golf course next door, but it's a much more recent change which has really captured the local imagination. The bar near the entrance remains a good place for beer, nuts and pub chat, and drinkers are positively encouraged, though most will stay for one and head straight for the elegant new restaurant. Pale-toned walls, slate floors and high-backed velvet chairs strike a sophisticated note, taken up in a creative but affordable menu that shows sound culinary understanding: for an example of this generosity and balance, try grilled oysters in lime and chilli or sole in parsley butter with bean salad.

Food serving times:
Tuesday-Sunday:
12pm-2.30pm,
6.30pm-9.30pm
Closed 4 weeks in winter
Prices:
Meals: a la carte 15.00/25.00

Typical Dishes

Cheese soufflé

Steak with mushroom and chicken pâté

Chocolate and Grand Marnier crème

At Carvynick Golf and Country Club, 1.5mi North West of the junction of A30 and A3058. Parking

Tresco

015 **New Inn**

Tresco TR24 0QQ

Tel.: (01720) 422844 - Fax: (01720) 423200
e-mail: newinn@tresco.co.uk

 ✘rest 🚭 *VISA* Ⓜ©

 Skinners Tresco Tipple, Betty Stogs and Cornish Knocker Ale

 n hospitable stopping off point on your way, perhaps, to the Old Blockhouse or Tresco Abbey Gardens, this stone built former inn may prove difficult to leave. It has a charming terrace garden - with plenty of seating - and views that extend across the beautiful island. In keeping with its surroundings, the traditional bar is packed with nautical memorabilia; other lounges have a friendly, bustling ambience – it's where the locals congregate. Back outside, a large semi-decked sun lounge is a good place to tuck into an extensive "snacky" menu or indulge in blackboard seafood specials. The dining room (remember to book first) is a striking bistro-style restaurant serving traditional favourites. If, indeed, you haven't moved on, bedrooms are simple, well-kept and comfortable.

Food serving times:
Monday-Sunday:
    12pm-2pm, 6pm-9pm
(booking essential to non-residents) Accommodation rates include dinner

Prices:
Meals: a la carte 17.50/29.00
🛏 **16 rooms:** 75.00/230.00

Near Tresco Stores

Typical Dishes

Potted Brymer crab

Slow roasted belly of port

Chocolate mousse with clotted cream

Ashburton

016 Rising Sun

Woodland, Ashburton TQ13 7JT

Tel.: (01364) 652544 - Fax: (01364) 653628
e-mail: mail@risingsunwoodland.co.uk - Website: www.risingsunwoodland.co.uk

   room

 Princetown Jail Ale, Teignworthy Reel Ale, Springtide, Sharps Doom Bar, Cornish Coaster

In the depths of the rolling countryside, this old drovers' inn is one to remember for hot summer afternoons, when families can enjoy some fresh Devon air at one of the terrace picnic tables in the garden, but the cosy and very traditional bar comes into its own at the turn of the year. The blackboard menu gives credit where it's due to a huge supporting cast of Wessex farmers, brewers and other suppliers, and approachable bar staff will happily talk you through the choices. Fresh and appetising dishes could include pigeon or smoked trout salads and sea bass with balsamic sauce – it depends on the season, of course – but their hearty pies are perennially popular; beef and Devon blue cheese and venison with stout and juniper head a short list of favourites.

Food serving times:
Tuesday-Saturday:
  12pm-2.15pm, 6pm-9.15pm
Sunday: 12pm-3pm,
  7pm-9.15pm
Closed 25 December. Open
Bank Holiday Monday
Prices:
Meals: a la carte 14.50/21.95
6 rooms: 40.00/70.00

Typical Dishes

Crab tart, lemon and honey dressing

Roast duck with Kirsch

Devon apple cake

1.5mi East, off the A38 between Exeter and Plymouth. Parking

Beesands

017 **The Cricket Inn**

Beesands TQ7 2EN

Tel.: (01548) 580215
Website: www.thecricketinn.co.uk

 VISA AE MC

Fuller's London Pride, Bass

The owners lovingly call this bright, modernised establishment "the inn by the shore", which rather neatly sums up the fact that you can practically kick one of Start Bay's pebbles from the Cricket Inn's front door. This, of course, guarantees it's a busy watering hole when the sun's shining. It's formed from a couple of fishermen's cottages, and the airy, open-plan interior means there's plenty of room to grab a table and admire the view from one of the many windows. There's a hearty choice of modern British dishes, but in this location you can hardly pass up the seafood, which practically jumps from the Channel to the kitchen. Of the three light, spacious bedrooms, two boast sea views.

Food serving times:
Monday-Sunday:
12pm-2.30pm, 6pm-9.30pm
(check opening times in winter)
Prices:
Meals: a la carte 17.00/30.00
4 rooms: 60.00/70.00

2.25mi South East of Kingsbridge by A379. Parking

Typical Dishes

Seafood pancake

Monkfish in coconut and coriander

Cider and apple tart

Branscombe

018 Masons Arms

Branscombe EX12 3DJ

Tel.: (01297) 680300 - Fax: (01297) 680500
e-mail: reception@masonsarms.co.uk - Website: www.masonsarms.co.uk

     rest **VISA** **MC** **JCB**

 Otter Bitter and guest ales

The picturesque village of Branscombe is one of the joys of the East Devon coast, nestling piecemeal in a deep valley right next to the sea. At its heart lies this 14C creeper-clad inn, visible to anyone up in the hills. It has a wonderfully bustling atmosphere, built around the unspoilt bar where hotel guests and locals mingle with a pint. The hearty ambience is enhanced with the surrounding ancient ships' beams, slate floors, and stone walls; a huge central fireplace is regularly used to spit-roast joints of meat at lunchtime and in the evening: modern British menus are highlighted by crab and lobster landed on Branscombe's beach. Also finding favour are comforting favourites such as casserole of local beef and dumplings with horseradish sauce. Bedrooms are divided between inn and cottages opposite.

Food serving times:
Monday-Sunday:
12pm-2pm, 7pm-9pm
(bar lunch)
Prices:
Meals: a la carte 16.00/30.00
22 rooms: 45.00/150.00

Typical Dishes

Ceviche of Lyme Bay mackerel

Chicken, wild mushroom risotto

Iced hazelnut parfait

In the village centre.
Parking

Broadhembury

019 Drewe Arms

Broadhembury EX14 3NF
Tel.: (01404) 841267 - Fax: (01404) 841118
e-mail: fishytails@btconnect.com

🍷 🥧 **VISA** Ⓜ©

Otter Bitter, Ale, Bright, Head

A delightful village deserves a delightful pub, and in this village tucked away in East Devon they've struck gold. A quintessentially English setting places the 13C Drewe Arms next to a church and opposite a row of cottages the colour of clotted cream. Gloriously unimproved, the interior seems not to have changed for centuries. Unusually, the walls are covered with carved walking sticks, while farming implements and even an eel-catcher's basket hang from the ceiling. The quiet is broken only by the satisfied murmurs of those drinking at the neat little bar or eating in the two dining areas. Fish is the focus of the menus. Typically, you might find marinated herrings, roasted cod with anchovies or salmon fishcakes with tomato and dill sauce; dishes are reassuringly well executed and very tasty.

Food serving times:
Monday-Saturday:
    12pm-2pm, 7pm-9.30pm
Sunday: 12pm-2pm
Closed 25 December and 31 December
(booking essential) -
Seafood -
Prices:
Meals: a la carte 10.00/30.00

Typical Dishes

Crab thermidor

John Dory, anchovies and caper butter

Lemon posset, cream

5mi Northwest of Honiton by A373. Parking

Dalwood

020 **The Tuckers Arms**

Dalwood EX13 7EG

Tel.: (01404) 881342 · Fax: (01404) 881138
e-mail: tuckersarms@freeserve.co.uk · Website: www.tuckersarms.co.uk

 VISA **MC** *JCB*

Otter, O'Hanlon's Firefly, Royal Oak, Courage Directors

With its neatly trimmed thatch and little low windows, this medieval longhouse looks promising from outside, but it's a particular pleasure to find its style and history still so well reflected in the interior, both in the cosy lounge bar and the dining rooms. Plates and brasses decorate the beams and the venerable old stonework of the fireplace has been preserved. The cooking remains the big draw, though: a very affordable menu with a set-price option doesn't overlook local meat or seasonal game and has a good local reputation for its catch of the day: try smoked salmon cakes or John Dory in a delicate Devon cream sauce with asparagus, and follow it up with a tasty, traditional pudding like date and banana sponge, served with rum and toffee sauce.

Food serving times:
Monday-Sunday:
   12pm-2pm, 7pm-9.30pm
Closed 25-26 December
Prices:
Meals: 18.95 (fixed price dinner) and a la carte 18.95/22.50

🛏 **4 rooms:** 59.50

Typical Dishes

Smoked mackerel rarebit

Veal in white wine and cream sauce

Lemon meringue pie

3.5mi West of Axminster by B3261, off A35.
Parking

Doddiscombsleigh

021 **Nobody Inn**

Doddiscombsleigh EX6 7PS

Tel.: (01647) 252394 - Fax: (01647) 252978
e-mail: info@nobodyinn.co.uk - Website: www.nobodyinn.co.uk

   🍷   🍇   🚫   **VISA**   Ⓜ©

 Nobody Inn Bitter, Sharps Doom Bar, Crouch Vale Gold Extra

A ll roads may not lead to Doddiscombsleigh, but find the lanes that do, and you'll alight on a little piece of history in the rather eccentric shape of the Nobody Inn. An unfalteringly characterful part 16C interior leads you off down a warren of nooks and crannies; a veritable sense of history is all pervading. Food is ordered at the bar and you dine on uncovered tables, sitting perhaps on an ancient settle. Local ingredients are all over the menu, such as fish from Dartmouth, quail from local farms and fruit from nearby orchards. If you've been traipsing round Dartmoor all day, then you might require a modest room here, but remember to book early.

Food serving times:
Monday-Sunday:
    12pm-2pm, 7pm-10pm
Closed dinner 25 December, 26 December, dinner 31 December and 1 January
Prices:
Meals: a la carte 18.00/26.00
🛏 **7 rooms:** 30.00/80.00

Typical Dishes

Gravadlax with garlic mayonnaise

Fillet of beef, tarragon cream sauce

Sticky toffee pudding

10mi Southwest of Exeter by B3212 off B3193.
Parking

Haytor Vale

022 Rock Inn

Haytor Vale TQ13 9XP

Tel.: (01364) 661305 - Fax: (01364) 661242
e-mail: inn@rock-inn.co.uk - Website: www.rock-inn.co.uk

  ☜room *VISA*

Dartmoor Best, Old Speckled Hen

 In a pleasant little village near the eastern tip of Dartmoor stands this characterful looking pub with a long-standing owner. It was originally a coaching inn dating back to the mid-18C, and this is evidenced by the covered entrance and stone trough beside old stables. There are nooks and crannies a-plenty; the warren of rooms adds to the gloriously rural appeal of the place. Horse-brasses, unsurprisingly, are ubiquitous. Food orders are taken at the bar by a very pleasant team. Cooking is sound and satisfactory with an interesting meat menu, which might include pan-fried local pheasant breast on cider and fennel seed cabbage with a Merlot jus, shallots and roast walnuts, or suprême of Devon chicken on coconut risotto.
Accommodation is provided in the shape of surprisingly spacious and well-kept bedrooms.

Food serving times:
Monday-Sunday:
   12pm-2pm, 7pm-9.30pm
Closed 25 December
Prices:
Meals: 20.95 and a la carte 16.00/25.00
🛏 **9 rooms:** 65.50/95.95

Typical Dishes
Salad of warm duck, citrus dressing
Fillet of red bream, pesto dressing
Mango crème brûlée

3.5mi West of Bovey Tracey by B3387. Parking

Holsworthy

023 The Rydon Inn

Holsworthy EX22 7HU

Tel.: (01409) 259444 - Fax: (01409) 259186
e-mail: info@rydon-inn.com - Website: www.rydon-inn.com

Sharps Doom Bar, Ring o' Bells Triple H

Tired of life out of a suitcase, two world travellers have decided to put down roots in rural Devon. Their joint venture, the Rydon Inn, actually centres on the stylish modern extension to the 300 year old pub, a bright rotunda with big cross-beams and broad picture windows giving lovely views over the fields. The adjoining bar still welcomes a young local crowd for a pint or three on a Friday night, though the restaurant is a touch smarter in tone, its tables set with candles and fresh flowers. Plenty of thought goes into composing an interesting modern menu that might take in lobster ravioli, braised shank of Devon lamb or a creamy blueberry cheesecake. A concise "little ones" menu sees younger diners well catered for.

Food serving times:
Monday-Sunday:
  12pm-2pm, 6.30pm-9pm
Closed 25-26 December and 2 weeks October
Closed Monday in winter
Prices:
Meals: a la carte 16.95/27.95

Typical Dishes

Whisky-dressed Gravadlax

Rack of lamb, gooseberry and mint

Cheesecake

On A3072 1mi West of Holsworthy. Parking

Horn's Cross

024 **The Hoops Inn**

Horn's Cross EX39 5DL

Tel.: (01237) 451222 - Fax: (01237) 451247
e-mail: information@hoopsinn.co.uk - Website: www.hoopsinn.co.uk

Hoops Old Ale, Jollyboat Freebooter, Old Speckled Hen, Bass

An old wayside inn since the Middle Ages, this sizeable thatched pub still has plenty to offer the passer-by, including those who need a bed for the night – four rooms in the main house are particularly comfortable, but there are a further eight "standard" ones at the back. Its handsome bar preserves its wooden settles, bowed ceiling beams, cups, tankards and porcelains, not to mention traces of the well which once supplied water for home-brewed ales. A wide-ranging menu covers everything from lunchtime ploughmans and bar favourites, through afternoon teas to tasty dishes like seafood pie, lamb with rhubarb jus and sticky toffee pudding. A pretty terrace looks out over the water garden.

Food serving times:
Monday-Sunday:
    12pm-3pm, 7pm-9.30pm
Closed 25 December
Prices:
Meals: a la carte 16.00/28.00
13 rooms: 60.00/90.00

Typical Dishes

Crab cakes with lobster sauce

Roast lamb, mint, cinnamon and onion

Treacle tart

0.5mi West on A39 going to Clovelly. Parking

Knowstone

025 ## The Masons Arms Inn

Knowstone EX36 4RY

Tel.: (01398) 341231
Website: www.masonsarmsinn.com

 VISA AE M©

Tawny Real Ale

N estled most serenely in a tiny
hamlet just off the southern tip of
Exmoor is this very attractive,
yellow painted, part 13C little thatched
inn. It's tremendously characterful inside,
heavily beamed with flagged floors and a
cosy front snug bar where locals gather to
sup Exmoor ale drawn from the barrel. Go
down some ruggedly ancient stone steps
to find yourself in a candlelit dining room:
you could be feasting 700 years ago!
Rickety wood tables, benches and chairs
are haphazardly set about the place;
however, there's nothing haphazard
about the food, which, surprisingly in this
tucked-away part of Devon, comes with
Gallic inspiration. Try terrine Provençale,
followed by cassoulet, and finish off with
pear and lemon tart.

Food serving times:
Monday-Saturday:
12pm-3pm, 6pm-9pm
Sunday: 12pm-3pm
Closed Monday lunch
Prices:
Meals: a la carte 22.00/26.00

Typical Dishes

Lobster fricassee

*Fillet steak with wild
mushrooms*

Raspberry Charlotte

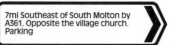
7mi Southeast of South Molton by
A361. Opposite the village church.
Parking

Lifton

026 Arundell Arms

Fore Street, Lifton PL16 0AA

Tel.: (01566) 784666 - Fax: (01566) 74494
e-mail: reservations@arundellarms.com - Website: www.arundellarms.com

   rest **VISA** **AE** **(i)** **(MC)**

 Courage Best, Bass, Sharps Doom Bar

Sandwiched idyllically between Dartmoor and Bodmin Moor, in a valley of five rivers, this ancient coaching inn can trace its roots back to Saxon times; its pleasant, ivy-clad exterior is the mainstay of the village's main street. This is a well looked after and seriously run establishment with a recently created reception area and extended bar that's always busy. There's a comfy, classic country house lounge to indulge a pre-prandial before heading into the grand dining room with its high ceiling, large windows, warm yellow walls and opulent feel. Service can tend towards the formal but is never less than pleasant. English and French cuisine predominates: local produce, including fish caught by guests, is to the fore.

Food serving times:
Monday-Sunday:
  12pm-2.30pm, 6pm-10pm
Closed 24-25 December
Prices:
Meals: 24.50/34.00 and a la carte 20.00/40.00
27 rooms: 89.00/136.00

Typical Dishes
Scallops with saffron and chives

Thyme roasted beef, shallot purée

Rhubarb dessert trio

0.5mi off A30. Parking

Lydford

027 Dartmoor Inn

Moorside, Lydford EX20 4AY

Tel.: (01822) 820221 - Fax: (01822) 820494
e-mail: info@dartmoorinn.co.uk

🍷 *VISA* Ⓜ️Ⓒ JCB

Otter, Dartmoor Best, Fuller's London Pride

A bracing walk round Lydford Gorge can build a serious appetite, and there's no better way of satisfying it than a visit to this locally renowned inn on the edges of Dartmoor. As befits its location, it boasts a pleasing rustic character, and enough dining areas to satisfy a coachload of gourmands. Open fires and arty prints on the walls create just the right feeling of relaxation. Good value set menus have earned the Dartmoor a Michelin Bib Gourmand: local produce is much in evidence in modern menus influenced by Mediterranean and local styles. On any given day, you might be able to savour chicken liver parfait, followed by lamb shank shepherds pie, finishing with a home-made, naughty but nice chocolate ice cream with chocolate sauce.

Food serving times:
Monday-Sunday:
12pm-2.15pm,
6.30pm-9.30pm
Closed 3 days at Christmas and Bank Holidays
Prices:
Meals: a la carte 18.75/29.50

Typical Dishes
Goat's cheese and red onion tart
Mixed grill of fish
Rhubarb and black treacle pudding

1mi East on A386.
Parking

Marldon

028 **Church House Inn**

Village Rd, Marldon TQ3 1SL

Tel.: (01803) 558279 - Fax: (01803) 664865

Dartmoor Best, Fuller's London Pride, Greene King IPA and Abbot

Visitors to Torbay might like to make an excursion from the delights of Torquay and Paignton to this nearby, attractive inn by the church in Marldon: the pub itself is well signposted. It's a listed, whitewashed Georgian structure of 14C origins, and its characterful aspect continues inside with beams, rough stone walls and flagstone floors. There's a large central bar with adjoining rooms which tend to be used for dining but you can eat anywhere: you'll find plenty of drinkers mingling with diners. The bustling atmosphere doesn't faze the waiting staff: there's an invariably friendly service. Blackboard menus offer plenty of choice from the traditional to the more modern, with a guarantee that the vegetables have come from the village's allotment!

Food serving times:
Monday-Sunday:
    12pm-2pm, 7pm-9.30pm
Prices:
Meals: a la carte 21.00/27.00

Typical Dishes

Seared duck breast, honey dressing

Rack of lamb, redcurrant jus

Chocolate brownie

Off A380 between Torquay and Paignton - well signposted. Parking

Noss Mayo

029 Ship Inn

Noss Mayo PL8 1EW

Tel.: (01752) 872387 - Fax: (01752) 873294
e-mail: ship@nossmayo.com - Website: www.nossmayo.com

 Exmoor Gold, Spitfire, Tamar, Drayman

Go down a winding South Hams road to get to this idyllically located pub, a stirring dash of white in a delightful inlet surrounded by hills. At high tide, entry is via a back door at first-floor level, but when the tide's out, you can scamper over the beach to the front entrance. The oldest part of the Ship dates from the 1700s; now it's a gleaming, modern place with lovely local prints, glossy wood furniture and piles of books and newspapers - there are games to play as well, like Scrabble and chess. Upstairs a maritime air pervades the restaurant. Friendly staff serve up an extensive menu, ranging from the simple to the adventurous with a good helping of local seafood. Afterwards, go for a stroll in the delightful village, cross the inlet to visit the equally charming Newton Ferrers, or set off on a salty walk up the South West Coast Path.

Food serving times:
Monday-Sunday:
12pm-9.30pm
Closed dinner 25 December
Prices:
Meals: a la carte 18.75

10.5mi Southeast of Plymouth by A379 off B3186.
Restricted parking, particularly at high tide

Typical Dishes

Tomato and juniper soup

Seafood brochette

Apricot, walnut and ginger pudding

Parracombe

030 Fox & Goose

Parracombe EX31 4PE

Tel.: (01598) 763239 - Fax: (01598) 763621
e-mail: foxandgoose@mrexcessive.net - Website: www.foxgoose.com

     room VISA MC

 Exmoor Ale, Fox, Barn Owl Amber Wheat Ale

The pleasant pub by the stream has, like the rest of Parracombe, taken progress at its own pace: you can still make out today's village of quiet, narrow streets in the sepia photos from the pub's early days, hung here and there among the books, plants, prints and hunting trophies of the main bar. The landlord takes charge in the kitchen and makes good use of the ingredients close to hand: blackboard menus list meats supplied by nearby farms, fish from the local boats – turbot, for example, served with a sundried tomato risotto – and homemade ice creams and desserts, including a good, hearty apple pie. Two simple, pine fitted rooms are fine for an overnight stop.

Food serving times:
Monday-Sunday:
   12pm-2pm, 6pm-9.30pm
Prices:
Meals: a la carte 15.00/30.00
2 rooms: 45.00

Typical Dishes

Homemade pâté, toast

Steak and seaweed pie

Lemon pudding, ice cream

5mi Southwest of Lynton by B3234
off A39.
Parking

Peter Tavy

031 Peter Tavy Inn

Peter Tavy PL19 9NN

Tel.: (01822) 810348 - Fax: (01822) 810835
e-mail: peter.tavy@virgin.net

Princetown Jail Ale, Summerskills Tamar, Sharps Doom Bar, Blackawton Tavy Tipple, Sutton Dartmoor Pride

A matter of yards from St Peter's Church, and the River Tavy, this tiny country pub soon fills up; with good-spirited locals clustered round the bar for a chat in the evening, it certainly has the right kind of sound as you open the door. Two dining rooms with very low beams and close-set chairs and benches can be a bit of a squeeze, too, but once you're settled, an attentive landlord and his team will see you well looked-after. Chabichou goat's cheese and pancetta salad, mildly spicy chicken and prawns and sticky toffee pudding with thick Devon cream are typical of a sound menu with a touch more variety than you might first expect. If the weather's set fair, ask about walks around the surrounding moorland to build up a serious appetite!

Food serving times:
Monday-Sunday:
12pm-2pm, 6.30pm-9pm
Closed for dinner 24, 26 and 31 December and all day 25 December
Prices:
Meals: a la carte 12.65/25.20

Typical Dishes

Sweet potato and watercress soup

Medallions of beef with hogs pudding

Sticky toffee pudding

3mi Northeast of Tavistock by A386. Parking

Rockbeare

032 Jack in the Green Inn

London Rd, Rockbeare EX5 2EE

Tel.: (01404) 822240 - Fax: (01404) 823445
e-mail: info@jackinthegreen.uk.com - Website: www.jackinthegreen.uk.com

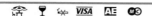

 Otter Ale, Ruddles, JIG

This whitewashed pub has been heavily extended, but still retains an air of the traditional with its carpets and beams. The lounge bar has banquette seating and dark wood tables, but the more characterful – and touch more sophisticated – place to eat is the restaurant, which spans three rooms in the oldest part of the premises. You can eat from the range of dishes listed on the blackboard or from a regularly changing fixed price menu, both of which provide good value. Cooking in the modern British style is accomplished and well presented. Typically, expect fillet of smoked haddock topped with welsh rarebit, or rack and braised shoulder of Whimple lamb with Meaux mustard.

Food serving times:
Monday-Sunday:
    12pm-2pm, 6pm-10pm
Closed 25 December-2 January
Prices:
Meals: 24.95 and a la carte 20.00/24.95

Typical Dishes
Saffron scallops
Chicken, truffle sauce, asparagus
Fried figs, raspberries and honeycomb

6.25mi East of Exeter by A30. Parking at the back

Slapton

033 **Tower Inn**

Church Rd, Slapton TQ7 2PN

Tel.: (01548) 580216

e-mail: towerinn@slapton.org - Website: www.thetowerinn.com

🍷 🛏room *VISA* AE MC JCB

Adnams Bitter, Tribute, Badger Tanglefoot and guest beers during the summer

Built in 1347, this remarkably preserved inn once belonged to the Collegiate Chantry of St Mary, and the old church tower still keeps watch over a charming pub garden. Inside, inviting flagged and beamed bar-parlours – one with a fireplace stripped back to the old stone – connect with a slightly smarter dining room strung with hop bines. In such characterful old surroundings, it comes as quite a surprise to see a number of more contemporary dishes among the classics: generous, well-prepared platters of piquant antipasti are something of a speciality. Two simple little bedrooms in the annex are designed with stopovers in mind.

Food serving times:
Monday-Sunday:
    12pm-2pm, 7pm-9.30pm
Prices:
Meals: a la carte 20.00/28.00
🛏 **3 rooms:** 40.00/60.00

Typical Dishes

Smoked mackerel, eel, salmon and prawns

Sea bass, glazed crab

Cherry soup, balsamic ice cream

6mi Southwest of Dartmouth by A379.
Parking

Staverton

034 Sea Trout Inn

Staverton TQ9 6PA

Tel.: (01803) 762274 - Fax: (01803) 762506
e-mail: enquiries@seatroutinn.com - Website: www.seatroutinn.com

    ⌚rest **VISA** **AE** **⓿⓿**

 Palmers IPA, Copper, Gold

Idyllically placed between Dartmoor and the sea, this traditional Devonian inn is used to being busy, and you're immediately struck by the efforts of the polite and easy-going young staff. The smoothly run ambience means that visitors tend to find equal enjoyment between the bar, terrace or separate linen-clad conservatory restaurant: you can indulge drinks or a meal at either, feeling relaxed and unhurried whichever alternative is taken. Ingredients are refreshingly local: sausages, bacon, poultry and cheeses are produced on nearby farms; the fish is landed at Brixham, just 10 miles away. Overnight rest may be taken in one of the pretty, cottage-style bedrooms, before the morning's activities begin: a walk by the Dart, perhaps, or visits to Buckfast Abbey, the Otter Sanctuary or one of many National Trust properties nearby.

Food serving times:
Monday-Sunday:
12pm-2pm, 6.45pm-9pm
Prices:
Meals: a la carte 16.00/24.00
🛏 **10 rooms:** 50.00/80.00

Typical Dishes

Scallops, basil and parmesan crust

Sea trout, lemon crab risotto

Ginger rhubarb tart

3.5mi North of Totnes by A384. Parking

Stokenham

035 Tradesman's Arms

Stokenham TQ7 2SZ

Tel.: (01548) 580313 - Fax: (01548) 580657
e-mail: thetradesmansarms@tiscali.co.uk - Website: www.thetradesmansarms.com

VISA · M© · JCB

Bass, Sutton XSB, Plymouth Pride, Brakspear

A glistening seven-mile finger of golden coastline runs along this part of South Hams, and the nearby Tradesman's Arms is the kind of pub whose charm fits in seamlessly with such enviable surroundings. It's a part-thatched, 14C building that used to serve as workmen's cottages. You have the choice of two separate rooms in which to idle away time looking across a green and pleasant South Devon valley, a pint of real ale at your side. There's the main bar with its stone fireplace and beamed ceiling, or a non-smoking alternative. Both rooms serve the same menu, based around fish and game which, naturally enough, are fresh from the most local of sources: typically, Brixham fish or scallops from Start Bay.

Food serving times:
Monday-Sunday:
  12pm-2.30pm, 7pm-9.30pm
(booking essential)
Prices:
Meals: a la carte 17.15/26.85

Typical Dishes

Scallops with chorizo

Sea bass, seasonal vegetables

Raspberry frangipane, clotted cream

5.5mi East of Kingsbridge on A379.
Parking

Tuckenhay

036 The Maltsters Arms

Bow Creek, Tuckenhay TQ9 7EQ

Tel.: (01803) 732350 - Fax: (01803) 732823
e-mail: pub@tuckenhay.demon.co.uk - Website: www.tuckenhay.com

   VISA **M©**

 Princetown IPA, Teignworthy and a selection of guest ales

As implied by its name, this is a former Devonshire malt house dating from the 1800s sited idyllically on the Tuckenhay Creek, when the tide's in, that is. The Maltsters, once owned by TV chef Keith Floyd, is personally run and enjoys a cosy, quaint feel, with a little "pubby" bar and adjacent dining area with further "overflow" room. On busy summer days, a terrace at the side of the creek has its own bar and barbeque. Modern British cooking is the order of the day here, and there's ample choice of meat and local fish dishes, as well as a very good selection of wines by the glass. Families are provided with a "Real Food For Children" menu, so you'd be ill-advised to expect chicken nuggets or even chips

Food serving times:
Monday-Sunday:
12pm-3pm, 6.30pm-9.30pm
Closed 25 December
Prices:
Meals: a la carte 17.00/25.00
🛏 **5 rooms:** 65.00/110.00

Typical Dishes
Smoked fish platter

Veal escalope, prawn and mushroom sauce

Baileys and clotted cream cheesecake

3.75mi South East of Totnes, near the mouth of the river. Parking

Bridport

041 West Bay

Station Road, West Bay, Bridport DT6 4EW

Tel.: (01308) 422157 - Fax: (01308) 459717
e-mail: karen.trimby@btopenworld.com

 ⚒ ⚭room *VISA*

Copper Ale, Palmers IPA, 200

Sitting just yards from the harbour, there's been a pub on this spot since 1739 and you can still imagine the smugglers and crusty seafarers planning their moonlit jaunts. The front of the bar is still popular with the locals, and the low-beamed ceiling adds to the intimate atmosphere. Behind the bar is the slightly more formal restaurant with its neat arrangement of pine tables and chairs. A blackboard menu offers an extensive range of refreshingly local seafood, which is delivered twice a day. Lunchtime offers a lighter option. In this part of the world, eating al fresco comes naturally, and a summer terrace gives an opportunity to catch up with news from Lyme Bay's fossil gatherers. It's a busy place, so make sure you book first. Four simple bedrooms await upstairs.

Food serving times:
Monday-Saturday:
   12pm-2pm, 6.30pm-9.30pm
Sunday: 12pm-2.30pm
Open dinner Bank Holiday Sundays
booking essential
Prices:
Meals: a la carte 15.00/25.00
4 rooms: 50.00/70.00

1.75mi South of Bridport by B3157. Near the harbour. Parking

Typical Dishes

Scallops, black pudding and fennel

Sea bass with noodles

Vanilla crème terrine, fruit coulis

Corscombe

037 The Fox Inn

Corscombe DT2 0NS
Tel.: (01935) 891330 - Fax: (01935) 891330

⇌room 🚭 **VISA** **AE** **MC** **JCB**

🍺 *Exmoor Ale, Butcombe Bitter and occasional guest ales*

Sticky soot, built up over time, lies ingrained on the walls above the fireplaces here. It's one of many endearing features of this mightily charming 17C pub, which boasts several fascinating areas. Two stone floored main bar rooms are intimate and dripping with rural ambience, typified by pews, slate-clad bar and scrubbed pine furniture. Country style imbues the extremely characterful breakfast room, where the first meal of the day is cooked on the Aga; look out for the dog that rests there. A mellow old conservatory has a large table constructed from one strip of oak felled in the 1987 storms. And the food? Dine on well-judged traditional dishes using the best seasonal produce, including well-renowned blackboard fish specials. There are wonderful bedrooms, too, endowed with cosy, rustic warmth.

Food serving times:
Monday-Sunday:
12pm-2pm, 7pm-9pm
Closed 25 December
Prices:
Meals: a la carte 19.00/28.00
🛏 **4 rooms:** 55.00/100.00

Typical Dishes

Gratin of crab, sea bass and bream

Brill, sweet potato and coriander mash

Sticky toffee pudding

3.5mi Northeast of Beaminster.
Parking

Evershot

038 Acorn Inn

28 Fore St, Evershot DT2 0JW
Tel.: (01935) 83228 - Fax: (01935) 83707
e-mail: stay@acorn-inn.co.uk - Website: www.acorn-inn.co.uk

 🍷 ⊱room **VISA** **AE** **MC** **JCB**

 Up to 3 guest ales offered

This neat 16C inn in sleepy Evershot still feels like a proper village local, with friendly neighbourhood rivalries kindled at the skittle alley and cooled off with pints of Devon guest ales and ciders, but the oak-panelled main bar, warmed by an open fire in winter, also attracts diners from further afield. Two further rooms in pale wood are just for dining. British pub favourites appear alongside classic dishes with a light modern touch and plenty of local produce; a blackboard menu lists daily changing seafood specials. Smart, cottage-style bedrooms with exposed beams and some thoughtful individual touches stay on the right side of twee.

Food serving times:
Monday-Sunday:
12pm-2pm, 6.30pm-9.30pm
Prices:
Meals: a la carte 18.00/30.00
🛏 **9 rooms:** 75.00/130.00

Typical Dishes
Medley of mushrooms
Scallops with saffron and white wine
Chocolate brownies, cappuccino sauce

7mi Northeast of Beaminster by B3163.
Parking

Farnham

039 The Museum Inn

Farnham DT11 8DE

Tel.: (01725) 516261 - Fax: (01725) 516988
e-mail: enquiries@museuminn.co.uk - Website: www.museuminn.co.uk

   VISA **MC**

  Ringwood Best, Timothy Taylor, Summer Lightening

Standing at the main crossroads of the village, the original, part-thatched Museum Inn has long since received an addition here and an extension there, but the pub as it stands today seems not only smart, bright and well-tended, but seamlessly characterful too. Diners have the choice of four dining rooms, furnished with antique dressers and scrubbed tables and decorated with curiosities from old paintings to stags heads, but as they don't take bookings here, you may be asked to take a seat in the bar first before heading through for classic-contemporary dishes like chicken parfait, duck confit and haddock and mustard risotto. Spacious, quite luxuriously styled bedrooms really are a cut above the average inn; if you don't feel quite ready for bed, the residents lounge might tempt you with a cosy fire and plenty of reading matter.

Food serving times:
Monday-Saturday:
  12pm-2pm, 7pm-9.30pm
Sunday: 12pm-3pm,
  7pm-9.30pm

Closed 25 December, dinner 26 December and dinner 31 December

Prices:
Meals: a la carte 20.50/29.00
🛏 **8 rooms:** 65.00/120.00

7.5mi Northeast of Blandford Forum by A354.
Parking

Typical Dishes

Pressed skate wing with lemon

Salad of guinea fowl

Iced raspberry parfait

Plush

040 Brace of Pheasants

Plush DT2 7RQ

Tel.: (01300) 348357

e-mail: albu@tinyworld.co.uk - Website: www.thebraceofpheasants.co.uk

Butcombe, Otter, Palmers Copper, Fuller's London Pride

The Giant of Cerne Abbas is not much more than a (giant's) stone-throw from this gloriously secluded 16C thatched inn, which revels in a pleasant rural setting midway between Dorchester and Blandford Forum. In keeping with the surroundings and exterior, the pub – formerly two thatched cottages and a smithy - has a cosy, characterful interior, dominated by the large bar where locals gather to sup pints or partake of the robust, tasty cooking, which has earned a solid local reputation. The same is served in a slightly more formal parlour, or non-smoking dining area for families. There's a pretty rear garden for summer use, with the woods and bridleways of the Piddle valley beyond.

Food serving times:
Tuesday-Sunday:
12.30pm-2.30pm,
7.30pm-9.30pm

Closed 25 December. Open Bank Holiday Mondays

Prices:
Meals: a la carte 21.00/29.00

🛏 **4 rooms:** 60.00/75.00

Typical Dishes

Blue cheese soufflé

John Dory, lime hollandaise

Panna cotta with marinated baby figs

1.5mi North of Piddletrenthide.
Parking

Amberley

042 The Amberley Inn

Amberley GL5 5AF

Tel.: (01453) 872565 - Fax: (01453) 872738
e-mail: theamberley@zoom.co.uk - Website: www.theamberley.co.uk

 🍷 **VISA** **MC**

 Uley Old spot, Archers Best, Wickwar Bob

With refurbishments only completed in 2004, this charming Cotswold inn is now the stylish star turn of its pleasant hamlet. It's surrounded by countryside and close to Woodchester Park National Trust Garden and a host of ancient monuments, but it holds an attraction of its own: the wood-panelled bar, with its plump banquette cushions and polished tables and chairs, has the fresh scent of renewal. No less impressive is the menu, which boasts a well-balanced and well-executed mix of modern and traditional dishes with prominent use of Gloucestershire ingredients. Look out, too, for the pub's popular tapas selection. The restaurant offers seasonal, fixed price menus – slightly more adventurous than in the bar. Well-ordered, pretty bedrooms are now very much part of the premises.

Food serving times:
Monday-Sunday:
    12pm-2pm, 7pm-9pm
Prices:
Meals: 27.95 (fixed price dinner)
🛏 **12 rooms:** 59.00/89.00

Typical Dishes

King scallops, celeriac purée

Pigeon en croûte

Valrhona chocolate fondant

1mi North of Nailsworth.
Parking

Arlingham

043 Old Passage Inn

Passage Rd, Arlingham GL2 7JR

Tel.: (01452) 740547 - Fax: (01452) 741871
e-mail: oldpassageinn@ukonline.co.uk - Website: www.fishattheoldpassageinn.co.uk

 Bass

Originality is the keyword to this bright green painted inn, perched in an isolated spot where the Severn starts to twist and turn. Any resemblance to a cosy, small-town country inn ends at the dining room, where gastronomic ambitions spiral off on a modern tangent. All efforts go into an accomplished seafood menu; cooking is bold, generous and suitably rustic. A small private dining area at the front can be booked for special occasions. The inn's three bedrooms are funky. They're called Red Mullet, Yellow Finned Tuna and Green Lipped Mussel, and they're all strikingly modern, bright, hi-tec and highly individual. Each has a kingsize bed, and each has a tall DIY cupboard from which, in the morning, Continental breakfast is rather surprisingly, and uniquely, served.

Food serving times:
Tuesday-Saturday:
　　　12pm-2pm, 7pm-9pm
Sunday:　　　　　　12pm-2pm
Closed 24-31 December
Prices:
Meals: a la carte 24.50/33.25
🛏 **3 rooms:** 55.00/85.00

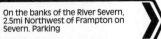

On the banks of the River Severn, 2.5mi Northwest of Frampton on Severn. Parking

Typical Dishes

Rich fish soup

Skewered monkfish and scallops

Crème brûlée

Barnsley

044 Village Pub

Barnsley GL7 5EF

Tel.: (01285) 740421 - Fax: (01285) 740929
e-mail: reservations@thevillagepub.co.uk - Website: www.thevillagepub.co.uk

   ✂room *VISA* Ⓜ⑤

 Local ales available

A really special place – too good and too affordable to save for special occasions. Renovated with impeccable taste, five connecting rooms of this part-17C inn lead from gleaming oak floors to spotless flagstones, bright botanical prints and Regency colours to Persian carpets and wingback chairs; the elegant, beamed bedrooms in French country style are every bit as inviting. The real highlight, though, is the daily-changing menu. Dilligently sourced produce, local and organic where possible, and a dash of originality raise appetising modern dishes well above the norm: try tagliatelle with a rich, dark venison and chicken liver sauce, haddock with potato and bacon salad and a deliciously buttery banana cheesecake. Keen and accommodating staff make sure you're well looked-after and a Bib Gourmand award highlights the good value for money.

Food serving times:
Monday-Friday:
    12pm-2.30pm, 7pm-9.30pm
Saturday: 12pm-3pm,
                7pm-10pm
Sunday: 12pm-3pm
Prices:
Meals: a la carte 20.00/30.00
🛏 **6 rooms:** 80.00/125.00

4mi North East of Cirencester, on the B4425 〉〉

Typical Dishes

Steamed mussels, cider, onion and sage

Pork chop, bubble and squeak

Apricot almond tart

Bledington

045 Kings Head Inn

The Green, Bledington OX7 6XQ

Tel.: (01608) 658365 - Fax: (01608) 658902
e-mail: kingshead@orr-ewing.com - Website: www.kingsheadinn.net

🍷 ⅙room *VISA* **AE** **MC**

🍺 *Hook Norton and guest ales*

A charming Cotswold setting and a warmly welcoming pub: what could be more idyllic on a perfect summer's day? The Kings Head traces its origins back to the 15C, and in all that time it can rarely have looked more inviting: it certainly entices the Morris dancers who happily congregate each summer on the green outside to perform the Bledington Dances. The place oozes style, with stone and wood floors, real fires and an archetypal modern country pub feel. Printed evening menus identify a solid traditional base, with good use of local produce: meat is bought from a renowned Cotswold butcher, fresh Cornish fish arrives daily, and vegetables are from nearby Evesham Vale. Bedrooms hold the promise of comfy country repose: a low-beamed stairway leads the way.

Food serving times:
Monday-Sunday:
12pm-2pm, 7pm-9pm
Closed 25-26 December
Prices:
Meals: a la carte 9.50/12.95
🛏 **12 rooms:** 50.00/95.00

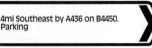

Typical Dishes

Lime marinated kipper fillets

Marinated chicken breast, herb rösti

Mango cheesecake

4mi Southeast by A436 on B4450. Parking

Calcot

046 **The Gumstool Inn**

Calcot GL8 8YJ

Tel.: (01666) 890391 - Fax: (01666) 890394
e-mail: reception@calcotmanor.com - Website: www.calcotmanor.co.uk

Butcombe Bitter, Wickwar Bob, Archers Best, Sharps Doom Bar

The cheerful, civilised Gumstool proudly nurtures its own identity beside an impressive neighbour – Calcot Manor - in one of Gloucestershire's most pleasing locations. It boasts a bustling intimacy, as locals and hotel guests mingle. Gingham curtains, hop bines and a leather armchair by the open fire lend traditional flavours to a generally modern ambience. Rustic but comfy about sums it up. You'll eat well here: bold, imaginative cooking is invariably flavoursome, with influences drawn from the Mediterranean. Dishes can be taken in ample (starter), or generous, portions. Staff create a very relaxed style, but you'll always feel you're being well looked after.

Food serving times:
Monday-Friday:
    12pm-2pm, 5pm-9,30pm
Saturday: 12pm-9,30pm
Sunday: 12pm-9pm
(booking essential)

Prices:
Meals: a la carte 18.50/25.00
30 rooms: 150.00/ 300.00

Typical Dishes

Avocado pear, salmon mousse

Thai lamb curry

Chocolate and orange tart

3.5mi West of Tetbury on A4135. Parking

Chipping Campden

047 Eight Bells Inn

Church St, Chipping Campden GL55 6JG

Tel.: (01386) 840371 - Fax: (01386) 841669

e-mail: neilhargreaves@bellinn.fsnet.co.uk - Website: www.eightbellsinn.co.uk

      VISA **MC** **JCB**

Hook Norton Best, Old Hooky, Marston Pedigree, Goffs Jouster

With its typical gables, little leaded windows and steep-pitched roof, the charming 14C Eight Bell Inn stands out even in well-preserved Chipping Campden. It once housed the stonemasons working on the nearby bell-tower, and history is still writ large on the rustic interior. The ancient beams over the bar are now studded with brasses and hung with mugs, and a glass plate set into the floor reveals an old passage running from St. James' Church, thought to have been used for escaping the persecutions of the Reformation or the dangers of the Civil War rather than for discreet exits after last orders. A succinct modern menu and specials board balances the eclectic and the traditional: chunky baguettes are a popular choice at lunch. Pine-fitted bedrooms in bright blues and yellows provide the essentials.

Food serving times:
Monday-Sunday:
12pm-2.30pm,
6.30pm-9.30pm
Closed 25 December
Prices:
Meals: a la carte 18.00/26.00
4 rooms: 50.00/95.00

In centre of town.
Unlimited parking on road

Typical Dishes

King scallops in Parma ham

Chicken on asparagus and ham risotto

Mandarin crèpes

Chipping Campden

048 King's Arms

The Square, Chipping Campden GL55 6AW

Tel.: (01386) 840256 - Fax: (01386) 841598
e-mail: info@thekingsarmshotel.com - Website: www.thekingsarmshotel.com

 *VISA* **AE** **M⊙**

 Hook Norton Best and 1 guest ale

This archetypal Cotswold inn is a real treat. Behind the handsome 17C façade, two surprisingly spacious, antique-furnished rooms, decorated with pictures on a culinary theme, are the perfect place to enjoy a well-balanced menu with a hint of brasserie style – dishes like pork with apple and Calvados, or asparagus salad, make the most of local produce in all its seasonal variety. Countless delightful details raise the bedrooms well above the usual pub standard: impeccably tasteful and never fussy, some even have oak four-poster beds. The pretty rear courtyard, bordered with lavender, is blissfully quiet after the bustle of the town in summer.

Food serving times:
Monday-Sunday:
  12pm-6pm, 6.30pm-9.30pm
Closed 24-25 December
Prices:
Meals: a la carte 20.00/28.00
🛏 **12 rooms:** 90.00/150.00

In centre of town.
Residents only parking or parking in the square

Typical Dishes

Goat's cheese and aubergine salad

Roast monkfish, red wine jus

Sticky toffee pudding

Clearwell

049 # The Wyndham Arms

Clearwell GL16 8JT

Tel.: (01594) 833666 - Fax: (01594) 845666
e-mail: res@thewyndhamhotel.co.uk - Website: www.thewyndhamhotel.co.uk

Freeminer Brewery Speculation Ale, Freeminer Bitter

Visitors are spoiled for choice in this part of the Forest of Dean: the Clearwell Caves and medieval Castle are close at hand, while the Perrygrove Railway is just up the road. Paying a visit to this Cotswold style pub, dating back 600 years, fits in seamlessly on the tourist trail. A pleasant outside terrace is a good spot for summer relaxing; inside, there's much character to admire, particularly in the two-roomed restaurant, which proudly boasts flagstones, bare white walls, rafters, chimney, old bread baking oven in a corner, and paintings for sale on the walls. Hearty, well-cooked, keenly priced dishes keep locals and tourists alike happy: typical dishes might include lightly spiced crab cake with chilli jam; roast rump of lamb on ratatouille with a redcurrant jus; or roasted bell peppers stuffed with couscous.

Food serving times:
Monday-Saturday:
    12pm-2pm, 7pm-9.30pm
Sunday: 12pm-2.30pm,
      7pm-9pm

Prices:
Meals: 14.90/17.00 and a la carte 17.00/27.50
🛏 **18 rooms:** 55.00/95.00

Typical Dishes

Spiced crab cake, chilli jam

Venison and juniper berry stew

Vanilla panna cotta

By the Cross in the village. Parking

Clifford's Mesne

050 Yew Tree

Clifford's Mesne GL18 1JS

Tel.: (01531) 820719 - Fax: (01531) 820912
e-mail: paul@yewtreemayhill.freeserve.co.uk - Website: www.theyewtreeinn.co.uk

 Wye Valley Butty Bach, Fuller's London Pride, Shepherd Neame Spitfire

Allow yourself plenty of time to find this little village, hidden in a wooded corner of the Herefordshire borders. What was once a sadly run-down old place has been restored through the efforts of a dedicated couple, who have definitely put their mark on the place: dog lovers will be pleased to see man's best friend getting the recognition he deserves in the lounge décor and the five acres of thriving garden are now patrolled by talkative ducks and geese. There's a ringingly enthusiastic welcome for everyone and no effort spared in the service, while regional produce is the key to an appealing modern menu, which is a touch lighter at lunch: try straw-smoked haddock with poached duck's egg or lemon tart with homemade prune and Armagnac ice cream.

Food serving times:
Tuesday-Saturday:
   12pm-3pm, 7pm-11pm
Sunday: 12pm-3pm
Closed 2-21 January
Prices:
Meals: 27.00 (fixed price lunch) and a la carte 19.45/34.50
2 rooms: 55.00/70.00

Typical Dishes

Mushroom risotto

Turbot, Champagne and basil sauce

Millefeuille of strawberries

2mi Southwest of Newent.
Parking

Cockleford

051 **The Green Dragon Inn**

Cockleford GL53 9NW

Tel.: (01242) 870271 - Fax: (01242) 870171

e-mail: green-dragon@buccaneer.co.uk - Website: www.green-dragon-inn.co.uk

VISA AE M©

 Hook Norton, Butcombe, Courage Directors and 1 monthly changing guest ale

The classic direction "in the middle of nowhere" is a pinpoint indication for this authentic old Cotswold pub in a delightfully remote setting along a country road. A typical honey-gold stone façade serves notice of the warm ambience within: beams, log fire and an authentic rustic style dating back to the 17C. Take your pick of three rooms around the double bar – one is particularly devoted to dining. There's an elaborate choice of menu with a touch of Italian inspiration, so you might find roast fig, taleggio and Parma ham bruchetta for starters, followed by fried gnocchi with white truffle oil, Parmesan and oyster mushrooms for main course. Visitors to the area may wish to stay overnight in plain, simple yet well-equipped bedrooms.

Food serving times:

Monday-Friday:
12pm-2.30pm, 6pm-10pm

Saturday: 12pm-10pm

Sunday: 12pm-9.30pm

Prices:

Meals: a la carte approx. 25.00

 9 rooms: 57.00/70.00

Typical Dishes

Crab and lobster risotto

Ribeye steak, roasted cherry tomatoes

Fruit crumble

5mi South of Cheltenham by A435. Parking

Coln Saint Aldwyns

052 **The Courtyard Bar (at New Inn at Coln)**

Coln Saint Aldwyns GL7 5AN

Tel.: (01285) 750651 - Fax: (01285) 750657
e-mail: stay@new-inn.co.uk - Website: www.new-inn.co.uk

Butcombe, Wadworth 6X, Hook Norton Best

This delightful, ivy-wreathed 16C inn, with pretty bedrooms in floral patterns, makes a perfect destination for an indulgent long weekend in the country, but you don't have to be a guest to make the most of the Courtyard Bar. Discreetly spaced tables and charming, serenely efficient service would not seem out of place in the more formal restaurant, but there's more than a measure of proper pub intimacy to the place, especially when they fire up the old stove on frosty evenings. Affordable cuisine in contemporary style: ask for a place on the terrace in summer.

Food serving times:
Monday-Sunday:
     12pm-2pm, 7pm-9pm
(bookings not accepted)
Prices:
Meals: 35.00 and a la carte 17.00/25.00
14 rooms: 100.00/130.00

Typical Dishes

Welsh rarebit

Confit of crispy pork, plum sauce

Panettone bread and butter pudding

3mi North of Fairford.
Parking

Didmarton

053 Kings Arms

The Street, Didmarton GL9 1DT

Tel.: (01454) 238245 - Fax: (01454) 238249

e-mail: kingsarms@didmarton.freeserve.co.uk - Website: www.kingsarmsdidmarton.co.uk

   VISA M©

 Four or more from Wickwars Cotswold Way, Uley Bitter, 2 Bath Ales, 2 Sharps Ales and Butcombe

This handsome 17C former coaching inn looks most resplendent in its honey coloured overcoat - fitting apparel for a trusted Cotswold family member. Inside is just as good. Hops clamber over beams and local stone merges seamlessly with terracotta walls. A bright and cheerful fire-lit bar with oak settles is perfect for a winter's evening. During the summer months, there's an ideal garden setting for drinks and gentle slumbers. The bright dining room offers a reassuringly hearty menu of tried-and-tested dishes which might include local sausages with buttered mash and onion gravy, or fresh Cornish crab. Smart, pine-fitted bedrooms are good for a pub. Wake refreshed for trips into nearby Malmesbury or Tetbury.

Food serving times:

Monday-Friday:
12pm-2pm, 7pm-9.30pm

Saturday: 12pm-2.30pm, 7pm-9.30pm

Sunday: 12pm-2.30pm, 7pm-9pm

Prices:

Meals: a la carte 14.00/28.00

🛏 **11 rooms:** 45.00/80.00

Typical Dishes

Pigeon breast, red onion marmalade

Venison casserole

Blood orange cheesecake

5.5mi Southwest of Tetbury on A433. Parking

Ewen

054 **Wild Duck Inn**

Drake's Island, Ewen GL7 6BY

Tel.: (01285) 770310 - Fax: (01285) 770924
e-mail: wduckinn@aol.com - Website: www.thewildduckinn.co.uk

👁 ♓ ♈ **VISA** **AE** **MC**

Theakston Best, Old Peculier, Sharps Doom Bar, Wells Bombardier, Duck Pond, Courage Directors

Equally remarkable on the inside and the outside, this privately owned Elizabethan house seems almost too imposing to have started life as a mill, but though the ancient oil paintings do have a hint of stateliness about them, there's an unmistakeable pub atmosphere to the place: intriguing artefacts and bushy swags of hops decorate a series of intimate bar-rooms. Upstairs and in the modern wing, imaginatively styled bedrooms, two with four-poster beds, all share the same richly comfortable ambience. An extensive daily menu, supplemented by blackboard specials, combines modern and traditional dishes and includes a good choice of fresh fish landed at Brixham. Weather permitting, the giant chess set on the terrace offers a more intellectual way to decide who picks up the bill for lunch.

Food serving times:
Monday-Saturday:
12pm-2pm, 7pm-10pm
Sunday:
12pm-2pm,
7pm-9.30pm

Prices:
Meals: a la carte 25.00/30.00
🛏 **12 rooms:** 60.00/130.00

Typical Dishes
Scallops, rocket and watercress salad

Lemon sole, salmon potato cake

Sticky toffee pudding

3.25mi Southwest of Cirencester by A429.
Parking

Frampton Mansell

055 **White Horse**

Cirencester Rd, Frampton Mansell GL6 8HZ
Tel.: (01285) 760960

Uley Bitter, Hook Norton Best Bitter, Arkell's Summer Ale

From dismal nonentity to bright, modern gastropub, it's been a busy few years for The White Horse, and the friendly, responsive service suggests a team enjoying their success. More cheerful-looking than you would ever guess from the outside, the interior divides into a cosy and very relaxed bar, where they serve snacks and baguettes at lunchtime, and a colourful dining room offering a more ambitious menu. Fairly priced dishes, typically including grilled sardine fillets and roasted tomato, rich chicken liver parfait and sea bass on warm baby vegetables, blend bold, contemporary flavours with a streak of originality. An ever-growing local reputation means it's worth getting there early at weekends.

Food serving times:
Monday-Saturday:
  12pm-2.30pm, 7pm-9.45pm
Sunday: 12pm-2.30pm
Closed 24-26 December and 1 January
Prices:
Meals: a la carte 20.00/27.00

Typical Dishes
Grilled sardines
Belly of pork, spring onion mash
Peaches, cardamon and cinnamon

7mi West of Cirencester by A419. Parking

Lower Oddington

056 **Fox Inn**

Lower Oddington GL56 0UR

Tel.: (01451) 870555 - Fax: (01451) 870666
e-mail: info@foxinn.net - Website: www.foxinn.net

  room

Hook Norton, Abbott, Archers, Wadworth 6X

A charming village deserves a charming pub, and Lower Oddington has one, an ivy-covered inn not far from the 11C church. There's a well cared-for atmosphere in the smartly cosy dining rooms – beams and fireplaces, nooks and crannies, books and candlelight – although the first impression, on most nights of the week, is of friendly chat and activity. Imperturbable young staff have it all under control, even during the busiest lunchtimes, serving enjoyable, flavoursome cooking with its share of British classics like steak and kidney pudding and Bakewell tart. Seafood fans will want to try the potted shrimps, or even ask in advance about their special fish days. The food is so popular that they've had to build a new kitchen to cope with demand. Three delightful bedrooms, sumptuously furnished with antiques, are always in immaculate order.

Food serving times:
Monday-Saturday:
  12pm-2pm, 6.30pm-10pm
Sunday: 12pm-2pm,
       6.30pm-9.30pm
Closed 25 December and Sunday dinner November-March
Prices:
Meals: a la carte 17.95/24.95
3 rooms: 68.00/95.00

3mi East of Stow-on-the-Wold by A436. Parking

Typical Dishes

Mushroom and Roquefort tart

Sea trout, creamed fennel and chives

Mango crème brûlée

Paxford

057 Churchill Arms

Paxford GL55 6XH

Tel.: (01386) 594000 - Fax: (01386) 594005
e-mail: info@thechurchillarms.com - Website: www.thechurchillarms.com

  ☓room **VISA** M© JCB

 | *Hook Norton Best and 1 guest ale*

This well-kept, instantly likeable pub is a confirmed local favourite and even at its busiest – when service can start to fray a little at the edges – a laid-back atmosphere still prevails: it's usual to see locals, walkers and visitors to nearby Hidcote Manor propping up the bar and chatting as they patiently bide their time for a table. It's worth the wait; fresh, contemporary, seasonal cooking, using fine ingredients from trusted regional suppliers, is served up at prices which are generous going on philanthropic, hence the Bib Gourmand award. Recent successes, typically robust and enjoyable, include asparagus with shallot dressing and smoked goose, crisp, full-flavoured duck confit with cauliflower purée, and a rich chocolate torte. Simple, stylish rooms, half in the modern extension, make a good base for a weekend in the Cotswolds.

Food serving times:
Monday-Sunday:
    12pm-2pm, 7pm-9pm
Prices:
Meals: a la carte 18.50/28.00
🛏 **4 rooms:** 40.00/70.00

Typical Dishes

Smoked goose with asparagus

Ham hock, creamed cauliflower

Almond roulade

3mi East by B4035.
On street parking

Poulton

058 Falcon Inn

London Rd, Poulton GL7 5HN

Tel.: (01285) 850844 - Fax: (01285) 850403
e-mail: info@thefalconpoulton.co.uk - Website: www.thefalconpoulton.co.uk

  VISA **MC**

 Hook Norton Best, West Berks Good Old Boy, Bath Ales Gem

More contemporary inside than the exterior suggests, the thoroughly refitted Falcon has, if anything, gained in neighbourly good nature since its conversion to a dining pub. Relaxed and friendly in atmosphere, there's a main room with a log fire, seagrass carpets, scrubbed pine tables and mix-and-match chairs and pews, and more dining space in the converted skittle alley, from where you can peek into the kitchen and see how lunch is coming on. Two old friends with enthusiasm to burn share the cooking and put their faith in local suppliers; hearty Modern British dishes, never over-elaborate, range from crab cakes or blue cheese and spinach omelette to unstinting helpings of belly pork with lentils, followed by tasty chocolate brownies with ice cream. Well-balanced wine list.

Food serving times:
Monday-Sunday:
    12pm-2.30pm, 7pm-9pm
Fixed price lunch Sunday
Prices:
Meals: 20.00 and a la carte
18.95/29.95

Typical Dishes

Salad of seared beef fillet
Roast fillet of brill
Coconut panna cotta

Village on A417 between Cirencester and Fairford. Parking

Sapperton

059 The Bell

Sapperton GL7 6LE

Tel.: (01285) 760298 - Fax: (01285) 760761
e-mail: thebell@sapperton66.freeserve.co.uk - Website: www.foodatthebell.co.uk

   VISA

Hook Norton Best, Thatchers Scrumpy, Goffs Jouster, Uley Old Spot, Wickwar Cotswold Way

Over the past few years, a dedicated young team have really seen their efforts pay off. The Bell is a much-loved local institution: spotless, smart, uncluttered and wonderfully comfortable, with the warm glow of Cotswold stone inside and out. A well thought-out repertoire, plus daily specials, finds room for pub favourites and appetising modern dishes which make the most of whatever's in season: fortifying midwinter fare includes local pheasant and wild mushrooms braised in wine – tender, earthy and rich – and a moist, dark date and toffee pudding. There are some invigorating walks through woods and meadows, and a log fire and a big wood-burning range to welcome you back, or tables in the courtyard if the sun is shining.

Food serving times:
Monday-Sunday:
    12pm-2pm, 7pm-9.30pm
Closed 25 December and occasional Mondays
Prices:
Meals: a la carte 16.00/30.00

Typical Dishes

Home-smoked cod

Shank of lamb, creamed leeks

Fresh berries in Cointreau

5mi West of Cirencester by A419. Parking

Southrop

060 **The Swan**

Southrop GL7 2NU

Tel.: (01367) 850205 - Fax: (01367) 850555

VISA

Hook Norton, Abbot, Archer's and 2 guest ales

Looking little changed by the centuries, the ivy-covered inn has kept its characterful beamed ceiling, its log fire and its public bar, good for lighter lunches. The main dining room, though, is an altogether more formal affair, but no less welcoming for that. Here, the manager and chef bring their experience from Terence Conran's Bibendum to a contemporary menu with a subtle Mediterranean flavour and a touch of West End sophistication: expect anything from Spanish cured meats and foie gras terrine to monkfish with artichoke risotto or steak tartare. To round off the evening with some healthy competition, they even have a skittle alley for hire: try finding one of those in Kensington!

Food serving times:
Monday-Sunday:
  12pm-2.30pm, 7pm-10pm
Closed 25 December
Prices:
Meals: a la carte 17.00/34.00

Typical Dishes

Thai pork salad

Grilled quail, rosemary jus

Coconut parfait, mango compote

3mi North of Lechlade on Eastleach Rd. Parking on road

Stow-on-the-Wold

 061 **Eagle & Child**

Digbeth St, Stow-on-the-Wold GL54 1BN

Tel.: (01451) 830670 - Fax: (01451) 870048

e-mail: info@theroyalisthotel.co.uk - Website: www.theroyalisthotel.co.uk

 **VISA** **MC**

Hook Norton and 1 monthly changing guest ale

Not many pubs can boast a leper hole in their armoury (well, in the cellar, to be precise). But that's the case here, in a building that, over a thousand years ago, was a hospice sheltering lepers. It claims to be England's oldest inn, and can certainly boast some impressive history: the discovery of a Civil War Royalist commander's letter, a tunnel leading from the bar to the church opposite, and an ancient frieze. The rooms themselves have thousand year-old timbers. To get to them, go through the reception to the Royalist Hotel and cross the threshold of a pub where you'd feel cheated if there wasn't the tangible whiff of history and rustic charm (don't worry, there is). There's also a sunny, bright conservatory and a restaurant with soft lighting and beams serving well-priced modern menus with a distinct French influence.

Food serving times:
Monday-Thursday:
  12pm-2.30pm, 6pm-9.30pm
Friday-Saturday:
  12pm-2.30pm, 6pm-10pm
Sunday: 12pm-3pm,
            6pm-9.30pm

Prices:
Meals: a la carte 15.00/30.00

Typical Dishes

Chicken liver and mushroom parfait

Ginger and soy sea bass

Lemongrass brûlée

At the Royalist Hotel. Parking

Stow-on-the-Wold

062 Kings Arms

Market Sq, Stow-on-the-Wold GL54 1AF

Tel.: (01451) 830364 - Fax: (01451) 830602
e-mail: info@kingsarms-stowonthewold.co.uk - Website: www.kingsarms-stowonthewold.co.uk

Greene King IPA, Abbot Ale

 t takes something special to stand out in the middle of this seriously popular Cotswold town, but the Kings Arms – centrally prominent – may just stake such a claim. Dating from the 16C, its stone façade reflects warmly across the Market Square. Inside, the sunny ambience is no less pronounced: a rewarding mix of rustic and modern styles creates a friendly, relaxed feel. Subtly blended chairs, bare tables, leather sofas and casually placed books and magazines prove the ideal antidote to serious bouts of sightseeing. There are two dining areas: sit in Rennie Macintosh chairs and enjoy impressively simple, satisfying modern menus that have rightly been awarded a Michelin Bib Gourmand. Then retreat to one of the effortlessly stylish bedrooms with a faint air of the Bohemian.

Food serving times:
Monday-Friday:
    12pm-2.30pm, 6pm-9.30pm
Saturday: 12pm-2.30pm,
                            6pm-10pm
Sunday: 12pm-2.30pm,
                            7pm-9pm
Closed 1 week mid May and 1 week mid October
Prices:
Meals: a la carte 16.50/24.50
8 rooms: 90.00/120.00

On the Market Square, in the town centre.
Parking

Typical Dishes

Mussels with chorizo

Calves liver, Italian bacon and sausage

Pistachio and rhubarb pavlova

Tetbury

063 The Trouble House

Cirencester Road, Tetbury GL8 8SG

Tel.: (01666) 502206 - Fax: (01666) 504508
e-mail: enquiries@troublehouse.co.uk - Website: www.troublehouse.co.uk

 VISA AE M©

 Wadworth IPA, 6X, Westons Old Rosie Cider

Y ou might easily speed past this nondescript roadside inn, but you'd be missing some of the best pub food in England, known far and wide for its Michelin star. Imagination and quiet finesse bring out some great natural combinations of flavours in classic and modern British recipes. These can be deliciously simple and satisfying, like lardy cake and custard or tender liver with bacon, but more refined dishes lose none of their robust and moreish appeal: honey lacquered pork with cabbage in garlic and bacon cream, and rabbit with linguine, beans and peas are among the best. Grab a seat where you can in one of three low-beamed bars, with roaring fires and hop-trimmed beams: neat, down-to-earth and very welcoming.

Food serving times:
Tuesday-Saturday:
 12pm-2pm, 7pm-9.30pm
Closed 25 December-4
January and 1 week
September
Prices:
Meals: a la carte 25.00/31.00

2mi Northeast on the A433.
Parking

Typical Dishes

Foie gras and apple terrine

Ribeye steak béarnaise

Dessert plate

Upper Oddington

064 **Horse and Groom**

Upper Oddington GL56 0XH

Tel.: (01451) 830584 - Fax: (01451) 831496
e-mail: info@horseandgroom.co.uk - Website: www.horseandgroom.uk.com

    room **VISA** **MC** **JCB**

 Hook Norton, Flowers, Brakspear, Bass, Timothy Taylor Landlord, Adnams, Old Speckled Hen

More "well-kept" than "well-kept secret", this busy, part 16C former coaching inn loses nothing by its rural hamlet location. Indeed, the Irish owner's conviviality is a firm guarantee that word will spread. The interior is charming, its timbers and crackling fires distributed over a spacious three rooms; they're invariably buzzing as Assumpta, the owner, weaves from kitchen to table with honest, tasty home-made dishes. Service, mostly from efficient young travellers, is never less than warm and cordial. Those wanting to steer clear of Stow's heaving guesthouses can stay here – the single rooms have plenty of character, but their sloped ceilings and beams may prove a nuisance after a healthy intake of the inn's wet stuff!

Food serving times:
Monday-Sunday:
  12pm-2pm, 6.30pm-9pm
Prices:
Meals: a la carte 15.00/25.00
7 rooms: 49.00/69.00

2mi East of Stow-on-the-Wold by A436. Parking

Typical Dishes

Chicken liver parfait

Swordfish, lime and mango salsa

Lemon tart, lemon ice cream

Winchcombe

065 White Hart Inn

High St, Winchcombe GL54 5LJ

Tel.: (01242) 602359 - Fax: (01242) 602703

e-mail: enquiries@the-white-hart-inn.com - Website: www.the-white-hart-inn.com

🍷 ✂room *VISA* AE MC JCB

 Old Speckled Hen, Wadworth 6X, Greene King IPA, Bass,

Over the last few years, the team at The White Hart have transformed a neglected black-and-white timbered inn and built a devoted local following. The secret of their success? It's not the traditional look of the place so much as the feeling of heartfelt hospitality; the cheerfully attentive service brims with personality, and there's a pleasant surprise on the menu too. A broad selection offers a good spread of English and International dishes, but the Swedish specialities are the real treat: gravadlax and herring platters, meatballs, smorgasbord and fruit pancakes are all flavourful, authentic and moreish. Refurbished bedrooms are decorated on a theme: choose from Scottish, Swedish, New England and Moroccan.

Food serving times:
Monday-Sunday:
11am-10pm
Closed 25 December
Prices:
Meals: 16.95 (fixed price lunch) and a la carte 15.00/30.00
🛏 **8 rooms:** 75.00/125.00

Typical Dishes

Scandinavian seafood

Halibut, lobster sauce

Iced lingonberry and vodka parfait

In town centre.
Parking

Appley

066 Globe

Appley TA21 0HJ
Tel.: (01823) 672327

VISA Ⓜ

Cotleigh Tawny, Butcombe Blonde, Palmers IPA

Cosy and traditional, even pleasantly old-fashioned in some ways, the inn's welcoming interior shows the influence of a genial man who clearly sees himself as custodian of the Globe as well as its chef and long-standing landlord. The building itself has origins in the 1400s, but there's nautical history too, in the pictures, prints and photos of the Titanic decorating one wall, and a touch of nostalgia in the display case of die-cast Dinky and Corgi cars and vans. Hard to fault for generosity, the tasty, substantial pub cooking often has a subtle international touch; service is well-organised and invariably polite. If the sun's out, lounge with lunch and beers in the garden before setting off on a walk near the Devon border; if it's not, you could always ask to book the skittle alley.

Food serving times:
Tuesday-Sunday:
    12pm-2pm, 7pm-10pm
Closed 25-26 December.
Open Bank Holiday Mondays
Prices:
Meals: a la carte 17.00/25.00

Typical Dishes

Haddock chowder

Sea bass in tarragon butter

Chocolate and Baileys brûlée

6mi West of Wellington on A38.
Parking

Babcary

067 **Red Lion inn**

Babcary TA11 7ED
Tel.: (01458) 223230 · Fax: (01458) 224510

Hopback Crop Circle, Teignworthy Springtide, Butcombe

Set to one side, the bar of the Red Lion Inn cedes pride of place to two spacious, airy lounges. One's more particularly given over to eating, but they share a contemporary country style: oriental rugs, neatly set, rustic wooden tables and framed paintings and Red Lion posters on the walls. It's not over-formal, and this clearly suits a lively crowd of lunchers, from local families to passers-by who were lucky enough to drop in on spec.; service might slow a fraction on the busiest days, but a young team stays positive and polite. The chef's experience with Michel Roux is clear from a glance at the menu, where dishes with a classical edge include spicy chilli crab cakes and a plate of duck confit with braised lentils that wouldn't taste out of place in a family bistro in the Dordogne.

Food serving times:
Monday-Saturday:
    12pm-3pm, 7pm-9.30pm
Sunday: 12pm-3pm
Prices:
Meals: a la carte 15.00/28.00

Typical Dishes
Black pudding, poached duck salad

Chump of lamb, garlic mash potato

Glazed lemon tart

4.5mi Northeast of Ilchester by A37. Parking

Batcombe

068 **Three Horseshoes Inn**

Batcombe BA4 6HE

Tel.: (01749) 850359 - Fax: (01749) 850615

 Butcombe Golden Spring

This delightfully set rural pub is reached in true country fashion: down twisty country lanes until you get to the village church. The long, low bar which gives The Three Horseshoes its internal character is distinguished by its cream painted beams and planks and deep pink walls; an inglenook boasts a wood-burning stove, and there are cosy, cushioned window seats. The menus are of the modern variety, and come with some interesting combinations: typically, duck breast on sauteed courgette and bacon with gratin potatoes and honey and red wine jus. You can indulge in a pretty, stripped stone dining room, while a back terrace is an ideal place to sit on the grass in summer and inhale the sweet Somerset air.

Food serving times:
Monday-Sunday:
    12pm-2pm, 7pm-9.30pm
Closed 25 December
Prices:
Meals: a la carte 16.00/20.00

Typical Dishes

Smoked chicken and duck salad

Grilled chicken, crayfish tails

3mi North of Bruton by A359.
Near the church

Exford

069 Crown

Exford TA24 7PP

Tel.: (01643) 831554 - Fax: (01643) 831665
e-mail: info@crownhotelexmoor.co.uk - Website: www.crownhotelexmoor.co.uk

 VISA AE M⑤

 Exmoor Ale, Exmoor Gold, Cotleigh Tawny

Wonderfully located in the very heart of ruggedly beautiful Exmoor, it's no surprise to find local riders walking around the oldest coaching inn in the area. Step out to the rear and you'll find a lovely water garden and a trout stream meandering through gently sloping lawns. Come back in and find a seat in the front bar and lounge: a comfy, country-house style, open-plan area, with tables fashioned from barrels, old local photos on the walls and a huge stone fireplace around which the locals gather to chat about local goings-on: it's more comfortable than the parish pump, and the drink's better. The more formal restaurant is the place for ambitious, internationally influenced dishes; hearty shepherd's pie is on offer in the bar. Bedrooms here are individually styled, some with period features.

Food serving times:
Monday-Sunday:
12pm-2pm, 7pm-9.30pm
Prices:
Meals: 18.50/32.50

Typical Dishes

Smoked salmon and celeriac remoulade

Pan seared sea trout

Griottine cherry brûlée

In the village centre.
Parking

Holcombe

070 **The Ring o' Roses**

Stratton Rd, Holcombe BA3 5EB

Tel.: (01761) 232478 - Fax: (01761) 233737
e-mail: info@ringoroses.co.uk - Website: www.ringoroses.co.uk

 Otter, Blind Man's Golden Spring

As neatly maintained outside as it is inside, this old country inn has something of a personally run feel to it, and its owners certainly see it as more than just a village watering hole. A lobby to the right of the bar leads up to the bedrooms – somehow it's no surprise to find them spick and span and all comfortably furnished, one with a four poster bed – while the lounge on the left leads into the restaurant. As you might expect, lunchtime sees a slightly more limited selection, but the full evening menu ushers in a more original range, encompassing fried dim sum, crispy gougons of salmon and guinea fowl on parsnip and juniper mash. If you're planning on staying for a while, Wells, Longleat and Bath are all a convenient drive away.

Food serving times:
Monday-Friday:
12pm-2pm, 7pm-9pm
Saturday-Sunday:
12pm-1.30pm, 7pm-9pm
Closed 1-2 January
Prices:
Meals: a la carte 18.45/28.15
8 rooms: 65.00/85.00

Typical Dishes

Mousseline of chicken and Stilton

Veal, sage and ham

Orange and passion fruit trifle

4.5mi Northeast of Shepton Mallet by A367.
A few hundred yards outside of village. Parking

Ilchester

071 ## Ilchester Arms

The Square, Ilchester BA22 8LN

Tel.: (01935) 840220 - Fax: (01935) 841353

Website: www.ilchester-arms-hotel.co.uk

  rest **VISA** **AE** **MC**

Butcombe

First licensed in 1686, this impressive looking Somerset pub shows its age with appropriate dignity, the profusion of ivy on its exterior just adds a little more rural charm. It stands proudly in the village centre, a relaxing oasis from the hustle and bustle of nearby Yeovil. Public areas are relaxing and intimate, typified by two small lounges and an airy, wood decorated bar - like being down at the local, which many of the customers are. A bistro continues this informal theme, its daily changing blackboard menus have a hearty and familiar ring. At any given time you might try rich, rosemary scented lamb casserole with spring vegetables, confit of duck with garlic crust and cassoulet beans or seared calves liver with onions, bacon and mash. Sizable bedrooms have a good range of facilities.

Food serving times:
Monday-Saturday:
12pm-2.30pm, 7pm-9.30pm
Sunday: 12pm-2.30pm
(bar lunch)
Prices:
Meals: a la carte 12.00/25.00
7 rooms: 60.00/75.00

Typical Dishes

Crispy duck pancakes

Honey roast duck, potato rösti

Chocolate tart, Grand Marnier sauce

In the town centre.
Parking

Kingsdon

072 Kingsdon Inn

Kingsdon TA11 7LG
Tel.: (01935) 840543 - Fax: (01935) 840916

Otter, Butcombe, Cotleigh Barn Owl

This part 17C thatched inn knows how to pack 'em in. The best advice is: "Get here early!" Punters are drawn by the unadulterated charm of the place, as well as its rather handy position just off the A303 in a picturesque village near the attractive town of Somerton. It possesses bags of character: low bowed ceiling, wood burning stove, stripped pine built-in wall seat, scatter cushions and stone floors. Four snug, adjoining rooms provide dining options; there's a pleasant garden too. Traditional, popular dishes – and lots of them – show up on a busy looking blackboard menu: everything from whitebait to lambs liver to goats' cheese salad.

Food serving times:
Monday-Saturday:
12pm-2pm, 7pm-9.30pm
Sunday: 12pm-2pm,
7pm-9pm
Closed 25-26 December and 1 January
Booking essential
Prices:
Meals: a la carte 15.00/23.20

Typical Dishes

Crab and prawn mornay

Duck in scrumpy sauce

Sticky ginger pudding, ginger ice cream

2.5 mi South East of Somerton on B3151. Parking

Lovington

073 Pilgrims

Lovington BA7 7PT

Tel.: (01963) 240600

e-mail: thejools@btinternet.com - Website: www.thepilgrimsatlovington.co.uk

VISA **AE** **MC**

 Cottage Champflower Ale

You'd probably not stop here at first sight: Pilgrims doesn't look anything special from the outside. But its slogan – 'the pub that thinks it's a restaurant' - gives a hint of what to expect inside. Beyond the front door, there's a transformation. It does, indeed, have a smart, pleasant restaurant style: deep burgundy and exposed stone walls, coir mat flooring and bright, cheerful watercolours mostly by a local village artist. The bar isn't forgotten; it's traditional in character, with flag floors and low beams. Cookery books are piled on a piano and matchboxes from around the world decorate the walls. Menus, in the modern style, revel in interesting variations: try, perhaps, tempura of prawns with soy and lime sauce; asparagus and butter bean risotto with Parmesan and, for dessert, chocolate marquise with orange crème anglaise.

Food serving times:
Tuesday-Saturday:
    12pm-2.30pm, 7pm-11pm
Sunday: 12pm-2pm
Closed last 2 weeks October
Closed Tuesday lunch
Prices:
Meals: 16.00/19.00 and a la carte 21.00/32.00

4mi South West of Castle Cary by B3152 and A371 on B3153. Parking

Typical Dishes
Trio of smoked fish
Monkfish, scallops, bacon and mushrooms
Lemon posset, blackcurrants in cassis

Lower Vobster

074 The Vobster Inn

Lower Vobster BA3 5RJ

Tel.: (01373) 812920 - Fax: (01373) 812350
e-mail: vobsterinn@btinternet.com

 Butcombe Bitter, Fuller's London Pride, Courage Best

V ery much the centre of its tiny Somerset village, the Vobster Inn, run by a husband and wife team, takes its duty seriously and does its best to keep everyone happy, from young families and older couples, out enjoying the sun at the terrace tables, to the unhurried neighbours enjoying a slow pint inside. Adjoining the bar, a long lounge serves as the restaurant, its walls painted with grapes and lined with posters, labels, wine racks and even old wine cases. Sensibly allowing room for market-fresh specials, the menu starts with Fowey mussels, smoked salmon or generous slices of duck terrine, then offers "Ten from the grill" – including steaks and more local fish – with your choice of sauce. Try Falmouth plaice and chips with caper and anchovy butter, and don't pass up a good selection of cheeses.

Food serving times:
Monday-Sunday:
12pm-3pm, 7pm-10pm
Closed 25th December
Prices:
Meals: a la carte 14.00/28.00

Typical Dishes

Crayfish salad

Wild bass with samphire

Chocolate marquise, mango sorbet

5.5mi West of Frome via Mells.
Parking

Luxborough

075 Royal Oak of Luxborough

Exmoor National Park, Luxborough TA23 0SH

Tel.: (01984) 640319 - Fax: (01984) 641561
e-mail: info@theroyaloakinnluxborough.co.uk - Website: www.theroyaloakinnluxborough.co.uk

  VISA **AE** **MC**

Cotleigh Tawny, Exmoor Gold, Palmers 200, IPA

It's as though a spaceship was directed to land a pub in the most idyllic position possible, and dropped it right here, in the fold of the rolling Brendon Hills, surrounded by picture postcard cottages. Tear yourself away from the remote setting to step into a low beamed and log fired bar featuring an impishly accurate cartoon of one of the regulars (who may well be sitting there with pipe and pint). Invitingly furnished dining rooms in deep olive tones lead off from here; another rustic bar keeps them company and the atmosphere carries over from here. Suppliers knock at the front door with their produce, so there's no shortage of local inspiration: chicken with bacon lardons, cider, cream and local apple brandy is a satisfying blend of West Country flavours.

Food serving times:
Monday-Sunday:
12pm-2pm, 7pm-9pm
Closed 25 December
Prices:
Meals: a la carte 16.95/26.50
12 rooms: 55.00/85.00

Typical Dishes
Smoked haddock and poached egg
Lamb in filo pastry, with roast garlic
Treacle tart

5mi South of Dunster by A396.
Parking

Mells

076 **Talbot Inn**

Selwood St, Mells BA11 3PN

Tel.: (01373) 812254 - Fax: (01373) 813599
e-mail: roger@talbotinn.com - Website: www.talbotinn.com

Butcombe, London Pride, Smiles

Seamlessly blending in with homes along the same street, this utterly charming 15C stone-built coaching inn boasts an immediate impact with its cobbled courtyard containing Provençal style French chairs and vine-covered pergola. The effect continues in a pleasant, intimate main bar, where dried hops cling to the beams and green candles flicker in old wine bottles. Here, indulge in hearty, traditional bar meals with daily changing blackboard dishes or a more serious dinner menu with fish specials from Brixham. You can also eat in a large tythe barn, its ancient character recently enhanced by a mural depicting life in Mells through the ages. Bright, pretty, individually appointed bedrooms make a night's stopover worthwhile.

Food serving times:
Monday-Sunday:
12pm-2.30pm, 6.45pm-11pm
Closed 25-26 December, 1 January and Bank Holiday Mondays
Prices:
Meals: a la carte 20.40/27.75
🛏 **8 rooms:** 55.00/125.00

Typical Dishes

Mussels in white wine

Roast duck, braised red cabbage

White chocolate cheesecake

4mi West of Frome.
Parking

Midford

077 Hope and Anchor

Midford BA2 7DD

Tel.: (01225) 832296 - Fax: (01225) 832296
Website: www.hopeandanchormidford.co.uk

 VISA **MC**

 Butcombe, Bass, Sharpes Cornish Coaster, Otter Best, Funky Monkey and 3 Bath ales offered

Finding somewhere to eat and drink in Bath in the height of the tourist season can be a problem, but this part 18C inn may, in its own cosy little way, provide the answer. It's only four and a bit miles away, but offers its own package of charm, character – and creepers running up the walls. Once you've climbed the steep brick steps from the car park, you arrive at a pleasantly enclosed rear terrace, the ideal spot to shake off post-Bath fatigue. Inside is warm, friendly and snug; the bar boasts an impressive selection of real ales. Sit on tapestry cushions and eat roast veal chop with sauté potatoes or lamb cutlets and new potatoes; polish off the same traditional dishes in the dining room, only this time in much older, more formal surroundings. Friendly, efficient young staff are always on their toes but, thankfully, off yours.

Food serving times:
Monday-Saturday:
12pm-2pm, 6pm-9.30pm
Sunday: 12pm-9pm
Closed 25-26 December
Booking esssential
Prices:
Meals: a la carte 15.00/21.00

Typical Dishes
Smoked duck on Chinese leaves

Venison with sloe gin and blueberries

Baileys cheesecake

4.5mi South of Bath by A367 on B3110. Private parking, access to rear terrace by very steep steps. Parking

Monksilver

078 **Notley Arms**

Monksilver TA44 JB

Tel.: (01984) 656217

 VISA ① ⑩ JCB

 Smiles Best, Wadworth 6X, Exmoor Ale

A corkscrew drive through the hills to this engagingly situated pub on the edge of Exmoor is effort well rewarded. The Notley's roughly textured exterior finds reflection in nearby cottages of chocolate-box charm, while inside, the subtly lit bar-cum-dining room is calm, down-to-earth and immediately likeable. A ticking clock whiles away time above the log fire; candles and seasonal fresh flowers lend a pretty touch to the wooden tables. Unfussy, keenly priced meals, from filled pittas up to full dinners, show real confidence in the quality of Brendon Hills suppliers: there's no fried food to be found here. You can expect home-made pasta or savoury steamed puddings; ostrich, too, from a local farm, reflects the owner's South African origins. Afterwards, indulge in delicious fruit crumbles and locally churned ice-cream.

Food serving times:
Monday-Sunday:
    12pm-2pm, 7pm-9pm
Closed 25 December
Bookings not accepted
Prices:
Meals: a la carte 15.00/20.00

Typical Dishes

Home-made soup

Fresh salmon fishcakes

Treacle tart

3mi South of Williton on B3188.
Parking

Montacute

079 Phelips Arms

The Borough, Montacute TA15 6XB

Tel.: (01935) 822557 - Fax: (01935) 822557
Website: www.phelipsarms.co.uk

 VISA AE MC

🍺 *Palmers Copper Ale, IPA and Zoo*

Montacute derives most of its fame from the stirring Montacute House, owned by the National Trust, but this attractive part-17C sand coloured inn provides another reason to turn off the A303. It's a good, traditional pub with a light modern makeover: refurbishment in 2004 gave the owner the chance to add his own photos and paintings to the walls. Bright lights and swirly carpet are offset with dark wood tables and chairs given a modern lift by bright red and blue curtains and cushions. The contemporary touches carry over to the cooking, which boasts some interesting, eclectic choices. Fresh dishes range from homemade burgers and chips to scallops with sweet chilli and crème fraiche, or monkfish with crab spring roll and Thai dressing. There's also a tapas menu and homemade pickles and chutneys are displayed at the bar.

Food serving times:
Sunday-Monday:
12pm-2.30pm
Tuesday-Saturday:
12pm-2.30pm, 7pm-9pm
Closed 25 December
Prices:
Meals: a la carte 20.25/31.75
🛏 **4 rooms:** 45.00/70.00

Typical Dishes

Dorset crab, mango and ginger

Lemon sole and salmon paupiette

Treacle pudding

5mi West of Yeovil by A3088. Public parking in the square opposite

Stanton Wick

080 **Carpenters Arms**

Stanton Wick BS39 4BX

Tel.: (01761) 490202 - Fax: (01761) 490763
e-mail: carpenters@buccaneer.co.uk - Website: www.the-carpenters-arms.co.uk

 ⟱ 🍷 ⤢room 🍽 **VISA** **AE** **M⊙**

Bass, Butcombe, Wadworth 6X, Courage

Hard to believe, judging by its 21C ambience, but the Carpenters Arms is actually a group of converted miners' cottages. Now it glows with a pubby contentment, typified by terracotta carpeting, candles in wine bottles, built-in wall seats and, of course, the original exposed stone walls. A big log fire roars in winter. Its long, low exterior is offset with bright flowers and the tranquility of the surrounding countryside. For diners, a snug inner "parlour" awaits with fresh flowers on the tables and beams above. Modern cooking prevails, proof of popularity confirmed by the number of tables taken. Typical dishes include Cajun chicken with minted yoghurt, Thai monkfish curry, or roast duck breast and baby spinach with thyme and sherry vinegar jus. Upstairs: sizable, pine furnished bedrooms in subtle floral patterns.

Food serving times:
Monday-Saturday:
12pm-2pm, 7pm-10pm
Sunday: 12pm-2.30pm,
7pm-9pm
Closed dinner 25-26 December
Prices:
Meals: a la carte 20.00/26.00
🛏 **12 rooms:** 64.50/89.50

9mi South of Bristol by A37 off A368.
Parking

Typical Dishes

Warm smoked duck, rocket salad

Trout fillets, lemon and chive butter

Rosemary crème brûlée

Triscombe

081 Blue Ball Inn

Triscombe TA4 3HE
Tel.: (01984) 618242 - Fax: (01984) 618371

 🍺 Cotleigh Tawny, Exmoor Gold, Stag, HSD, Tribute, Otter, Butcombe Gold

A walk in the gorgeous Quantocks means sustenance along the way, so arm yourself with a map and pitch up at the Blue Ball in good time for lunch. It's a wonderfully inviting place - long and low and sloping on three levels: you can't go far wrong with a 15C thatched and stone-built former stables. There are fires on each level and beech partitions. A central bar leads to two dining areas where the menus are imaginative, wide ranging and full of local ingredients. Hungry ramblers can get chunky baguettes at lunchtime; more serious diners can feast on Spanish style lamb and aïoli; wild bass with slow roast tomatoes, rosemary and garlic, or duck breast and confit leg, onion marmalade and spiced orange butter.

Food serving times:
Monday-Sunday:
12pm-2pm, 7pm-9pm
Closed 25 December, dinner 26 December and dinner 1 January
(booking essential)
Prices:
Meals: a la carte 20.00/32.00

Typical Dishes

Asparagus

Rabbit with lemongrass

Chocolate and pistachio dessert

4.5mi North of Bishops Lydeard by A358..
Parking

Winsford

082 Royal Oak Inn

Exmoor National Park, Winsford TA24 7JE

Tel.: (01643) 851455 - Fax: (01643) 851009
e-mail: enquiries@royaloak-somerset.co.uk - Website: www.royaloak-somerset.co.uk

Butcombe, Brakspear

Facing the shaded green and its trim cottages, the old Royal Oak, its thatched roof turned and folded, stands at the heart of Winsford, a charming village best known for its little interlacing streams and its old packhorse bridge across the River Exe. Inside the pub, one cosy lounge leads into another, their original rural style proudly preserved, to the delight of visitors from out of town; cushioned benches are grouped to form intimate little booths. Out-and-out English cooking seems right at home here, and a no-nonsense menu sticks to the classics, from lunchtime pies and sandwiches in the bar to generous plates of steak and kidney pudding with tasty rhubarb crumble and cream to follow. After lunch, Exmoor beckons, with mile upon mile of heather upland and wooded valleys to be explored.

Food serving times:
Monday-Sunday:
11.30am-2pm, 7pm-9.30p,
Prices:
Meals: a la carte 17.50/25.00
14 rooms: 136.00/160.00

5mi North of Dulverton by B3223.
Opposite the village green. Parking

Typical Dishes

Prawn cocktail

Pork tenderloin, garlic cream sauce

Crème caramel

Axford

083 Red Lion Inn

Axford SN8 2HA

Tel.: (01672) 520271 - Fax: (01672) 521011
e-mail: indo@redlionaxford.com - Website: www.redlionaxford.com

Hook Norton Best, Fuller's London Pride and guest ales

This brick-and-flint inn of early 19C pedigree immediately impresses as a warm and welcoming place. The top area is a lovely lounge bar with roaring fire and a gaggle of contented smokers, and there are fresh flowers on the main bar. Throughout the remainder of the inn a wide range of pictures by local artists is on sale. The blackboard choice of dishes is split into starters, mains and fish and are, largely speaking, from a traditional base. They're served in either the neatly kept dining room, full of old and new silver and china jostling for attention, or conservatory, where tankards hang beseechingly from the ceiling. There's one more blackboard, announcing wines by the glass, and when the scoffing and quaffing are done, diners are invited to fill in a card and be kept informed on future menus and events.

Food serving times:
Monday-Sunday:
12pm-2pm, 7pm-9pm
Prices:
Meals: a la carte 20.00/40.00

Typical Dishes

Tuna, mango and lime

Lamb on sweet potato mash

Raspberry cheesecake

4mi East of Marlborough on Mildenhall Rd. Parking

Codford St Mary

084 George

High St, Codford St Mary BA12 0NG
Tel.: (01985) 850270

  ⇖room **VISA** **MC** **JCB**

Ringwood Best, Butcombe Best, Hook Norton

The wild expanse of Salisbury Plain stretches away from this whitewashed 18C pub-hotel in a pretty village. Culture prevails in the Woolstone Theatre opposite; The George, meanwhile, makes a successful appeal to other senses. A charming refurbishment over the course of 2004 created an inviting bar area: whet the appetite by relaxing with a drink and a magazine in the lounge before heading to the restaurant where "pubby" style lunch menus give way to a concise, daily changing evening menu that uses fresh ingredients to good effect: try, perhaps, Black Forest ham, Parmesan crisp and white truffle oil for starters, followed by black bream and lobster ravioli with asparagus and crab reduction. If thoughts of the dark Plain are too much to contemplate at night, stay in one of their clean, simple bedrooms.

Food serving times:
Monday: 12pm-2pm, 7pm-9.30pm
Wednesday-Sunday:
    12pm-2pm, 7pm-9.30pm
Prices:
Meals: a la carte 22.00/35.00
⇔ **3 rooms:** 45.00/65.00

Typical Dishes

Scallops, lime vinaigrette

Duck, mushroom risotto, raspberry jus

Passion fruit soufflé

7mi Southeast of Warminster by B3414 off A36.
Parking

Corsley

085 Cross Keys

Lyes Green, Corsley BA12 7PB
Tel.: (01373) 832406 - Fax: (01373) 832934
Website: www.crosskeysatcorsley.com

 VISA **MC** **JCB**

 Henry's IPA, Wadworth 6X, Summersault plus guest beers

A typically rural pub in a typically rural area: all the credentials for a satisfying experience in deepest Wiltshire. The owners of this charming old pub go out of their way to create a warm, relaxed feel, from the bright, colourful walls filled with local photos and prints, to the friendly, even lightly jokey service. Choose between dining areas either embellished by fresh flowers or tubby candles. Either way you'll eat at scrubbed tables from an extensive menu featured on three blackboards. Dishes are keenly priced, freshly prepared, and very tasty, carefully utilising local supplies and suppliers. Try something from the notable fish range.

Food serving times:
Monday-Saturday:
12pm-2.15pm, 7pm-9.30pm
Sunday: 12pm-2.15pm,
7.15pm-9pm
Restricted opening Christmas
Prices:
Meals: a la carte 10.50/27.75

Typical Dishes

Scallops, bacon and mushrooms

Sea bass, raspberry and ginger dressing

Deep fried ice cream

5mi North West of Warminster by A362. Parking

Heytesbury

086 **Angel Inn**
High St, Heytesbury BA12 0ED

Tel.: (01985) 840330 - Fax: (01985) 840931
e-mail: admin@theangelheytesbury.co.uk - Website: www.theangelheytesbury.co.uk

Ruddles County, Moorland Original, Greene King IPA

In a pretty village on the edge of Salisbury Plain stands this attractive roadside 17C inn. Its appeal continues to grow as improvements reach completion: there's now a delightful courtyard terrace and stylish, refurbished ground floor, boasting a cosy lounge with soft leather tub seats, roaring fire, and, further along, snug though spacious bar. To one side, an elegant, contemporary restaurant completes the picture. Modern pub classics go down well at lunch, as you would expect but, in the evening, things move on with a particularly interesting a la carte that's well prepared and cooked with precision. Staying overnight is a wise move here. Cosy, well-appointed bedrooms have been undergoing refurbishment.

Food serving times:
Monday-Sunday:
   12pm-2.30pm, 7pm-9.30pm
Closed dinner 25 December
Prices:
Meals: a la carte 12.00/35.00
8 rooms: 65.00/75.00

Typical Dishes

Home-cured salmon

Pork fillet, black pudding croquette

Iced passion fruit parfait

4mi Southeast of Warminster by B3414.
Parking

Hindon

087 Angel Inn

Angel Lane, Hindon SP3 6DJ

Tel.: (01747) 820696 - Fax: (01747) 820054
e-mail: info@theangelathindon.co.uk - Website: www.theangelathindon.co.uk

Ringwood, Charles Wells Bombardier, Wadworth 6X

This characterful and historic former coaching inn is set in a charming village surrounded by rolling countryside. All the required elements for a classy Georgian hostelry are in place: bar with chunky wood tables, logs burning in the inglenook, plush comfy sofas, buzzy atmosphere. The restaurant, which leads off from here, is lent character by the wistful presence of candles, fresh flowers and framed local pictures on the wall. Dine in the modern style: shallot tarte Tatin with balsamic and rocquette salad; rolled pheasant terrine with apple, date and banana chutney; chump of lamb, rosemary and potato gnocchi with red wine jus, carrots and coriander. Puddings are equally rewarding, particularly the spiced Bramley apple crème brûlée with fresh fig and pomegranate. Cosy rooms add a final lustre.

Food serving times:
Monday-Saturday:
  12pm-2.30pm, 7pm-9.30pm
Sunday: 12pm-2.30pm
Closed 25 December
Prices:
Meals: a la carte 15.00/26.00
7 rooms: 75.00/85.00

Typical Dishes

Sardines, garlic, thyme and lemon

Warm poached salmon salad

Sticky toffee pudding

9.5mi South of Warminster by A350. Parking

Holt

088 Tollgate Inn

Ham Green, Holt BA14 6PX

Tel.: (01225) 782326 - Fax: (01225) 782805
e-mail: alison@tollgateholt.co.uk - Website: www.tollgateholt.co.uk

    VISA MC

A selection of guest ales offered

The locals of Holt have made this hearty old pub of Bath stone a wonderfully friendly place to be. Conviviality stretches across all areas, aided and abetted by strategically placed sofas and a log-burning stove. No one seems in a rush as they linger over newspapers and magazines. If and when you decide to eat you have a choice of two venues. A cosy room adjacent to the bar offers a traditional feel, while upstairs, in a former chapel, is a more formal restaurant with original chapel windows and lofty timbers. Local ingredients are proudly advertised on the menus, and dishes exhibit distinctly modern overtures. Bedrooms have a more traditional outlook, facing a paddock or old weavers' cottages.

Food serving times:
Tuesday-Saturday:
    12pm-2pm, 7pm-9pm
Sunday: 12pm-2pm
Closed first week January
Prices:
Meals: 11.95 and a la carte
20.00/28.50
4 rooms: 50.00/95.00

Typical Dishes

Pan fried foie gras on brioche

Beef Wellington

Hot banana bread, ice cream

3.25mi North of Trowbridge by B3106 off B3105.
Parking

Marden

089 The Millstream

Marden SN10 3RH

Tel.: (01380) 848308 - Fax: (01380) 848337
e-mail: mill.stream@virgin.net - Website: www.the-millstream.co.uk

   VISA

Wadworths JCB, 6X, Henrys IPA, Summersault

Look across the delightful garden to the river Avon from this recently enlarged, Vale of Pewsey pub. The pastoral delights to be enjoyed here are timeless; inside an appealing refurbishment has taken place: champagne is served by the glass in a bar that stays open all day. This old pub's recent makeover has nevertheless left it with much original character: pale beams, thick wattle walls in a mustard palette, log burners and antiques enliven the open-plan section. There are several dining areas, with vertical beams acting as dividers. Tables are in antique wood but the menus are of more recent vintage: much of the local produce is organic and fish is fresh from Looe. There's an excellent wine list; if you need help, the bubbly owner is only too keen to help.

Food serving times:
Monday-Thursday:
12pm-3pm, 7pm-9.30pm
Friday-Saturday:
12pm-3pm, 7pm-10pm
Sunday: 12pm-5pm
Closed 25 December and
Sunday dinner
Prices:
Meals: 25.00/35.00 and a la carte 17.00/30.00

Typical Dishes

Chicken tahini, falafel

Chargrilled pork chop, minted pea purée

Strawberry terrine

5.5mi Southeast of Devizes by A342.
Parking

Norton

090 Vine Tree

Foxley Road, Norton SN16 0JP

Tel.: (01666) 837654 - Fax: (01666) 838003

e-mail: tiggi@thevinetree.co.uk - Website: www.thevinetree.co.uk

Butcombe, Archers Village, St Austell Tribute, Wychwood Fiddlers Elbow, Hook Norton, Bath Ales Gem

Westonbirt Arboretum may be just up the road, but this lovely rural pub holds a certain al fresco secret too – an extensive terrace and spacious garden where summer afternoons drift by in the company of flower-filled urns and a trickling fountain. Step inside and, despite the draw of the sunshine, you might just decide that you want to stay put. It's an interior of low beams, deep red walls, scrubbed wooden tables and a bar that sells a fine selection of real ales and wines. There are four snug dining areas, too, with one more hidden away upstairs. Weekly changing menus boast dishes influenced by the seasons and the location; the cooking is confident and appealing.

Food serving times:
Monday-Thursday:
  12pm-2.30pm, 7pm-9.30pm
Friday-Saturday:
  12pm-2.30pm, 7pm-10pm
Sunday: 12pm-2.30pm,
                7pm-9.30pm

Closed 25 Deember

Prices:
Meals: a la carte 18.95/35.00
4 rooms: 45.00/85.00

Typical Dishes

Tea-smoked quail with foie gras

Turbot steak, pea purée

Peaches in Sauternes

3mi Southwest of Malmesbury.
Parking

Nunton

091 **Radnor Arms**

Nunton SP5 4HS
Tel.: (01722) 329722

  VISA

 Badger Best, Tanglefoot, Firsty Ferret

Over the last 250 years this homely inn in local brick has served Nunton well as a village butcher's, bakery and brewhouse, as well as the community watering-hole; now it's a well-liked, personally run drinking and dining pub, and the neighbours, and visitors, are no less appreciative. Simply styled inside, what really marks the place out is the warm-heartedness that comes across in the personal service, and the welcome as you walk to the bar, but the fortifying home cooking is just as generous: tasty asparagus accompanies a pile of crayfish tails, filling plates of liver and onions come with a mound of mash and comforting "nostalgia puds" round off the meal.

Food serving times:
Monday-Sunday:
    12pm-2pm, 7pm-9pm
Prices:
Meals: a la carte 16.95/25.00

Typical Dishes

Scallops with black pudding

Roast marinated lamb

Vanilla cheesecake

2.5mi South of Salisbury by A338.

Ramsbury

 The Bell

The Square, Ramsbury SN8 2PE

Tel.: (01672) 520230 - Fax: (01672) 520832
e-mail: info@thebellransbury.com - Website: www.thebellramsbury.com

VISA **MC**

Wadworth IPA, 6X, Bass

If this handsome period pub has a new lease of life, it's probably thanks to the new leaseholder. Though he's happiest on the first tee or the rugby touchline, behind the bar comes a close second, and he's found time to direct a renovation that feels true to the origins of the place. One half is given over to dining, the other, filled with light from the bow window, matches old pew seats with framed black and white photos; even with an encouraging crowd of regular drinkers and diners, it feels pleasantly spacious. An abbreviated lunch menu manages to offer decent variety, from pints of prawns and gazpacho to haddock risotto or sausage and mash, and is just as well-presented as the evening list, which introduces a few surprises: when was the last time you saw lamb sweetbreads on a pub menu? Don't forget the shaded garden in hot weather.

Food serving times:
Monday-Saturday:
 12pm-2.30pm, 7pm-9.30pm
Sunday: 12pm-2.30pm
Prices:
Meals: 14.00/28.00

Typical Dishes

Foie gras and chicken livers

Duck leg, niçoise salad

Mango crème brûlée

4.5mi Northwest of Hungerford by B4192.
Parking

Rowde

093 George & Dragon

High Street, Rowde SN10 2PN
Tel.: (01380) 723053 - Fax: (01380) 724738
e-mail: gd-rowde@lineone.net

 ✆ ⤢ *VISA* Ⓜ©

Butcombe, Milk Street Brewery

The lazy waters of the nearby Kennet and Avon Canal create the ideal mood for a visit to this divinely characterful pub in the Vale of Pewsey. Its epicentre is a gorgeous stone fireplace crackling heartily in the darker months. The low timbered ceiling just adds to the feeling of rich warmth; outside, summer sunshine can be enjoyed in a smart little garden. There are two areas in which to dine - adjacent to the fire or in a non-smoking dining room - but either way, you can't go wrong. Menus place the emphasis on seafood with plenty of daily changing specials, and the cooking is simple, robust and classic, its keen pricing evidenced by a Michelin Bib Gourmand. As well as good value menus, you can also rely on polite, friendly service.

Food serving times:
Tuesday-Saturday:
    12pm-2pm, 7pm-9pm
Closed 25 December and 1 January
- Seafood - (booking essential)

Prices:
Meals: 13.50 and a la carte 20.00/35.00

Typical Dishes
Warm scallops and bacon salad

Pan fried monkfish, couscous salad

Iced lime soufflé

2mi Northwest of Devizes by A361 on A342..
Parking

Semington

094 **Lamb on the Strand**

99 The Strand, Semington BA14 6LL

Tel.: (01380) 870263 - Fax: (01380) 871203

Butcombe Bitter, Ringwood Best and guest ales

This ivy clad, red brick inn is a rather diverting attraction on the busy road out of Trowbridge. It has a characterful feel, its 18C origins typified by the low beams; a woodburner and log fire adds to the pleasing ambience. A series of pleasantly furnished rooms affords lots of space to relax with a pint of real ale or a glass of wine from the landlord's carefully selected list. If the weather's good, eat outside in the attractive walled garden. Menus are traditional and extensive; consistently fresh food is served with abundant use of local produce: the mouth-watering cheese pudding is a sure-fire hit. Service is invariably efficient, friendly and helpful.

Food serving times:
Monday-Saturday:
12pm-2pm, 6.30pm-9pm
Sunday: 12pm-2pm
Closed 25-26 December and 1 January
(booking essential)
Prices:
Meals: a la carte 16.25/19.00

Typical Dishes

Grilled figs with chorizo

Smoked chicken, avocado pear and bacon

Chocolate mousse cake

2.5mi Northeast of Trowbridge by A361.
Parking

Upton Scudamore

095 **Angel Inn**

Upton Scudamore BA12 0AG

Tel.: (01985) 213225 - Fax: (01985) 213225
e-mail: theangelinn-uptonscudamore@btopenworld.com - Website: www.theangelinn-wiltshire.co.uk

   VISA

Wadworth 6X, Butcombe and 1 guest ale

To the east the vast expanses of Salisbury Plain offer a rather forbidding prospect, but in this cosy 16C inn all is relaxed and cheerful. The patrons see to that, running the Angel in their own personalised and dedicated way; the warm character of the establishment all adds to the experience. There's a lovely, sunny rear terrace with barbeque for summer days, but the interior's no less inviting, rustic charm seamlessly linked to rural setting. Scrubbed wooden floors, cosy sofas and candlelight will make you want to linger. Fine cooking will have much the same effect. Appealing, modern dishes are supplemented by blackboard fish specials: try, perhaps, roast scallops with chilli jam followed by roast monkfish with spinach and new potatoes. Simple but comfortable rooms are invariably spotless.

Food serving times:
Monday-Sunday:
  12pm-2pm, 7pm-9.30pm
Closed 25-26 December and 1 January
Prices:
Meals: a la carte 15.00/25.00
10 rooms: 60.00/78.00

Typical Dishes
Warm chicken, bacon and Brie salad

Grilled sea bass, crushed potatoes

Crème brûlée, oranges

2.5mi North of Warminster by A350. Parking

Whitley

096 Pear Tree Inn

Top Lane, Whitley SN12 8QX

Tel.: (01225) 709131 - Fax: (01225) 702276
e-mail: sales@peartreeinn.co.uk

Box Tunnel Vision, Stonehenge Pigswill, Palmers Copper, Bath Barnstormer

Though not far from Bath, visitors to this attractive Cotswold stone inn may be tempted to stay put once they've indulged what's on offer here. A pleasant front garden leads in to what can best be described as a stylish country dining pub and restaurant. Owners are keen to stress the amount of home produced food that goes into their menus: soups, sausages, bread, sorbets and ice cream are all made on the premises and Wiltshire suppliers provide game and meat. End results are a pleasing amalgam of traditional and modern dishes with a European accent. Staying overnight is a pleasure: bedrooms drip with contemporary style. There's impressive use of beautiful local oak and re-claimed barn doors; you'll also find top quality linen, the very best toiletries, and super-smart chrome fittings.

Food serving times:
Monday-Thursday:
    12pm-2pm, 6.30pm-9.30pm
Friday-Saturday:
    12pm-2pm, 6.30pm-10pm
Closed 25-26 December and 1 January
Prices:
Meals: 15.00/21.00 and a la carte 21.00/30.00
🛏 **8 rooms:** 75.00/100.00

Typical Dishes
Pigeon salad

Roast monkfish in Parma ham

Strawberry trifle, basil syrup

1.5mi Northwest of Melksham by A365 on B3353.
Parking

*I*n recent years, the restored Jewellery Quarter, Brindleyplace and Centenary Square, not to mention the shops and bars of Mailbox and the new Bullring, have brought revival and recognition to ever-evolving Birmingham. But not far from Britain's hard-wrought second city, Coalbrookdale, picturesque Ironbridge and the towns of The Potteries and The Black Country offer poignant reminders of the industries that made them and shaped their working way of life. Further afield, and further back in time, Warwick and world-famous Stratford span the centuries, while the reflections of Viking and Celtic art at Kilpeck Church look back to a more ancient past. Explore prosperous period towns like Ludlow and Lichfield, visit the cathedral cities of Hereford and Worcester or take in some of England's most captivating countryside, from the upper Wye to the lower Peaks, by way of Elgar's beloved Malverns and Housman's "blue remembered hills". The discoveries continue in the region's pubs and inns, with cider and orchard fruits from the Vale of Evesham, Herefordshire beef, Gloucester's well-known cheeses and, most famously of all, the Burton beers which transformed the Great British Pint over 200 years ago.

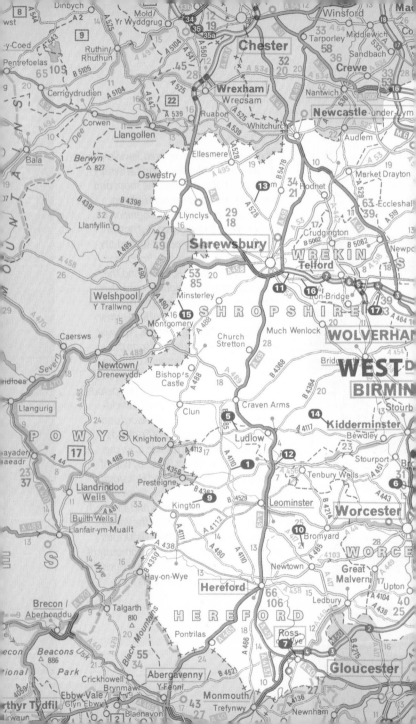

Aymestrey

001 **Riverside Inn**

Aymestrey HR6 9ST

Tel.: (01568) 708440 - Fax: (01568) 709058
e-mail: theriverside@btconnect.com - Website: www.theriversideinn.org

 VISA

 A selection of ales from Woods Brewery, Wye Valley Brewery

This aptly named 16C inn stands rather idyllically by a stone bridge over the river Lugg in a country setting of nearby castles and hill forts. Ludlow's not too far away, either. The imposing black and white timbered exterior gives a broad hint of what to expect inside, where, from a small central bar, three interconnecting rooms put on their rustic best with a display of rafters, stone walls, fresh flowers and hops. Menus are broadly English in design, and extremely local in content: fruit and vegetables are grown in the kitchen gardens. Dishes include baked fillet of halibut with spinach and prawn sauce or Herefordshire duck and wild mushroom sauce. Afterwards, walk along the Mortimer Trail and sleep in stylish bedrooms in the redesigned outbuildings.

Food serving times:
Monday-Sunday:
   12pm-2.15pm, 7pm-9.15pm
Closed 25 December
Prices:
Meals: a la carte 18.00/25.00
5 rooms: 40.00/85.00

Typical Dishes
Vodka cured trout, honey and mustard

Chicken stuffed with black pudding

Chocolate cheesecake

7mi Northwest of Leominster by A44, B4529, and B4360 on A4110
Situated on the banks of the River Lugg. Parking

Clent

002 Bell & Cross

Holy Cross, Clent DY9 9QL
Tel.: (01562) 730319 - Fax: (01562) 731733

    VISA Ⓜ©

Banks Bitter, Mild, Marstons Pedigree, Timothy Taylor, Hook Norton

A lovingly tended garden and a little terrace make this pretty, early-19C inn a natural choice for summer days, but it's far from just a fair-weather pub. Five charming rooms and a traditional tap room – with a listed bar, no less – are so cosy that you'll be tempted to linger over that last drink, and attentive young staff certainly make you feel welcome. A tasty seasonal menu, with blackboard specials, is devised in part by the England football team's chef-by-appointment, who takes charge in the kitchen when not putting fire in the bellies of Sven's Men. Diners without a big match after lunch should let the training regime slide and treat themselves to sea bass with asparagus risotto or tarte Tatin with Calvados crème fraiche.

Food serving times:
Monday-Sunday:
12pm-2pm, 6.30pm-9.30pm
Closed 25-26 December
Prices:
Meals: a la carte 18.50/26.50

Typical Dishes

Thai prawns, mango and pomegranate

Lamb, rosemary jus

Strawberry and mascarpone sable

1.5mi North of Belbroughton
Parking

Cutnall Green

003 ## The Chequers

Kidderminster Road, Cutnall Green WR9 0PJ
Tel.: (01299) 851292 - Fax: (01299) 851744

 Timothy Taylor Landlord, Hook Norton, Banks Bitter and regularly changing guest ales

This half-timbered roadside pub isn't too much to look at, but inside it's a different story. The bar boasts modern decor in traditional surroundings, typified by sandblasted pale beams, tiled floor and leather tub chairs. There's an adjacent, most welcoming Garden Room: lilac soft furnishings and a plush sofa, surrounded by hanging tankards. Richly coloured walls with wine-themed paintings invoke a modern country style. The pub's owner is Roger Narbert, who's chef to the England football team, but expect more than pasta or chicken: menus boast great choice from traditional favourites to up-to-the-minute and highly interesting. Service is invariably courteous, efficient and enthusiastic.

Food serving times:
Monday-Saturday:
  12pm-2pm, 6.30pm-9.15pm
Sunday: 12pm-2.30pm,
                      7pm-9pm
Closed 25 December, dinner 26 December, 31 December and dinner 1 January
Prices:
Meals: a la carte 15.00

Typical Dishes
Goat's cheese, spinach, red onion tart
Smoked haddock, poached egg
Sticky toffee pudding

3mi North of Droitwich Spa on A442. Parking

Dunhampton

004 Epic

Ombersley Rd, Dunhampton DY13 9SW

Tel.: (01905) 620000 - Fax: (01905) 621123
e-mail: epic.dunhampton@virgin.net - Website: www.epicbrasseries.com

 VISA AE M©

 Timothy Taylor Landlord, Marstons Pedigree

If ever an establishment was named with simple, pinpoint accuracy, then surely this is it. Epic, standing hard on a West Midlands A road, is a pub conversion of suitably large proportions. The spacious interior has a slightly retro ambience; the open-plan design allows for some banquette seating in a pleasingly simple, airy format of well-spaced wooden tables. There's an al fresco alternative enabled by a small garden and decking area. Choose from a menu that offers a balanced, varied selection of tried-and-tested favourites alongside sound contemporary dishes. Seasonal, fresh ingredients are used to good effect, and well-drilled staff offer a friendly and efficient service.

Food serving times:
Monday-Saturday:
  12pm-3pm, 6.30pm-9.30pm
Sunday: 12pm-3pm
Prices:
Meals: a la carte 25.00/35.00

Typical Dishes
Goat's cheese, tomato and shallots

Daube de Boeuf

Chocolate fondant, pistachio ice cream

1.75mi North of Ombersley by A449 (Southbound).
Parking

Leintwardine

005 **Jolly Frog**

The Todden, Leintwardine SY7 0LX

Tel.: (01547) 540298 - Fax: (01547) 540105
e-mail: jaynejollyfrog@aol.com - Website: www.jolly-frog.com

 VISA MC JCB

2 weekly changing guest beers

R un with personality and imagination, the Jolly Frog is the kind of place that rewards a little light curiosity, hidden around the next hedgerow bend in the gentle folds of Herefordshire. Once inside, you'll discover four cosy adjoining rooms with a fascinating collection of rustic bits and pieces, a library of over 850 cookery books and a small delicatessen, but the cuisine itself more than holds the attention, spanning a commendably well-priced table d'hôte menu, an extensive choice of shellfish and interesting specials-board diversions: enthusiastic staff take the time to put you in the picture and remain quick off the mark with smooth and effective service. Though less French than the name might imply, it is definitely part of "l'Angleterre profonde", intimate, relaxing and true to its surroundings.

Food serving times:
Tuesday-Sunday:
12pm-2.30pm, 6pm-10.30pm
Closed 25 December
- Seafood specialities -
Prices:
Meals: 12.95 and a la carte
15.00/25.30

Typical Dishes

Goat's cheese hash brown

Hake, butter bean and spinach stew

Trio de cafe

7mi West of Ludlow on A4113
Parking

Ombersley

006 Kings Arms

Main Rd, Ombersley WR9 0EW

Tel.: (01905) 620142 - Fax: (01905) 621084
e-mail: dgpendry@aol.com

 Banks Bitter, Marstons Pedigree, Everards Tiger and Adnams Broadside

This impressive black and white timbered pub owes its origins to the 15C, which has endowed it with much character. There are a whole array of snug corners, knick-knacks and curios, arranged over a large area beneath beamed ceilings. Dining is a relaxed, casual affair: the tables aren't set for eating, but the enthusiastic staff go into overdrive once you've ordered. The large menus cover a whole range of classic pub dishes with an extensive blackboard of daily specials that emphasise seafood. It's robust, rustic and tasty. A hearty meal might include the heart-warming homemade vegetable soup for starters, followed by an equally satisfying shepherd's pie.

Food serving times:
Monday-Sunday:
12.15pm-2.15pm,
6.15pm-10pm

Closed 25 December and dinner 31 January

Prices:
Meals: 9.95 (fixed price lunch) and a la carte 19.50/27.50

Typical Dishes

Asparagus hollandaise

Spring lamb cutlets, rosemary jus

Banana pancakes, toffee sauce

In the village centre
Parking

Ross-on-Wye

007 **The Lough Pool Inn**

Sellack, Ross-on-Wye HR9 6LX
Tel.: (01989) 730236 - Fax: (01989) 730462

 🍷 *VISA* Ⓜ©

John Smith Cask, Old Speckled Hen, Mutleys Mongrel, Wye Valley Bitter, Butty Bach

This black and white inn is in a wonderfully rural spot in Herefordshire, an ideal location for garden and terrace dining in the summer months. It's a solid traditional establishment with exposed stone, flag flooring and lots of space to wander around with a pint of local ale. No trouble in spotting the dining areas: they're painted bright yellow with red cedar-stained pine flooring. Menus change frequently, depending on ingredients. The excellent modern style of cooking has earned the Lough Pool a Michelin Bib Gourmand and good local produce is unerringly to the fore. Try, perhaps, smoked haddock and green herb tart for starters; mint and garlic marinated spring chicken with chorizo and leek risotto for main course. If room allows, finish with rum and vanilla pannacotta with shortbread.

Food serving times:
Monday-Sunday:
      12pm-2pm, 7pm-9pm
Closed Sunday dinner and Monday October-March
Prices:
Meals: a la carte 19.50/27.50

Typical Dishes
Goat's cheese soufflé, almond sauce

Beef and ale stew

Orange cake with clotted cream

3.25mi Northwest of Ross-on-Wye by B4260 and A49 on Hoarwithy rd Parking

Stoke Prior

008 Epic

68 Hanbury rd, Stoke Prior B60 4DN

Tel.: (01527) 871929 - Fax: (01527) 575647

e-mail: epic.bromsgrove@virgin.net - Website: www.epicbrasseries.com

     VISA **AE** **MC**

Hook Norton, Marston Pedigree and regular guest ales

The only remnants here of its days as a roadside pub are the tiled floor and odd rafter. Otherwise this stylish establishment has benefited greatly from a major facelift and extensions. At the centre, a large modern bar with comfy sofa lounge area. All around, an airy dining space with lots of glass, brick and wood, which has been cleverly worked into the modern design. The overall feel is one of effortless style, accentuated by comfortable seating at smart wood tables with good accessories. Menus are large and dominated by popular modern classics at reasonable prices: a Michelin Bib Gourmand is proof positive on that score. Service is efficient from staff who are used to being busy.

Food serving times:
Monday-Saturday:
12pm-3pm, 6.30pm-9.30pm
Sunday: 12pm-3pm
Prices:
Meals: a la carte 25.00/32.00

Typical Dishes
Chicken liver parfait
Smoked haddock, bubble and squeak
Chocolate fondant, pistachio ice cream

2.25mi Southwest of Bromsgrove by A38 on B4091
Parking

Titley

009 **Stagg Inn**

Titley HR5 3RL
Tel.: (01544) 230221 - Fax: (01544) 231390
e-mail: reservations@thestagg.co.uk - Website: www.thestagg.co.uk

 VISA

 Timothy Taylor Landlord, Hobsons Best Bitter, Town Cider, Old Henry

A carefully cultivated network of local suppliers, a real regard for quality and exemplary belief in value for money have made this one of Britain's Michelin star-rated pubs. The menu changes every five or six weeks, but the cooking itself, assured and original with a hint of classic French flair, is a model of consistency, allowing fresh, natural flavours to shine through. Sweet, glistening scallops are balanced by pea purée, bacon and a dab of mint oil, crisp rösti and buttery leeks make a deliciously simple foil to tender, marjoram-stuffed pork tenderloin, and peaches poached in muscat need only a light parfait to accompany them. Comfortable, softly lit surroundings and pleasant, intelligent service contribute to a really memorable experience. Two rooms above the pub, and more in the part-Georgian vicarage down the road.

Food serving times:
Monday-Saturday:
  12pm-2pm, 6.30pm-9.30pm
Sunday: 12pm-2pm
Closed first 2 weeks
November, 25-26 December
and Bank Holiday Mondays
Closed Tuesday - (set meal
Saturday dinner and Sunday
lunch)
Prices:
Meals: 13.90 and a la carte
22.00/25.00
 5 rooms: 50.00/110.00

Typical Dishes

*Scallops, curried celeriac
purée*

*Lamb, sweetbreads, rosemary
and garlic*

Lemon tart

3.5mi Northeast of Kington on B4355
Parking

Ullingswick

010 Three Crowns Inn

Bleak Acre, Ullingswick HR1 3JQ

Tel.: (01432) 820279 - Fax: (0800) 515338
e-mail: info@threecrownsinn.com - Website: www.threecrownsinn.com

 Hobsons Best and a selection of guest ales from Wye Valley

On one of Herefordshire's many quiet roads stands this difficult-to-miss red brick, timbered establishment blending in perfectly with its rural setting. You step straight into a wonderfully beamed bar boasting exposed brickwork and a cosy wood counter with benches and pews strewn around. Hops dangle from the rafters, sepia prints hang on the walls: all in all it's thoroughly pleasant and deserving of its loyal local following. The food's quality and keen pricing has earned a Michelin Bib Gourmand – it has a rustic, robust quality and tasty, local produce is proudly in evidence, not least vegetables and herbs from the kitchen garden. The type of dish that might whet your appetite is pork cutlet with cider sauce; Scrumpy Jack sausages, mash and onion gravy; or a delectably strong flavoured, though light and fluffy Cheddar cheese soufflé.

Food serving times:
Tuesday-Sunday:
   12pm-2.30pm, 7pm-9.30pm
Closed 2 weeks Christmas
Prices:
Meals: 12.95 (fixed price lunch) and a la carte 12.95/24.75

Typical Dishes

Smoked salmon

Lamb, persillade crust, lavender jus

Muscat wine caramel, Armagnac prunes

1.25mi East
Parking

Atcham

011 The Mytton and Mermaid

Atcham SY5 6QG

Tel.: (01743) 761220 - Fax: (01743) 761292
e-mail: admin@myttonandmermaid.co.uk - Website: www.myttonandmermaid.co.uk

 Woods Shropshire Lad, Ruddles, Salopian Icon

This redbrick, ivy-clad pub was built in 1735 and stands proudly on the banks of the Severn, opposite the National Trust's Attingham Park. The quirky bar is named after local 19C squire Mad Jack Mytton, who'd appreciate the warm, friendly atmosphere that prevails here. There's a log fire, sofa and large tables where you can linger over lunch or dinner. The easy-going restaurant – which has a separate identity but is really in the same room – sports smart, polished tables and menus full of good, traditional dishes that change with the seasons. The relaxed style carries over into a pleasant riverside drawing room and a series of stylish, individually decorated bedrooms with antique and modern furniture.

Food serving times:
Monday-Sunday:
12pm-2.30pm, 5.30pm-10pm
Closed 25 December
Prices:
Meals: 27.50 and a la carte
21.00/28.00
🛏 **20 rooms:** 60.00/135.00

Typical Dishes

Gazpacho
Lobster tart, citrus salad
Iced raspberry parfait

3mi Southeast of Shrewsbury by
A5064 on B4380
Parking

Brimfield

012 Roebuck Inn

Brimfield SY8 4NE

Tel.: (01584) 711230 - Fax: (01584) 711654
e-mail: peter@theroebuckinn.com - Website: www.roebuckinn.com

   VISA **MC**

 Tetley Cask, Woods Parish and weekly changing guest ale from local microbreweries

It takes something special in the gastronomic stakes to be especially noticed in the Ludlow area, and the Roebuck comes up with the goods – or, rather, the inventive menus. Slap bang in the middle of an attractive village just south of the famous town, it's every inch the epitome of a classic country pub, filled with rustic objects, curios and polished older wood furniture over four cheery rooms. A spick-and-span dining room has felt the benefits of tender loving care. Dishes are likewise freshly inspired: fillet of wild venison on celeriac rösti with a sloe gin and bay sauce; monkfish layered with roasted peppers and basil, wrapped in Parma ham; or the "famous fish pie" served very hot. Sleep overnight in homely bedrooms.

Food serving times:
Monday-Sunday:
11.30pm-3pm,
6.30pm-9.30pm
Closed 25-26 December
Prices:
Meals: a la carte 14.45/27.95
3 rooms: 45.00/70.00

Typical Dishes

Smoked fish ravioli

Steamed fillet of sole

Prune and Armagnac sponge pudding

4.25mi South of Ludlow by B4361 and A49

Burlton

013 Burlton Inn

Burlton SY4 5TB
Tel.: (01939) 270284 - Fax: (01939) 270204
e-mail: bean@burltoninn.co.uk - Website: www.burltoninn.co.uk

 Banks House Beer and 3 guest ales

Not the prettiest of buildings, but this 18C Shropshire stalwart knows how to pack 'em in – so much so that early in 2004 some bigger, better adjustments and refurbishments gave the old place more room to breathe. Nothing of the buzzy, bustling atmosphere has been lost, though. The compact, raftered bar crackles along in sympathy with the log fire, and the food – like the real ale generously stocked – goes down a treat, oiled by smooth service from a polite, friendly crew. It's rustic food, home-cooked and fresh. Just the names are enough to make your mouth water: steak, kidney and beer pie; asparagus and pecorino ravioli; veal loin chops topped with Dijon mustard; Tuscan pork. To the rear, smart bedrooms complete the picture – make sure you don't miss out on the first rate breakfasts.

Food serving times:
Monday-Sunday:
 12pm-2pm, 6.30pm-9.45pm
**Closed 25-26 December,
1 January and lunch Bank
Holiday Monday**
Prices:
Meals: a la carte 16.00/27.45
🛏 **6 rooms:** 50.00/80.00

Typical Dishes

Crab and asparagus tartlet
Honey glazed chicken breast
Chocolate rum slice

8mi Northwest of Shrewsbury on A528
Parking

Hopton Wafers

014 The Crown Inn

Hopton Wafers DY14 0NB

Tel.: (01299) 270372 - Fax: (01299) 271127
Website: www.crownathopton.co.uk

     VISA **AE** **MC**

 Hobsons Best, Timothy Taylor Landlord, Woods Parish

Being so close to a dining hotspot like Ludlow, you'd expect good food to go with the territory. So it proves with this handsome, foliage-clad, 16C one-time coaching inn, surrounded by some of middle England's finest countryside, and not too distant from the historically important Ironbridge. Spacious gardens, overlooking a duck pond and great for summer dining, lead up to a timbered bar with inglenook fireplace, the taproom bright with flowers and wall paintings. There are two places to eat: the bar or more formal dining room. Both offer an extensive and rewarding choice of traditional dishes, well-prepared and sourced with finest Shropshire dale produce. Sleep off your indulgences in very pleasant bedrooms featuring most modern comforts

Food serving times:
Monday-Sunday:
12pm-2.30pm,
6.30pm-9.30pm
(bar meals Sunday, Monday and lunch)
Prices:
Meals: a la carte 12.00/25.00
🛏 **7 rooms:** 49.50/80.00

Typical Dishes

Scallops on black pudding

Lamb shank in red wine

Saffron poached pears

Between Cleobury Mortimer and Ludlow on A4117
Parking

Marton

015 **The Sun Inn**

Marton SY21 8JP
Tel.: (01938) 561211

VISA **MC** *JCB*

Hobsons Best

A real family-run place, the simply styled Sun makes a creditable – and pretty successful – effort to be all things to this quiet Marches village, with dartboard, pool table and light snacks in a cosy front bar and a reassuringly homely dining room with neat linen-clad tables and floral patterns. The Shropshire-bred chef makes a point of using local ingredients and the modern country cooking, nourishing and enjoyable, has a real flavour of the season to it: on crisp autumn evenings, the daily menus might offer cream of potato and leek soup followed by hare with braised cabbage. Genial service from the owners helps things along nicely.

Food serving times:
Tuesday: 7pm-9pm
Wednesday-Saturday:
            12pm-2pm, 7pm-9pm
Sunday: 12pm-2pm
(booking essential)

Prices:
Meals: 16.00 (fixed price lunch) and a la carte 16.50/30.00

Typical Dishes

Pike sausage, creamed potatoes

Roast loin of veal

Rhubarb brûlee, elderflower sorbet

7mi Southeast of Welshpool on B4386
Parking

Norton

016 Hundred House

Bridgnorth Rd, Norton TF11 9EE

Tel.: (01952) 730353 - Fax: (01952) 730355
e-mail: reservations@hundredhouse.co.uk - Website: www.hundredhouse.co.uk

 A selection of guest ales offered

You know you've arrived somewhere with a hugely individual character when you arrive at Hundred House. The extensive rear herb garden is a particular joy and supplies the kitchen with much delightful produce, not least the delectable soft fruit for dessert, or the dried flowers that cascade from beams. The pub has its origins in the 14C and, in the best sense, it shows: rafters, quarry tiled floors, open fires and venerable dark oak. You can eat almost anywhere; if a hike along the Wrekin has bolstered a hearty appetite, try the likes of lamb casserole with mixed vegetables or prime Shropshire sirloin. Tasty banana and walnut bread with vanilla ice cream is also popular with the regulars. Lovely bedrooms offer half testers, four posters and a boundless variety of country comforts.

Food serving times:
Monday-Sunday:
12pm-2.15pm,
6.15pm-9.30pm

Prices:
Meals: a la carte 17.00/30.00
10 rooms: 69.00/135.00

Typical Dishes
Smoked duck pancake
Pork with fennel and olive stuffing
Raspberry, lemon curd meringue

7mi South of Telford on A442
Parking

Weston Heath

017 **The Countess's Arms**

Weston Heath TF11 8RJ
Tel.: (01952) 691123 - Fax: (01952) 691143

VISA AE M

A selection of up to 4 regularly changing guest beers

When the owners removed the internal walls and floors of The Plough at Weston Heath – a rather sombre boozer – and replaced them with polished wood floors and smart, part-brick, part-emulsioned walls, The Countess's Arms was born. In came a large, modern bar and open fire, a restaurant extension and an upstairs gallery. Shiny tables were put in all these areas, and menus of well-prepared, home-cooked dishes began to earn a good local reputation. Now the pub, and its modern country dining, is a bustling fixture on the A41. Accomplished main courses you could try range from peppered fillet of beef medallions with horseradish dumplings, braised root vegetables and red wine jus to flaked cod, fried potato and spring onion hash with rocket and aïoli.

Food serving times:
Monday-Saturday:
12pm-2.30pm,
6.30pm-9.30pm
Sunday: 12pm-8.30pm
Closed 25 December
Prices:
Meals: a la carte 15.00/20.00

5.5mi Northeast of Shifnal by B4379 and A5, on A41
Parking

Typical Dishes

Seafood dim sum

Piri piri chicken

White chocolate and ginger crème brûlée

Ardens Grafton

018 **Golden Cross**

Wixford Road, Ardens Grafton B50 4LG

Tel.: (01789) 772420 - Fax: (01789) 773697

 Tetley Cask and up to 4 guest ales offered

Popular destinations in this part of the world are not confined to nearby Stratford, as witnessed by the large number of satisfied visitors enjoying the ambience of this slickly run pub. It has a very pleasant feel, both inside and out. A large rear garden and terrace is ideal for summer dining; the roomy interior has a distinctly rural character, typified by the exposed beams, open fire and scrubbed wooden tables and chairs. A separate dining room gives off a more formal air; a la carte menus bear the hallmarks of modern British tastes and are very freshly prepared with vibrant use of local ingredients; the blackboard daily specials offer a distinct seasonal base.

Food serving times:
Monday-Saturday:
 12pm-2.30pm, 6pm-9.30pm
Sunday: 12pm-9pm
Prices:
Meals: a la carte 16.00/25.00

Typical Dishes

Peach and Parma ham salad

Pork chop, apple mash

Duo of chocolate mousse

5mi South West of Stratford-upon-Avon by A46. Parking

Armscote

019 **The Fox and Goose Inn**

Armscote CV37 8DD

Tel.: (01608) 682293
Website: www.foxandgoose.co.uk

🍷 **_VISA_** **AE** **M©** **JCB**

Fox & Goose own Bitter brewed by Brakspear, Old Speckled Hen

The blacksmith who once worked here at his forge would be amazed at its 21C transformation. The Fox and Goose embraces modernity but doesn't forget its past. Flagstones, wooden pews and a log fire all have pride of place here. They syncopate smoothly with an upmarket ambience elsewhere in the pub. The small bar has warm red walls; they're cream in the larger, stylish eating area. Imaginative and traditional blend cleverly in the cooking stakes: you might try roast lamb shoulder with rosemary and redcurrant jus; or poached smoked haddock with spinach, poached egg and chive sauce. Service is helpful and attentive; bedrooms, eccentrically styled, are named after Cluedo characters - candlestick and lead piping not included, thank goodness...

Food serving times:
Monday-Sunday:
  12pm-2.30pm, 7pm-9.30pm
Closed 25-26 December and
1 January
Prices:
Meals: a la carte 22.00/28.00
🛏 **4 rooms:** 50.00/90.00

Typical Dishes

Chicken liver parfait
Scallops with sweet chilli oil
Vanilla panna cotta

2.5mi North of Shipston-on-Stour by A3400
Parking

Aston Cantlow

020 King's Head

Bearley Rd, Aston Cantlow B95 6HY
Tel.: (01789) 488242 - Fax: (01789) 488137

🍷 🚭 **VISA** **AE** **MC**

Hook Norton Old Hooky, Greene King Abbot

This is a pub that's used to welcoming Stratford overspill, those who need a little respite from the intensity of Shakespeare's birthplace. It's a 15C whitewashed inn with black timbers set in a pretty village, with pleasant terrace and garden for summer visitors. The interior oozes charm with several cosy areas to choose from. There's a crackling log fire, low ceiling and polished flag flooring, plus rustic benches next to window tables, where you can watch the world go by. The attractive restaurant has a modern country style, reflecting the modish appeal of the menus, whose influence ranges from British and Mediterranean to the downright exotic (as in chilli and lime chicken kebabs with peanut dressing). Expect great service, too, generally with an Antipodean accent.

Food serving times:
Monday-Sunday:
12pm-2pm, 7pm-9.45pm
Closed 25-26 December
Prices:
Meals: a la carte 18.00/27.00

Typical Dishes
Whisky and honey cured salmon

Duck supper

Lime leaf and cardamon panna cotta

3mi South of Henley-in-Arden, off B4089
Parking

Farnborough

021 Inn at Farnborough

Farnborough OX17 1DZ
Tel.: (01295) 690615 - Fax: (01295) 690032
e-mail: enquiries@innatfarnborough.co.uk - Website: www.innatfarnborough.co.uk

VISA AE ① MC JCB

Greene King Abbot, Hook Norton, Charles Wells Bombadier

The historic village of Farnborough is home to two distinctive buildings: the National Trust owned Farnborough Hall and this Grade II listed 17C inn, at the heart of the community for nearly 400 years. Expectations are fully endorsed upon crossing the threshold. A homely interior is dressed in full sympathy with the age of the building: there's a warm glow from the open fire, flag stoned floor and country knick-knacks. A homely bar offers a promising selection of real ales and diners will appreciate the frequently changing menus; much time and effort goes into sourcing local ingredients, resulting in carefully prepared, tasty dishes with a modern flourish. Upstairs, in a sharp break from the rural treats below, is an eye-catching private meeting room with a zebra-striped ceiling.

Food serving times:
Monday-Sunday:
12pm-3pm, 6pm-11pm
Closed 25 December
Prices:
Meals: 12.95 and a la carte
18.00/28.00

Typical Dishes
King scallops, local asparagus
Lamb with spinach and potato gratin
Local cheeseboard

6mi North of Banbury on A423.
Parking

Great Wolford

022 Fox & Hounds Inn

Great Wolford CV36 5NQ

Tel.: (01608) 674220 - Fax: (01608) 674160
e-mail: info@thefoxandhoundsinn.com - Website: www.thefoxandhoundsinn.com

⇔room

A selection of up to 4 real ales offered

It takes something special to catch the eye in an area as rich in delights as the Cotswolds, but this 16C inn passes the test with flying colours. It's located in the heart of a delightful village, its honey coloured exterior luring the visitor into a series of hugely characterful rooms with bags of period appeal, typified by exposed beams with hop bines, an ancient bread oven, lovely open log fire and solid stone floor. Select from a good array of wines and local real ales and dine at candlelit tables; there's a daily changing blackboard menu of well executed, hearty, fresh fare, that puts many local ingredients to good use. In warmer months, make for the summer terrace. Stay overnight in cosy, well-kept bedrooms.

Food serving times:
Tuesday-Saturday:
　　　12pm-2pm, 7pm-9pm
Sunday:　　　12pm-2pm
Closed 2 weeks January
Prices:
Meals: a la carte 15.00/30.00
🛏 **3 rooms:** 50.00/80.00

Typical Dishes

Duck spring roll

Guinea fowl with poached apricots

Lemon and almond tart

4mi Northeast of Moreton-in-Marsh by A44. Parking

Henley-in-Arden

023 Crabmill

Preston Bagot, Claverdon, Henley-in-Arden B95 5EE
Tel.: (01926) 843342 - Fax: (01926) 843989
e-mail: thecrabmill@amserve.net - Website: www.thecrabmill.co.uk

    VISA AE MC

Tetleys, Wadworth 6X, Old Speckled Hen

A delightful rural hideaway, but one which doesn't quite leave its urbane smartness behind: a surprisingly spacious contemporary interior mixes smooth blond wood with ancient cross-beams and wattle walls, the warmth of a real fire and squishy tan leather sofas, so comfortable they demand a real battle of wills for a trip to the bar. A touch of brasserie style comes across in the competent cooking, with dishes like roast pigeon breast and mash, or pepper sirloin and chips, but it's the kind of food you can linger over, and you may find that hearty ramble up and down the Warwickshire hills being put back by another round. The staff look almost as nonchalant as the customers – the emblemed T-shirts are the clue – but provide prompt and conversational service with that noticeable bit extra. Justifiably popular, so consider booking.

Food serving times:
Monday-Saturday:
12pm-2.30pm,
6.30pm-9.30pm
Sunday: 12.30pm-3.30pm
Closed 25 December
(booking essential)
Prices:
Meals: a la carte 20.00/28.00

Typical Dishes
Crab with zucchini and orange pancakes
Rack of lamb, feta and tapenade
Baileys cheesecake

1mi East of Henley-in-Arden on A4189
Parking

Ilmington

024 ## The Howard Arms

Lower Green, Ilmington CV36 4LT

Tel.: (01608) 682226 - Fax: (01608) 682226

e-mail: info@howardarms.com - Website: www.howardarms.com

 Everards Tiger, North Cotswold Genesis and 1 guest ale

Wander in to this charming 16C inn for a quiet lunchtime pint and you may be surprised by the buzz of activity, but there's usually room for everyone in a spread of smartly kept rooms and snugs, decorated with prints, portraits and old photographs. Cheerful local staff are used to being busy and will talk you through the large weekly menu chalked up above the fireplace. Classic country cooking, done well, takes in dishes like steak and ale pie, pork in sage, honey and cider and pigeon with carrot and ginger purée. Three well-fitted bedrooms with an agreeable mix of antiques and country fabrics all share a view of the village green: if you do decide to stay, don't miss the famous paintings and porcelain at nearby Upton House, a stroll around the enchanting Hidcote Manor Gardens or a trip to Stratford-upon-Avon.

Food serving times:
Monday-Thursday:
12pm-2pm, 7pm-9pm
Friday-Saturday:
12pm-2pm, 7pm-9.30pm
Sunday: 12pm-2.30pm,
6.30pm-8.30pm
Closed 25 December
(fixed price Sunday lunch)
Prices:
Meals: 18.50 and a la carte
22.00/25.00
3 rooms: 77.00/115.00

4mi Northwest of Shipston-on-Stour
Located in the centre of the village.
Parking

Typical Dishes

Cheese soufflé

Pork with apples, cream and Calvados

Baked banana pudding, ginger ice cream

Tanworth-in-Arden

025 **The Bell**

The Green, Tanworth-in-Arden B94 5AL

Tel.: (01564) 742212

e-mail: reservations@thebellattanworthinarden.co.uk - Website: www.thebellattanworthinarden.co.uk

 VISA · AE · MC

 Fuller's London Pride, Hook Norton Old Hooky, Black Sheep

A very handily located pub, only 20 minutes from Stratford and five minutes from main motorway access, The Bell sits proudly in its pretty village location, close to an 11C church and providing sustenance to the occasional summer invasion of Morris dancers. Its premises embrace a recently added delicatessen and post office; a good deal of time, effort and money has been invested in the pub, too, and there's now a pleasing rustic-contemporary mix with a spacious, popular bar and an intimate main dining room that boasts squashy leather sofas and polished wooden tables. The wide ranging menus cover an interesting modern range: for instance, you might order baby Thai fish and oatmeal cakes with ginger and tomato sauce, followed by Moroccan chicken, couscous and raita. The modern theme is continued with designer-led bedrooms.

Food serving times:

Monday-Saturday:
12pm-2pm, 6.30pm-9pm

Sunday: 12pm-3pm

Closed dinner 25-26 December and 2-3 January

Prices:

Meals: a la carte 12.00/24.00

🛏 **4 rooms:** 60.00/70.00

Typical Dishes

Arabic mezze

Roast monkfish tail, baby leeks

Selection of cheeses

4.5mi North West from Henley-in-Arden by A3400 and Tanworth Road. 5 minutes from main motorways. Close to Church. Parking

Warwick

026 The Saxon Mill

Coventry Road, Guys Cliffe, Warwick CV34 5YN

Tel.: (01926) 492255 - Fax: (01926) 623903
e-mail: saxonmill@hotmail.com - Website: www.saxonmill.co.uk

 No real ales offered

Eating out on the river Avon takes on an excitingly literal meaning at this attractive converted water mill, as a spacious dining terrace juts out over the water. If the weather's too inclement to go al fresco, then there's ample room inside. A contemporary lounge has modern leather seats and sofas to sink into; get your drinks from a marble topped bar. Upstairs, a restaurant with heavily beamed ceilings has an open plan kitchen and rotisserie. Chunky wood tables complete the picture of solid rusticity. Extensive menus range from salad and pizza to specials off the rotisserie. If you're staying put in the bar, you can watch the river running below through special glass sections.

Food serving times:
Monday-Friday:
12pm-2.30pm
Saturday: 12pm-6pm
Sunday: 12pm-4.30pm
Closed 25 December
(booking essential)
Prices:
Meals: a la carte 20.00/30.00

Typical Dishes

Roast mushrooms, garlic and dolcelatte

Spit roast chicken

Vanilla and chocolate cheesecake

1.5mi North of Warwick on A429.
Parking

Barston

027 **Malt Shovel**

Barston Lane, Barston B92 0JP
Tel.: (01675) 443223 - Fax: (01675) 443223

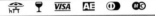

 No real ales offered

Past Solihull and right out into the countryside, this well-managed rural pub is worth having up your sleeve for a city getaway; you shouldn't expect to have it all to yourself – it's not a ticking-clock-snoozing-dog local – but the bustling atmosphere is at least half the pleasure. The terrace at the back, overlooking a large lawned garden, makes for pleasant al fresco eating, though they only take bookings for the restaurant, which opens for dinner. With its banquettes, colourful paintings, big metal-topped bar and busy kitchen on view behind glass, the main part of the pub has made a subtly modern style its own, without losing too much of its country character: the same could be said for its robust cooking which features daily fish specials and uses seasonings from the pub's own herb garden.

Food serving times:
Monday-Saturday:
12pm-2.30pm,
6.30pm-9.30pm
(lunch bookings not accepted)
Prices:
Meals: 25.00 and a la carte 12.00/25.00

Typical Dishes

Bang Bang Chicken
Gammon on butterbean mash
Chocolate marmalade tart

3.5mi South of Hampton-in-Arden by A452
Parking

Chadwick End

028 The Orange Tree

Warwick End, Chadwick End B93 0BN
Tel.: (01564) 785364 - Fax: (01564) 782988
Website: www.theorangetree.co.uk

VISA   AE   MC

Tetleys, Abbot IPA

Though pubby in style, this cream-painted conversion – only a few minutes from the NEC and a handful of enchanting National Trust properties - sits firmly in the country dining league. Sumptuous leather sofas beckon you into a smart, modern, split-level lounge and bar with definite restaurant sensibilities: varnished wooden tables with paper napkins, cushioned chairs and banquettes. Unless you're making your way to the patio, settle down and select a dish from the wide range available: everything from pizzas and pastas to rotisserie specials such as spit chicken with lemon and honey, or duck confit with pink peppercorn and smoked bacon mash.

Food serving times:
Monday-Saturday:
  12pm-2.30pm, 6pm-9.30pm
Sunday: 12pm-4.30pm
Closed 25 December and Sunday dinner
(booking essential)
Prices:
Meals: a la carte 21.00/30.00

Typical Dishes

Foie gras parfait

Roast chicken, confit garlic and mash

Ice cream

7mi Northwest of Warwick by A4141
A few minutes from the NEC. Parking

Hampton-in-Arden

029 The White Lion

10 High St, Hampton-in-Arden B92 0AA
Tel.: (01675) 442833 - Fax: (01675) 443168

🛏room **VISA** **MC**

 Hook Norton, Black Sheep

Set in a leafy village opposite the church, and very handy for the NEC in Birmingham, this 17C pub has Grade II listed status; surprisingly, though, when you step through the front door, there's an appealing modern rusticity on show, exemplified by stripped pine floors, pale beams and fresh flowers. The cosy front bar is where the locals gather, impressed by a fine range of real ales on offer; a separate side bar boasts welcoming, modern touches. To the rear, soft, neutral colours announce the dining room, a stylish place to eat, with ranks of mirrors and smart wicker chairs. Well cooked, interesting dishes offer a predominantly light touch, full of Italian elements, but reaching further afield for added inspiration in dishes like Moroccan spiced chicken with coriander noodles.

Food serving times:
Monday-Saturday:
12pm-2.30pm, 6.30pm-10pm
Sunday: 12pm-2.30pm
Closed Bank Holidays
Prices:
Meals: a la carte 19.80/28.90
🛏 **7 rooms:** 49.00/59.00
🍽 7.50

Typical Dishes

Crispy duck salad

Honey and mustard glazed ham, leek mash

Chocolate cake, amaretto ice cream

In the centre of town
Parking

Lapworth

030 ## The Boot

Old Warwick Rd, Lapworth B94 6JU

Tel.: (01564) 782464 - Fax: (01564) 784989
Website: www.bootatlapworth.co.uk

Old Speckled Hen, Wadworth 6X, Tetley Cask

Who'd believe Birmingham's just 10 miles up the road? Take a step outside the pretty village of Lapworth and discover this wonderfully rustic inn that pre-dates the adjacent Grand Union Canal by a few hundred years. It boasts a rabbit warren of beamed rooms to lunch in, the slightly gnarled tables adding to the charmingly frayed-round-the-edges feel. Don't look for an area set for dining, though, as cutlery arrives after you've ordered. There's a wide mix of styles from classic rustic pub fare to dishes with a decided European and Oriental influence - whatever takes your gastronomic fancy. As well as the bars, you can eat in a timbered upstairs dining room or on the terrace.

Food serving times:
Monday-Sunday:
   12.30pm-3pm, 7pm-10pm
Closed 25 December and
1 January
(booking essential)
Prices:
Meals: a la carte 18.00/25.00

Typical Dishes

Salmon fishcakes

Calves liver with onion mash

Rhubarb, vanilla and gin tart

2mi Southeast of Hockley Heath on B4439
Parking

Sutton Coldfield

031 **The Cock Inn**

Bulls Lane, Wishaw, Sutton Coldfield B76 9QL

Tel.: (0121) 313 3960

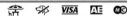

VISA AE MC

 Bass, Hook Norton and M&B Brew XI

Traditional on the outside, splendidly modern within. There's a confident, stylish ambience here, reflected in the buzz of the place. It's light and airy with wooden flooring and carvings and modern wood tables with discreet spot lighting. Some areas boast burgundy walls featuring framed wine labels; logs line another wall. There's a relaxing lounge area by the bar, and a cigar bar (apparently rather exclusive at weekends) opens onto a beer garden. Menus are original: they change seasonally, and have a section of little dishes alongside the well established grill rotisserie. The robust, modish cooking is mainly British, but other more eclectic elements vie for attention. All this, within minutes of the roaring M6 toll!

Food serving times:
No food service 25 December
Prices:
Meals: a la carte 15.00/28.00

Typical Dishes

Beetroot-cured gravadlax

Duck confit, green beans, butterbeans

Tarte Tatin

7mi East of Sutton Coldfield by A453 off A446. Parking

E. Baret / Michelin - (06 - Roubion)

- ☐ a. **D 17 road?**
- ☐ b. **N 202 road?**
- ☐ c. **D 30 road?**

The Michelin Atlases and new NATIONAL, REGIONAL, LOCAL and ZOOM map series offer clear, accurate mapping to help you plan your route and find your way.

Yorkshire, for many, means the countryside: a mind's-eye landscape of fells and fields spreading out from the Pennines, neat Dales villages above the Wharfe and the Swale, and Aysgarth Falls and Hardraw Force in all their secluded beauty. But the Ridings also lay claim to the genteel charm of Harrogate and Ripon, the striking ruins of Fountains Abbey and Rievaux and the unexpected brilliance of Vanburgh's Castle Howard, to say nothing of York, its medieval walled town and its awe-inspiring Minster. Industrial change has left its mark in the pit towns and the Steel City of Sheffield, but also in Leeds' rejuvenated centre and at Saltaire, the 19C mill village painted by Bradford-born David Hockney. The counties' pubs range from the proudly classic to the ceaselessly inventive, each striking its own balance with the famous local love of tradition: roast beef and Yorkshire pudding may have been adopted by the rest of Britain, but this is still the place to go for Wensleydale cheese, York ham, moorland game and parkin, the rich spiced oatmeal cake baked specially for Bonfire Night!

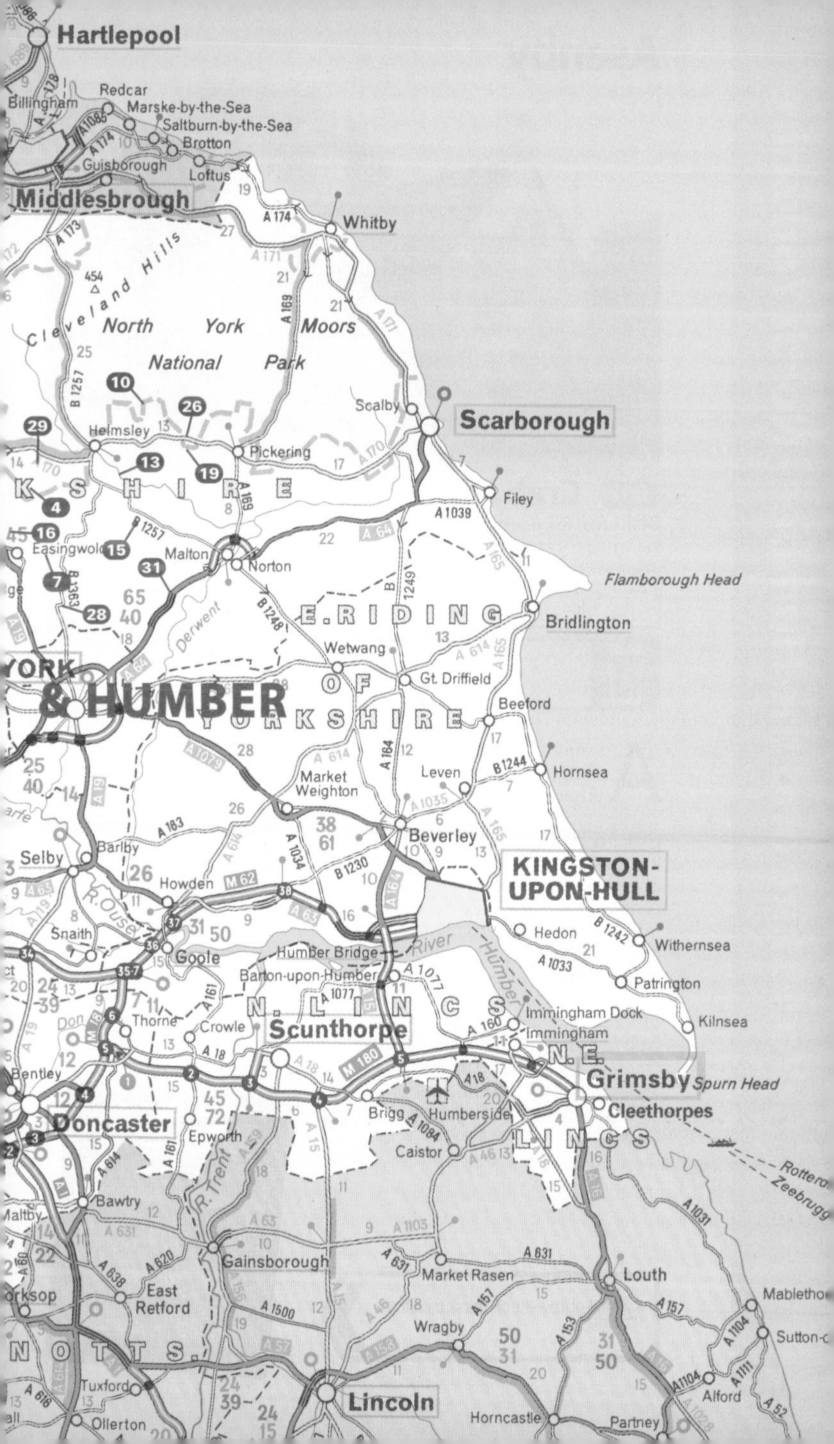

Hartlepool

Billingham Redcar
Marske-by-the-Sea
Saltburn-by-the-Sea
Guisborough Brotton
Loftus
Middlesbrough
A 174 Whitby

Cleveland Hills 454

North York Moors
National Park

Helmsley Scalby
Pickering Scarborough
Filey
Easingwold
Malton Norton A 1039
Flamborough Head
York & HUMBER
Wetwang Gt. Driffield Bridlington
E. RIDING
Beeford
OF YORKSHIRE
Market Leven Hornsea
Weighton
Selby Barlby Beverley
Howden KINGSTON-
UPON-HULL
Snaith Hedon Withernsea
Goole Patrington
Humber Bridge River
Barton-upon-Humber Kilnsea
Thorne Crowle Immingham Dock
Scunthorpe Immingham N.E.
Bentley Grimsby Spurn Head
Doncaster Brigg Cleethorpes
Epworth Humberside LINCS
Caistor
Bawtry
Maltby
Gainsborough A 631
Market Rasen Louth
East Mablethorpe
Retford Sutton
Wragby
NOTTS Horncastle
Tuxford Lincoln Alford
Ollerton Horncastle Partney

Asenby

001 Crab and Lobster

Dishforth Rd, Asenby YO7 3QL

Tel.: (01845) 577286 - Fax: (01845) 577109
e-mail: reservations@crabmanor.com

 🍽 🍷 ✂ ✗ **VISA** **AE** **MC**

 No real ales offered

As atmospheric in its own way as the nearby North York Moors, this bizarrely adorned thatched pub displays lobster pots, pews, a dentist's chair, rocking chair and fairground horses in its midst, but there's nothing eccentric in its widely acclaimed menus. A large conservatory, called the Pavilion, and terrace were added a couple of years ago, and there's also an atmospheric, pubby styled brasserie, plus a softly lit, formal restaurant. Together they concentrate primarily on one type of dish: seafood, with the same menu served in all the different areas. The result is locally acclaimed dishes; recent recommendations include king scallops, sea bass and lemon sole.

Food serving times:
Monday-Sunday:
  12pm-2.30pm, 7pm-9.30pm
- Seafood -
Prices:
Meals: a la carte 25.00/50.00
🛏 **12 rooms:** 200.00

Typical Dishes

King scallops, sesame prawn toast

"Posh" fish and chips

Assiette of desserts

5.25mi Southwest of Thirsk by A168
Parking

Bolton Abbey

002 Devonshire Brasserie and Bar

Bolton Abbey BD23 6AJ

Tel.: (01756) 710710 - Fax: (01756) 710564
e-mail: reservations@thedevonshirearms.co.uk - Website: www.devonshirehotels.co.uk

       VISA AE ① M⊙

Black Sheep Best, Rigwelter, Wharfedale Folly

Located at one end of the exquisitely elegant Devonshire Arms Country House, this stylish modern brasserie with the informal atmosphere is a complete contrast. Exposed stone, flagged floors and open fires provide rustic charm, but allied to this, bright modern colours, sofas, armchairs and vivid contemporary art add lashings of style. A good value and extensive menu provides all kinds of dishes from classic to traditional and modern; it's this variety, as much as the sound Yorkshire ales, that draw such crowds, particularly at the weekend. If there's a hint of summer sun, dine outside with fine views of the Dales as a pleasant accompaniment. Afterwards, you could always pay a visit to the spectacular ruins of 12C Bolton Priory.

Food serving times:
Monday-Saturday:
12pm-2.30pm, 6.30pm-10pm
Sunday: 12pm-3.30pm,
5pm-9pm
(booking essential)
Prices:
Meals: a la carte 18.00/28.50
🛏 **41 rooms:** 160.00/220.00

Typical Dishes

Terrine of black pudding and cheese

Moroccan chicken

Poached rhubarb, raspberry sorbet

6mi East of Skipton by A59
Parking

Burnsall

003 The Red Lion

Burnsall BD23 6BU

Tel.: (01756) 720204 - Fax: (01756) 720292
e-mail: redlion@daelnet.co.uk - Website: www.redlion.co.uk

Theakstons Best, Old Speckled Hen, Timothy Taylor Landlord, Folly Ales

From its haunted medieval cellars to the sedate comfort of the sitting room, history is ingrained in every nook and creaking beam of this creeper-clad inn on the River Wharfe. The 16C bar does a pleasantly busy trade in sustaining and enjoyable lunches by the fire; a wooden propellor looks strangely in place on its ancient, oak-pannelled walls. They'll gladly lay a table for dinner here too, but the restaurant, its mullioned windows overlooking the green, adds a further touch of formality and old-world service. A countryman's pub at heart, the Red Lion has its own trout and grayling waters and access to enviable grouse beats, so naturally fish and game, not to mention fine local lamb, are well represented on a extensive, classic menu with a light modern lift. Bedrooms boast sloping floors, open fires and Victorian brass bedsteads.

Food serving times:
Monday-Sunday:
  12pm-2.30pm, 6pm-9.30pm
(fixed price dinner)
Prices:
Meals: 29.95 and a la carte
18.00/29.90
15 rooms: 60.00/150.00

Southeast of Grassington on B6160
Parking

Typical Dishes

Pork, partridge and venison terrine

Suckling pig

Chocolate bread and butter pudding

Byland Abbey

004 Abbey Inn

Byland Abbey YO61 4BD

Tel.: (01347) 868204 - Fax: (01347) 868678
e-mail: jane@bylandabbeyinn.com - Website: www.bylandabbeyinn.co.uk

🏠 ✗rest 🚭 **VISA** **Ⓜ️©**

Black Sheep, Tetley

A charming, part 17C country inn with a unique monastic connection: the story goes that Ampleforth monks helped to restore the old house using the old stones of the delapidated abbey opposite. Its main rooms are full of character, as you might expect, their old beams and stonework still in place – one is open plan with an atrium roof, which works surprisingly well. Hearty, traditional cooking revolves around favourites like game casserole, honey-glazed shank of lamb and mild curried chicken; oeufs Chimay, an occasional feature on the menu, actually owes its origins to Parisian high society rather than the Belgian Trappist orders. Comfortable and handsomely furnished bedrooms are particularly fine, with plenty of thoughtful little extras; two rooms enjoy views of the enchanting Early Gothic abbey ruins.

Food serving times:
Monday-Saturday:
    12pm-2pm, 6.30pm-9pm
Sunday: 12pm-2pm
Closed 24-25 December
Closed Monday lunch
Prices:
Meals: a la carte 19.00/30.00
🛏 **3 rooms:** 70.00/135.00

Typical Dishes

Smoked venison, plum, bramble chutney

Lamb shank, mint and redcurrant jus

Sticky toffee pudding

Opposite the ruins of Byland Abbey.
Parking

Carlton-in-Coverdale

005 **Foresters Arms**

Carlton-in-Coverdale DL8 4BB

Tel.: (01969) 640272
e-mail: richard@wensleydalebrewery.com - Website: www.wensleydalebrewery.com

Up to 4 in-house brewed ales plus guest ales

Between the moor and the river Cover, the quiet Dales village of Carlton is an ideal place to get away from it all. There's a pleasantly unhurried mood in the two beamed and flagged rooms of its pub, and ramblers can retrace the day's walk in the maps and prints which cover the walls; there's also seating outside if you want to take your beer out into the sun. Sound cooking on a traditional base goes well with a pint and certainly gets the locals' approval. If the pictures in the bar give you an appetite for more of the great outdoors, drive north to Aysgarth and its beautiful triple flight of waterfalls, made famous by the film Robin Hood, Prince of Thieves.

Food serving times:
Tuesday-Saturday:
    12pm-2pm, 6.30pm-9pm
Sunday: 12pm-2pm
Open Bank Holiday Monday
Prices:
Meals: a la carte 16.00/20.00
 3 rooms: 69.00

Typical Dishes

Goat's cheese salad

Roast duck breast, marmalade sauce

Sticky toffee pudding

4.5mi Southwest of Middleham by Coverdale rd
Parking

Constable Burton

006 Wyvill Arms

Constable Burton DL8 5LH

Tel.: (01677) 450581
Website: www.wyvill-arms.co.uk

   rest *VISA*

Black Sheep, John Smith's and guest beers

Abbeys and castles – Jervaulx, Richmond, Bolton – are all within a 10-mile radius of this early 20C pub, situated in a quiet village on the eastern edge of the Dales. There are some traditional elements here – the odd beam, a stone bar area, plenty of memorabilia – but the real attraction for visitors and walkers wearied by a hike in the surrounding countryside is the good choice of ales and locally renowned dishes, steaks being a speciality. There's a blackboard menu which holds some interest, or just enjoy hearty cooking that makes the most of Yorkshire produce: pan-fried duck breast with honey, aniseed and bitter orange marmalade; braised jarret of pork with sauerkraut, roasted garlic potatoes and pork jus; or ham shank with maple syrup on olive mash and parsley sauce.

Food serving times:
Monday-Sunday:
 12pm-2pm, 6.30pm-9pm
Prices:
Meals: a la carte 15.70/27.20
 4 rooms: 36.00/66.00

3.5mi East of Leyburn on A684
Parking

Typical Dishes

Wensleydale ham and cheese terrine

Monkfish in Parma ham

"Three Way brûlée"

Crayke

007 The Durham Ox

Westway, Crayke YO61 4TE
Tel.: (01347) 821506 - Fax: (01347) 823326
e-mail: enquiries@thedurhamox.com - Website: www.thedurhamox.com

 🍴 🍷 ✕=rest ✕ **VISA** **AE** **MC**

 Charles Wells Bombardier, John Smiths, Theakstons IPA, Tetleys

Seasonal Modern British cooking is the order of the day here: smoked haddock with black pudding, venison with hazelnuts and mushrooms and an excellent North Country cheeseboard sum up a satisfying selection which combines the robust and the sophisticated, sometimes in the same dish - a Michelin Bib Gourmand award shows just how well-priced and well-prepared it is. A smartly set yet cosy dining room is convivial enough, but the real heart of this personally run pub is the charming main bar, with its inglenooks, gnarled beams and three centuries of character; diners are made to feel very welcome in both. Out in the converted farm buildings, attractive country-style rooms manage to marry period-style furnishings with mod cons like music systems or spa baths. A real local favourite on all counts.

Food serving times:
Monday-Sunday:
  12pm-2.30pm, 6pm-9.30pm
Closed 25 December
Prices:
Meals: a la carte 12.00/25.00
🛏 **8 rooms:** 60.00/80.00

2mi East of Easingwold on Helmsley Road
Parking

Typical Dishes

Scallops, Gruyere and garlic butter

Confit of pork, mash potato

Rhubarb crème brûlee

Dalton

008 The Travellers Rest

Dalton DL11 7HU

Tel.: (01833) 621225
e-mail: daltontravellers@aol.com

  Ψ *VISA* *MC*

	Black Sheep

A traditional looking pub in a tiny village well off the beaten track - for anyone wanting to get away not just from the roar of the city but even from the quiet murmur of the town, this could be the place. It looks like a traditional pub inside as well as out, consisting of a bar lounge with open fire and bric-a-brac, and two other rooms with simple wood tables, chairs and benches. For dinner, the locals tend to turn out in force, and the reason is simple: the food's good – the blackboard menu's eclectic and traditional with modern twists, and it's decent value, too. Possibilities include Mediterranean vegetable tart with crumbled Emmental, salmon with prawn noodle salad, and rhubarb crème brûlée.

Food serving times:
Monday-Saturday:
7pm-9.30pm
Closed 25, 26 December, 1st, 2nd January
(dinner only)
Prices:
Meals: a la carte 17.50/26.50

Typical Dishes

Crab and Gruyère tart

Pork, black pudding, apple and Calvados

Apple tart, cinnamon ice cream

7.5mi Northwest of Scotch Corner by A66.

East Witton

009 **The Blue Lion**

East Witton DL8 4SN

Tel.: (01969) 624273 - Fax: (01969) 624189

e-mail: bluelion@breathemail.net - Website: www.thebluelion.co.uk

   VISA **MC**

 Theakstons, Black Sheep, Riggwelter

On the edge of the Yorkshire Dales, this 18C one-time coaching inn reigns supreme. It's appealing all round, from the 18C style wood floors and crimson ceiling to the old, faded pictures, open fires and beams with entwined dried flowers – and that's just the restaurant. Pop across to the bar and the character shows no sign of flagging. Or rather, the flagging spreads out right there beneath your feet. It underpins two rooms that boast a bubbly and appealing atmosphere. Wooden booths, pubby knick-knacks, simple tables and chairs and a large, self-assured, modern blackboard menu entice diners in large numbers: the place has a strong local reputation. No-one seems in a rush: many are staying in the comfy, individually decorated bedrooms.

Food serving times:

Monday-Saturday:
 12pm-2.15pm, 7pm-9.30pm

Sunday: 12pm-2.30pm,
 7pm-9.30pm

(booking essential)

Prices:

Meals: a la carte 19.00/31.00

🛏 **12 rooms:** 53.50/89.00

Typical Dishes

Black pudding

Lamb shank with spring onion mash

Bread and butter pudding with custard

3mi Southeast of Leyburn on A6108
Parking

Fadmoor

010 **The Plough Inn**

Main Street, Fadmoor YO62 7HY

Tel.: (01751) 431515 - Fax: (01757) 431515

Timothy Taylor Landlord, Black Sheep Best, Tetleys Cask

This neatly-kept little pub on the edge of the North York Moors has a solidly earned reputation and bustling atmosphere. Its position guarantees a good smattering of walkers, and the friendly welcome ensures word-of-mouth is always positive. There's a characterful interior, a cheery balance between the rustic and the elegant: coir floors, sturdy range doubling as open fire, yellow walls, rich furnishings. Sit at simple wooden tables and chairs in the bar or head instead for a cosy, linen-clad rear dining area. The same menus are served throughout: a neat blend of the traditional with the more contemporary. Typically, you might try homemade seafood pie, topped with mashed potato, or, a touch more elaborate, French style pork, marinated in garlic and herbs, served with a cider and Bramley sauce and balsamic reduction.

Food serving times:
Monday-Sunday:
12pm-1.45pm,
6.30pm-8.45pm
Closed 25-26 December
(booking essential)
Prices:
Meals: a la carte 16.00/25.00

Typical Dishes

Scallops, sweet chilli

Pork loin, cider and apple sauce

Banana and caramel sponge

2.25mi Northwest of Kirbymoorside
Parking

Ferrensby

011 The General Tarleton Inn

Boroughbridge Rd, Ferrensby HG5 0PZ
Tel.: (01423) 340284 · Fax: (01423) 340288
e-mail: gti@generaltarleton.co.uk · Website: www.generaltarleton.co.uk

🍷 🚫 **VISA** **AE** **MC**

Timothy Taylor Landlord, Black Sheep Best Bitter

The extended 18C pub, surrounded by North Yorkshire countryside, remains as characterful and well run as ever. Neatly painted beams, old stonework and open fires, not to mention a small collection of humorous prints and period pictures on the walls, all bring out the convivial character of the place, although the atmosphere is substantially more formal in the dining room. Blackboard specials, early evening menus and Sunday fish suppers suggest a kitchen happy to experiment and accommodate while keeping the Bib Gourmand-winning combination of affordable prices and flavourful, well-judged British cooking; dishes range from foie gras parfait to fisherman's pie or crispy pork with blue cheese polenta and porcini. Polite service may not add much, but detracts nothing from a really enjoyable lunch or evening out.

Food serving times:
Monday-Saturday:
   12pm-2.15pm, 6pm-9.15pm
Sunday: 12pm-1.45pm,
                      6pm-9.15pm

Prices:
Meals: 30.00 and a la carte
19.50/30.00
🛏 **14 rooms:** 74.95/110.00

Typical Dishes

Seafood in crisp pastry, lobster sauce

Confit of lamb, red wine thyme jus

Apple cobbler

From the A1 at Boroughbridge, take the A6055 road to Knaresborough, the inn is about 4 minutes drive. Parking

Galphay

012 Galphay Arms

Galphay HG4 3NJ
Tel.: (01765) 650133
e-mail: thegalphay@btopenworld.com

Black Sheep, Copper Dragon

Appealing and unfussy, the steady cooking at the Galphay Arms never strays far from its traditional roots, but makes good use of regional ingredients and brings out the flavours of the season with simplicity and clarity: you can't go far wrong with good potted Morecambe Bay shrimps, followed by a stew of local wild roe deer, mushrooms and shallots, with a glass of red or a Yorkshire ale. Choose one of the neatly set, marble-topped tables to one side, or a firelit bar in true country style with high backed leather chairs and a collection of hunting prints on the walls. All in all, a proper village pub with a relaxing, homely feel, for which the personable owners can take much of the credit.

Food serving times:
Wednesday-Monday:
12pm-2pm, 6.30pm-9.30pm
Closed 25 December and lunch 31 December
Prices:
Meals: a la carte 15.00/25.00

Typical Dishes

Home-smoked salmon

Venison, mushroom and currant sauce

Ice cream

4.5mi West of Ripon by B6265.
Parking

Harome

013 The Star Inn

High St, Harome YO62 5JE
Tel.: (01439) 770397 - Fax: (01439) 771833
Website: www.thestaratharome.co.uk

🍽 🍷 🍇 ⇥ ✕ *VISA* Ⓜ©

 John Smiths, Black Sheep and 1 guest ale

You'll need a hearty appetite as well as a fine palate to get the most from this deliciously characterful, 14C thatched inn at the tip of the North York Moors. Thoroughly deserving of its Michelin star, the aptly named pub not only provides an utterly charming dining room, but also superb, rich dishes, prepared with balance and panache, that show pride in its Yorkshire roots. The bar loses nothing by the dining room's starring role; it boasts Mousey Thompson's famous furniture and antiques, as well as solid stone floors, walls filled with period knickknacks, beam-and-plank ceiling, big log fire, and daily papers and magazines. As if that weren't enough, there's a cosy coffee loft in the eaves, an organic deli selling all manner of delicious goodies, al fresco options in garden or on front terrace, and stylish bedrooms for overnighters.

Food serving times:
Tuesday-Saturday:
  12pm-2pm, 6.30pm-9.30pm
Sunday: 12pm-6pm
Closed 25 December and
2 weeks January
(booking essential)
Prices:
Meals: a la carte 25.00/40.00
🛏 **11 rooms:** 120.00/210.00

Typical Dishes

Black pudding with foie gras

Roe deer, creamed juniper cabbage

Banana tart

2.75mi Southeast of Helmsley by A170
Parking

Hetton

014 Angel Inn

Hetton BD23 6LT

Tel.: (01756) 730263 - Fax: (01756) 730363
e-mail: info@angelhetton.co.uk - Website: www.angelhetton.co.uk

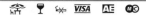 🕌 🍷 ✄ **VISA** **AE** **MC**

Black Sheep Bitter, Timothy Taylor Landlord, Copper Dragon

This hugely characterful pub started brewing and serving beer to cattle drovers 300 years ago. If they returned now, they'd probably recognise the same unimproved oak beams, nooks and crannies, but there's now a formal restaurant as well as a bar. The snug warren of rooms is invariably packed, so try and get there early to bag a table. Otherwise, wander around and admire the rural prints, old menus and various awards displayed around the walls. The wood bar displays well-priced blackboard specials, made up of classic and original dishes, some taking inspiration from France and Italy. Ingredients are mostly drawn from nearby sources: meats from the Dales, Lancastrian sausages and cheese, and fish from Fleetwood. Herbs are even more indigenous: from the Angel's own back garden. A Bib Gourmand winner.

Food serving times:
Monday-Saturday:
    12pm-2.30pm, 6pm-9pm
Sunday: 12pm-1.45pm
Closed 25 December and
1 week in January
Fixed price lunch Sunday,
fixed price dinner Monday-
Friday - (booking essential)
Prices:
Meals: 19.25/22.00 and a la carte 22.00/32.00
🛏 **5 rooms:** 170.00

Typical Dishes

Seafood, lobster sauce

Shoulder of lamb on thyme mash

Baileys crème brûlée

**5.75mi North of Skipton by B6265
Parking** 〉〉

Hovingham

015 **Worsley Arms**

High St, Hovingham YO62 4LA

Tel.: (01653) 628234 - Fax: (01653) 628130

e-mail: worsleyarms@aol.com - Website: www.worsleyarms.com

🍷 ⤬ *VISA* **AE** **MC**

Nick Stafford's Hambleton

Y ou can't fail to be impressed by this classic part-19C coaching inn set in a delightful village of Yorkshire stone. Step inside for instant confirmation that the Worsley is no run-of-the-mill establishment; handsome antiques, armchairs and sofas dotted around, along with books, pictures and a pleasantly quiet sitting room, give it the feeling of a modestly smart but welcoming country house. You can eat in the Cricketers, a pine-clad, pubby bar whose wine cellars are open for you to browse before lunch and dinner. There's a more refined dining room with a concise but balanced table d'hote menu making the most of fresh Yorkshire produce. Those staying overnight can settle into comfortable, individually styled bedrooms, two of which are in the cottages on the other side of the green.

Food serving times:
Monday-Sunday:
12pm-2pm, 6.30pm-9pm
Prices:
Meals: a la carte 20.00/30.00
🛏 **19 rooms:** 85.00/100.00

Typical Dishes

Chicken and bacon salad

Steak and kidney pudding, wine gravy

Lemon posset

Between Malton and Helmsley on B2157
Parking

Husthwaite

016　The Roasted Pepper

Low St, Husthwaite YO61 4QA

Tel.: (01347) 868007 - Fax: (01347) 868776
e-mail: info@roastedpepper.co.uk - Website: www.roastedpepper.co.uk

  VISA MC JCB

| | *No real ales offered* |

Turn off the A19 on your way to the North York Moors for an interesting culinary diversion. In the pretty little village of Husthwaite stands this immaculately whitewashed Victorian pub, given a 21C wash and scrub-up: this amounts to an interior best described as sunny, with a bright, contemporary red and yellow palette given full reign. The 19C hasn't been totally forgotten, though – the original brick and tile flooring is still intact. There's a small bar with a couple of tables for drinkers; it all starts to get serious with the dining area, where heavy wood tables and chairs, set with modern cutlery, lend the air of a restaurant. Menus are keenly priced at Bib Gourmand level, and have a distinctly Mediterranean theme, with tapas a key component. Anchovy and olive kebabs or Spanish hams and charcuterie put you in the picture.

Food serving times:
Tuesday-Saturday:
　12pm-2.30pm, 7pm-9.30pm
Sunday:　　　　12pm-2.30pm
Prices:
Meals: a la carte 15.00/25.00

Typical Dishes

Meat tapas platter

Griddled marlin, fennel rice

Lemon meringue ice cream

Between Thirsk and Easingwold off A19
Parking

Langthwaite

017 Charles Bathurst Inn

Langthwaite DL11 6EN

Tel.: (01748) 884567 - Fax: (01748) 884599

e-mail: info@cbinn.co.uk - Website: www.cbinn.co.uk

  VISA Ⓜ

 Theakstons Best Bitter, Black Sheep Riggwelter, John Smiths Cask

High in the windswept hills of Arkengarthdale, the well-run 18C inn is named after the old lord of the manor, whose "CB" monogram was stamped on the local lead from which he made his fortune: any cross-country ramble – and there are plenty – is likely to skirt more than one of his long-disused mines. Wood floors, open fires and photos of Herriot country add greatly to the charm of a neatly kept bar, which is perfect for a quiet pint or two, but owes much of its strong local reputation to its half-modern, half-traditional menu, painted afresh every day on two broad mirrors: there's more choice, and more demand, in the evenings. Spacious, individually decorated bedrooms with period pine furniture are good to come back to after a long day's walk.

Food serving times:
Monday-Sunday:
    12pm-2pm, 6.30pm-9pm
Closed 25 December and lunch November-February
Prices:
Meals: a la carte 17.50/25.00
🛏 **18 rooms:** 95.00

Typical Dishes
Chicken liver and black pudding salad

Chickpea and coriander fritters

Baileys ice cream

3.25mi Northwest of Reeth on Langthwaite rd
Parking

Leyburn

018 Sandpiper Inn

Market Pl, Leyburn DL8 5AT

Tel.: (01969) 622206 - Fax: (01969) 625367
e-mail: hsandpiper.99@aol.com

 🍷 ✂ **VISA** Ⓜ©

 Black Sheep Best and Special, Courage Directors, Daleside, Archers

A pub ideally placed for weary ramblers making their way from the Dales, this converted 16C stone house could just as easily be missed by them, as it's tucked away at one end of the market square and needs to be sought out. The effort's not wasted. Downstairs is a traditional pub, divided into cosy alcoves nestling under dark beams, with a log fire lighting the way. In the simply stylish – though rather subdued - dining room, it's bare wood tables by day, but linen at night. Good value blackboard menus offer rich pickings in the form of traditional fishcakes with chive beurre blanc, fillet of pork wrapped in Parma ham with sun dried tomatoes, or braised rabbit with wild mushrooms and thyme. For those who really are too weary, there are two comfy bedrooms upstairs.

Food serving times:
Tuesday-Thursday:
    12pm-2.30pm, 6.30pm-9pm
Friday-Saturday:
    12pm-2.30pm,
    6.30pm-9.30pm
Sunday: 12pm-2pm,
    7pm-9pm

Prices:
Meals: a la carte 19.00/27.25
🛏 **2 rooms:** 55.00/70.00

In town centre
Limited parking available ➤➤

Typical Dishes

Crab and salmon cake

Crispy duck, plum and orange sauce

Blackcurrant vacherin

Marton

019 ## The Appletree Country Inn

Marton YO62 6RD

Tel.: (01751) 431457

e-mail: appletreeinn@supanet.com - Website: www.appletreeinn.co.uk

 VISA **MC** **JCB**

John Smiths and 3 regularly changing guest ales

Spacious, warm and comfortable, a typical, family-run Yorkshire inn in a quiet village on the banks of the Seven, where the river runs down to the Vale of Pickering. In a rustic interior of exposed brick and timbers, well-spaced tables through three adjoining rooms mark this out as a dining pub first and foremost, so it's no surprise to find a touch of rather proper formality in the service. The cooking, too, works in its presentational flourishes, but it's not without its traditional, homespun side as well; among the typical dishes on a concise menu are mustard-dressed crispy duck, guinea fowl with wild mushrooms and griottine crème brulée.

Food serving times:
Wednesday-Sunday:
    12pm-2pm, 6.30pm-9pm
Monday: 6.30pm-9pm
Closed 25 December and
2 weeks January
Prices:
Meals: a la carte 17.50/30.00

Typical Dishes

Blue cheese and pear tart

Pork, mustard mash

Orange jelly, bitter chocolate sorbet

5.25mi West of Pickering by A170
Parking

Middleham

020 **White Swan**

Market Pl, Middleham DL8 4PE

Tel.: (01969) 622093 - Fax: (01969) 624551
e-mail: whiteswan@easynet.co.uk - Website: www.whiteswanhotel.co.uk

 VISA

 Black Sheep, John Smith's Cask

In a town now best known for its racehorses, where Richard III's white boar standard once flew from the now-ruined castle, The White Swan proves there's no accounting for some choices of pub names. A pleasant but unremarkable part of the market place, the old coaching inn saves the best for inside: the stone-floored bar with stove and inglenook is inviting enough, but the two cosy little rooms at the back are even nicer on a cold evening, and the neatly decorated bedrooms could be useful for an overnight stop. A sound, locally sourced English menu sticks to what it knows best with no over-reaching modern flourishes, preferring trusty favourites like beef and ale pie and chips and tasty desserts like lemon parfait. Run with quiet Yorkshire competence, it's a real asset to the town.

Food serving times:
Monday-Sunday:
12pm-2.15pm,
6.30pm-9.15pm
Closed 25 December
Prices:
Meals: 13.95 and a la carte
13.75/25.50
12 rooms: 47.50/79.00

Typical Dishes

Yorkshire feta, dried tomato salad

Pesto chicken, bacon cream sauce

Yorkshire cheeseboard

1mi from Leyburn on A6108. Parking

Moulton

021 **Black Bull Inn**

Moulton DL10 6QJ

Tel.: (01325) 377289 - Fax: (01325) 377422
e-mail: sarah@blackbullinn.demon.co.uk

 VISA **AE** **M©**

No real ales offered

There seems little to set the Black Bull apart from the other extended cottages in this North Riding village, until you step inside and find a long-established, traditional place of the sort that inspires real affection in its regulars. With a comfy seat and a pre-dinner drink in your hand, it's unexpectedly easy to feel at home in the neat, unshowy lounge bar, but though they serve a light menu here, the main feature is still to come. Besides two formal dining rooms in the main house, you can also sit down to dinner in a sumptuously comfortable 1930s Brighton Belle Pullman carriage: all of the respectful elegance of the Age of Steam, none of the points failures. Whatever you choose, a classic menu with an emphasis on seafood is served with a nice, straightforward friendliness.

Food serving times:
Monday-Saturday:
12pm-2pm, 6.30pm-10.15pm
Closed 24-26 December
- Seafood specialities -
Prices:
Meals: 18.95 (fixed price lunch) and a la carte 25.00/38.00

Typical Dishes

Lobster, pancetta and foie gras salad

Scallops, sea bass and langoustine

Blueberry panna cotta

4.25mi Northeast of Richmond by A6108
Parking

Osmotherley

022 Golden Lion

6 West End, Osmotherley DL6 3AA
Tel.: (01609) 883526 - Fax: (01609) 884000

   VISA MC JCB

Timothy Taylor Landlord, Jennings Bitter, Nick Stafford's Hambleton Ales

If you're walking the Cleveland Way, this old stone faced pub is like manna from heaven – it turns up right there on the path, so if you pay a visit, you're likely to meet fellow hikers. It's nothing very special to look at, and the interior isn't too much more than white walls and a few old pews, but the mix of ramblers, locals and those in search of a decent dinner keeps the atmosphere lively and friendly. What draws the dining fraternity here are the simple, well-constructed, keenly priced dishes that consistently hit the spot. Tried-and-tested meals are prepared with real care: steak and kidney with suet crust, mashed potatoes and peas; home-made meat lasagne with chips; calves liver with fried onions, mash and peas. Hearty fuel for heading to the hills.

Food serving times:
Monday-Sunday:
    12pm-3pm, 6pm-10pm
Closed 25 December
Prices:
Meals: a la carte 15.00/26.00

Typical Dishes

Crab mayonnaise

Steak and kidney suet pudding

Orange cake, marmalade cream

6mi Northeast of Northallerton by A684
Parking in village

Osmotherley

023 ## The 3 Tuns

9 South End, Osmotherley DL6 3BN

Tel.: (01609) 883301 - Fax: (01609) 883988

e-mail: enquiries@the3tuns.net

 ⌗ ✗=rest 🚫 **VISA** **AE** **MC**

Timothy Taylor Landlord

An unassuming pub on first sight – the modern sign outside is the first hint at the sympathetic refit that's taken place indoors. Pale oak panelling lightens rather than darkens the bar and restaurant, and combines surprisingly well with the retro design – there's more than a touch of re-interpreted Rennie Mackintosh in the pub's style. Three bedrooms in the pub and four in the cottage next door have been designed with similar care: they're spacious, comfortable and nicely maintained. Though you can wander in for a drink – and people do – the focus here is on food, served in a neatly set back room and also out on the front and back terraces: dishes like seared salmon and asparagus with pesto cream or a traditional crème brûlée form the core of a concise menu.

Food serving times:
Monday-Sunday:
12pm-2.30pm,
5.30pm-9.30pm

Prices:
Meals: a la carte 12.00/30.00
🛏 **7 rooms:** 49.00/65.00

6mi Northeast of Northallerton by A684
Parking

Typical Dishes

King scallops, duet of pesto
Beef fillet and langoustines
Chocolate fondue

Ramsgill-in-Nidderdale

024 Yorke Arms

Ramsgill-in-Nidderdale HG3 5RL

Tel.: (01423) 755243 - Fax: (01423) 755330
e-mail: enquiries@yorke-arms.co.uk - Website: www.yorke-arms.co.uk

 Black Sheep and 1 guest ale

Set in unspoilt countryside near Gouthwaite reservoir, this part 17C former shooting lodge is quite simply one of England's most charming inns. Handsomely styled with carved wooden furniture, antiques, oriental rugs and bright, gilt-framed oils, two welcoming dining rooms feel closer in atmosphere to a country house than a village pub, and the formal, structured service is that of a restaurant rather than an inn, but as a dining experience it's calm, refined and, at its best, quite delightful. Precise and consistent seasonal cooking balances classical style with a subtle regional identity and fully deserves its Michelin star: try brill with asparagus and girolle risotto, foie gras and pigeon terrine with fig chutney or braised hare on rosemary gnocchi. Good value lunch Monday to Saturday, lovely riverside terrace and stylish bedrooms.

Food serving times:
Monday-Sunday:
    12pm-2pm, 7pm-9pm
Accommodation rates include dinner
Prices:
Meals: 17.50/49.00 and a la carte 30.00/43.50
🛏 **13 rooms:** 105.00/340.00

Typical Dishes

Scallops, langoustine, butternut squash

Nidderdale lamb

Curd tart, rhubarb milkshake

5mi Northwest of Pateley Bridge by Low Wath Rd.
Parking

Scorton

025 Arden Arms

Atley hill, Scorton DL7 0JB

Tel.: (01325) 378678 - Fax: (01325) 378166
e-mail: info@ardenarms.co.uk - Website: www.ardenarms.co.uk

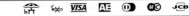

Timothy Taylor Landlord, Black Sheep Best

Halfway between the Dales and the North York Moors, this traditional pub is certainly in an out-of-the-way location, though for the ease-of-access minded, the A1 and Scotch Corner are comfortably close at hand. In sympathy with its surroundings, the Arden likes to keep things simple. It's not heavy on the character front, but there is a flagged floor and the odd piece of timber. Two cosy little rooms lead off the bar, and you can tuck into good value, modern or tried-and-tested dishes in any of these areas. The more adventurous blackboard specials are worth a shot, too. Sea bass with chorizo risotto and pineapple confit might well take your fancy, with orange and cardamom crème caramel to finish off. If your appetite's especially large, try the Arden hors d'oeuvres plate!

Food serving times:
Tuesday-Sunday:
   12pm-2.30pm, 6pm-9.30pm
Prices:
Meals: a la carte 16.50/25.00

Typical Dishes

Twice-baked soufflé

Whole Dover sole

Crème brûlée

On the edge of the Yorkshire Dales on the B1263. Parking

Sinnington

026 Fox and Hounds

Main St, Sinnington YO62 6SQ

Tel.: (01751) 431577 - Fax: (01751) 432791
e-mail: foxhoundsinn@easynet.co.uk - Website: www.thefoxandhoundsinn.co.uk

 Camerons, Black Sheep Special

Drive four miles out from the attractive market town of Pickering and you arrive in sleepy Sinnington on the river Seven, at the southern end of the North York Moors. The Fox And Hounds, an attractively extended 18C coaching inn, is the pivot around which community life revolves. Its characterful front bar is beamed and panelled in ancient oak, with old artefacts and a woodburner. Flop down there or retreat to the smart residents lounge with a pint of local ale. The restaurant, housed in a rear extension, has smart, linen-clad tables and impressive menus to match: slow roasted Goosenargh duck with red plum and sour cherry chutney, port and red wine reduction; or salad of pan seared halibut fillet with warm salad of roasted fennel, red onion, salmon, monkfish and basil. Bedrooms are pleasant and well kept.

Food serving times:
Monday-Saturday:
12pm-2pm, 6.30pm-9pm
Sunday: 12pm-2pm,
6.30pm-8.30pm

Closed 25 December
Prices:
Meals: a la carte 15.50/30.00
🛏 **3 rooms:** 59.00/100.00

Just off A170 between Pickering and Kirkymoorside. Parking

Typical Dishes

Stilton soufflé

Roast duck, honey and lavender sauce

Chocolate mousse

Skipton

027 # The Bull

Broughton, Skipton BD23 3AE
Tel.: (01756) 792065 - Fax: (01756) 792065
e-mail: janeneil@thebullatbroughton.co.uk - Website: www.thebullatbroughton.co.uk

Bull Bitter, Copper Dragon, Tetleys Cask

Don't let the busy A59 send you roaring off into the Pennines without a stop at this delightful country pub, located within the grounds of Broughton Hall Country Park Estate amid 3000 Yorkshire acres. It's a lovely old building which has been carefully refurbished to bring out the open log fire, rustic décor and intimate seating areas. The greetings are effusive, even from the pub cat. A selection of hand-drawn cask ales is always available, but pride of place-mat goes to the Bull's own beer brewed specially for them. The relaxing feel stretches to the dining rooms which envelop you in a web of warm stone. Chef makes good use of ingredients close to hand with produce from the Dales never far from your knife and fork; the pub's "everything home-made" credentials are worn as a badge of honour.

Food serving times:
Monday-Thursday:
    12pm-2pm, 6pm-9pm
Friday-Saturday:
    12pm-2pm, 6pm-9.30pm
Sunday: 12pm-6pm
Closed Bank Holiday Monday
Prices:
Meals: a la carte 15.50/22.48

Typical Dishes

Warm goat's cheese, tomato salad

Sausage and mash

Chocolate ice cream, raspberry coulis

3mi West of Skipton town centre on A59. In the grounds of Broughton Hall Country Park Estate. Parking

Sutton-on-the-Forest

028 **Rose & Crown**

Main St, Sutton-on-the-Forest YO61 1DP

Tel.: (01347) 811333 - Fax: (01347) 811444

e-mail: mail@rosecrown.co.uk - Website: www.rosecrown.co.uk

 Black Sheep Best, Timothy Taylors Landlord

Everyday pub name, exceptional pub cooking: crisp black pudding with quail's egg and pancetta, juicy pink lamb in thyme broth and deliciously smooth amaretto parfait are typical of a carefully sourced and precisely prepared repertoire that's won plaudits around the county and beyond. The smart, modern feel has softened slightly in a cosily rustic interior, but it's definitely a change for the better: it's unobtrusively stylish but still feels relaxed, and service is smooth and attentive without ever seeming stifling.The little seating and dining areas add a touch of intimacy, while the firelit bar, and the fair-minded value-for-money ethic, are in the best Yorkshire tradition. Good, frequently changing wine list. A Michelin Bib Gourmand winner for good food at moderate prices.

Food serving times:
Tuesday-Saturday:
        12pm-2pm, 6pm-9pm
Sunday: 12pm-2pm
Closed first 2 weeks January
Prices:
Meals: 12.95 and a la carte 16.00/30.00

Typical Dishes
Black pudding, honey and mustard

Ribeye steak, oxtail bourguignonne

Fig tarte Tatin

On B1363 North of York. Parking

Wass

029 Wombwell Arms

Wass YO61 4BE

Tel.: (01347) 868280 - Fax: (01347) 868039
e-mail: thewombwellarms@aol.com - Website: www.thewombwellarms.co.uk

      VISA MC

Timothy Taylor Landlord, Black Sheep

A drive north into the Howardian hills, past Coxwold and Byland Abbey, leads you to the tiny village of Wass and a country inn content to do what it does best. Its likeably old-fashioned bar in local stone has settles, stools and little tables for slow pint-supping, while three sympathetically redecorated dining rooms – bright and well-kept – make eating out seem easy and relaxed, rather than a matter of standing on ceremony. An appetising menu doesn't stint on variety, either: you might choose from pints of prawns, Whitby cod, roasts and grills or hearty casseroles made with Masham ale, though their meat pies are a matter of personal pride, too, and really call for one of their local beers. Pleasantly furnished rooms are a good stop-off if you're planning to tour the North York Moors.

Food serving times:
Monday-Friday:
    12pm-2pm, 6.30pm-9pm
Saturday: 12pm-2.30pm,
                6.30pm-9.30pm
Sunday: 12pm-2.30pm
Closed Monday January-March

Prices:
Meals: 12.45/20.00 and a la carte 18.00/31.00
🛏 **3 rooms:** 42.00/70.00

Typical Dishes

Black pudding, mushrooms and bacon

Wild boar sausage

Chocolate torte with hazelnuts

6mi Southwest of Helmsley by A170
Parking

West Tanfield

030 The Bruce Arms

Main St, West Tanfield HG4 5JJ

Tel.: (01677) 470325 - Fax: (01677) 470796
Website: www.brucearms.com

 No real ales offered

This thriving little Yorkshire pub looks no great shakes from the outside, despite the rather fetching creepers. Inside, though, a mini success story unfolds. Dating from 1820, it crams in timbers, log fire, heaps of local memorabilia, and a good local ales on tap. In 1997, it re-styled itself as a bistro and its well-prepared, interesting dishes get the thumbs-up from all comers. You can eat in the intimate bar, in a cosy dining room, or on the vine covered terrace in warmer weather. Home made dishes could include twice baked Wensleydale cheese soufflé for starters, followed by braised lamb shank, parsley mash and red wine gravy, or the rather exotic chicken breast with banana, smoked ham, coconut and mild curry sauce.

Food serving times:
Monday-Saturday:
  12pm-2pm, 6.30pm-9.30pm
Sunday: 12pm-2pm
Closed 2 weeks February
Closed Monday lunch
Prices:
Meals: a la carte 20.00/27.50
3 rooms: 40.00/60.00

Typical Dishes
Scallops, wild mushroom risotto

Rack of lamb

Chocolate brownie, hot black cherries

Between Marsham and Ripon on A6108
Parking

Whitwell-on-the-Hill

031 ## The Stone Trough Inn

Kirkham Abbey, Whitwell-on-the-Hill YO60 7JS

Tel.: (01653) 618713 - Fax: (01653) 618819

e-mail: info@stonetroughinn.co.uk - Website: www.stonetroughinn.co.uk

     VISA **M©**

 Black Sheep Best, Timothy Taylor Landlord, Theakstons Old Peculier, Malton Golden Chance and 1 guest beer

A truly idyllic spot on a summer's day – the Stone Trough Inn overlooks the ruins of 12C Kirkham Abbey and the long bend of the River Derwent. The pub itself is newer than it might first seem, and the skillful and sympathetic reconstruction looks still more authentic from the inside; a charmingly rustic, heavily beamed bar built of Yorkshire stone is full of little nooks and snugs. You can dine here, choosing from a varied selection of Modern British dishes and blackboard specials, or take your drinks through to the restaurant, which actually feels more like a big farmhouse kitchen, complete with pine tables and chairs. Here, again, the cooking is fresh and nicely judged, including dishes like chicken with bacon and Yorkshire blue cheese or loin of Northern lamb stuffed with apricots.

Food serving times:
Tuesday-Saturday:
  12pm-2pm, 6.30pm-9.30pm
Sunday: 12pm-2pm
Closed 25 December. Open Bank Holiday Mondays
Prices:
Meals: a la carte 20.00/27.75

Typical Dishes

Belly pork, sweet pepper relish

Smoked cheese soufflé

Apple, raisin and cinnamon filo roll

5mi Southwest of Malton by A64
Parking

Sheffield

032 Lions Lair

31 Burgess St, Sheffield S1 2HF

Tel.: (0114) 263 4264 · Fax: (0114) 263 4265
e-mail: info@lionslair.co.uk · Website: www.lionslair.co.uk

   VISA **MC**

 Tetleys, Black Sheep

The centre of Sheffield may not be the automatic choice for those in search of cosy rusticity, but this neat little pub hidden away in the heart of the city provides a number of pleasant surprises. It boasts a lovely enclosed rear terrace with the added attraction of stylishly nautical decking where summer barbeques and live music rustle the Yorkshire air, and a snug interior dining room with leather banquettes, pleasing mix of tables and popular, wide-ranging menus which are unfussy and freshly prepared. For starters, try the nibble platter, which includes marinated baby artichokes, toasted brioche with foie gras and Parmesan tuile, then move onto posh fish and chips served with Yorkshire caviar, boudin of guinea fowl with wild mushroom ragout, or honey glazed lamb shank.

Food serving times:
Monday-Saturday:
12pm-9pm
Sunday: 12pm-3pm
Closed 25-26 December and 1 January
Prices:
Meals: a la carte 15.00/25.00

Typical Dishes

Gateau of aubergine, cheese and lemon

Springbok, port jus

Spice and ginger nut crumble

Burgess St is off Parker's Pool, to the South of City Hall. Public Parking nearby

Totley

033 **The Cricket Inn**

Penny Lane, Totley S17 3AZ

Tel.: (0114) 236 5256 - Fax: (0114) 235 6582

e-mail: info@the-cricket.com - Website: www.the-cricket.com

  ⚡-rest

 Timothy Taylor Landlord, Stones

Among the copses and fields, where Sheffield's outermost suburbs blend into countryside, you'll find the home ground of Totley Cricket Club and, next to it, the trimly kept Cricket Inn. A traditionally informal bar is filled with the team's memorabilia; bats and bails, team photos, shots of cavalier strokemakers and hurricane 'quicks' all reflect the first love of the White Rose county. Nourishing and enjoyable food, prepared with culinary good sense, includes carrot soup with walnut pesto and homemade rolls, tasty steak and Brie sandwiches, pastas, pies and a fish special. The formal restaurant, with a menu to match, opens in the evening and for Sunday lunch; service is polite and friendly throughout. Afterwards, you could always stroll to the boundary and see if you can spot the next Trueman, Boycott or Vaughan...

Food serving times:
Tuesday-Saturday:
    12pm-2.30pm, 6pm-7pm
Sunday: 12pm-2.30pm
Closed 25 December and 1 January
(bar lunch only Tuesday-Saturday)

Prices:
Meals: a la carte 15.00/35.00

Typical Dishes

Lobster and lemon sole ravioli

Supreme of guinea fowl

Chocolate fondant

1mi South West of Sheffield by A621 (Baslow), after passing through Totley turn right into Hillfoot Road, down the hill and left into Penny Lane.

Addingham

034 Fleece

154 Main St., Addingham LS29 0LY

Tel.: (01943) 830491
e-mail: chris@monkmansbistro.fsbusiness.co.uk

 VISA ⓂⒸ

 Tetleys Cask, Timothy Taylor Landlord, Black Sheep

This good-looking, ivy-clad pub sits on the busy main street in Addingham, close to the southern 'gateway' to the Yorkshire Dales National Park. Its pleasing features extend across the threshold, where can be found open fires to entice chilled walkers on cold days, a solid stone floor, and rustic walls filled with country oriented prints, oils and general nick-nacks. It's all overseen in a very personally run style by the charming owner, and the homely ambience extends to the dining area, which boasts 1930s style tables. There's an appealing mix of dishes from the blackboard menu, the repertoire covering anything from queen scallops au gratin or prawn and mango cocktail to smoked haddock with wholegrain mustard sauce or pork and black pudding sausages with creamy mash: the sausages are straight from Lishmans, the local butcher.

Food serving times:
Monday-Saturday:
 12pm-2.15pm, 6pm-9.15pm
Sunday: 12pm-8pm
Prices:
Meals: a la carte 15.00/25.00

Typical Dishes

Antipasti, roast vegetables

Roast sea bass

Calvados bread and butter pudding

On the busy through road in the centre of Addingham. Parking

Halifax

035 ## Shibden Mill Inn

Shibden Mill Fold, Halifax HX3 7UL

Tel.: (01422) 365840 - Fax: (01422) 362971
e-mail: shibdenmillinn@zoom.co.uk - Website: www.shibdenmillinn.com

Shibden Mill Bitter, Theakstons XB, John Smiths and 2 regularly changing guest bitters

Only a mile or two outside the centre of Halifax, and the landscape of the Shibden Valley already feels properly rural. The old millpond has long since run dry, and the formal split-level dining room gives away little of the mill's history, but there's a more authentic country feel to the main bar. With a pleasantly haphazard mix of landscape prints, plates and bottles for decoration, it's spacious but still intimate, and frankly the more inviting choice, although the frequently changing menu, served throughout, has more in common with restaurant dining. Served in hefty pub portions, the rather complex dishes bear the hallmarks of fashionable cooking over the last decade and reveal a solid background in the Modern British kitchen. Individually styled rooms, being refurbished one by one, make this a useful overnight stop.

Food serving times:
Monday-Sunday:
    12pm-2pm, 6pm-9.30pm
Prices:
Meals: a la carte 14.95/25.00
⊨ **12 rooms:** 65.00/115.00

Typical Dishes

Belly pork, bean and fennel salad

Duck, roast beetroot

Almond and rhubarb tart, ginger custard

2.25mi Northeast by A58 and Kell Lane (turning left at Stump Cross pub), on Blake Hill Rd
Parking

Marsden

036 Olive Branch

Manchester Rd, Marsden HD7 6LU

Tel.: (01484) 844487
Website: www.olivebranch.uk.com

Holme Valley

Four wonderfully cosy rooms – feeling almost like interlinking snugs – make up the heart of this part 16C former cattle-drover's inn that matches exposed brick, pine antiques and framed sepia photographs with a light dash of modernity. Add to this the personable approach of the owners and its easy to see why the Olive Branch's reputation reaches well beyond Marsden itself. Up on the wall, the blackboard menu changes at the rate of a departures board: this might disconcert any chronically indecisive diners, but speaks well for the freshness of the diverse and tasty cooking. Flavourful seafood specialities are guaranteed, in any case, though you might well find baked field mushrooms with tomato sauce or pan-fried pork with sage among the other contemporary country dishes. Comfortable bedrooms. Moorland and canalside walks.

1mi Northeast on A62
Parking

Food serving times:
Tuesday-Friday:
  12pm-2pm, 6.30pm-9.30pm
Saturday: 6.30pm-9.30pm
Sunday: 12pm-2pm,
  6.30pm-9.30pm
Closed first 2 weeks January
Closed Tuesday lunch
Prices:
Meals: 16.95 and a la carte
23.75/30.50
3 rooms: 50.00/65.00
10.50

Typical Dishes

Scallops in lime, garlic and cheese

Duck, onion and sultana marmalade

Lemon tart

Shelley

037 Three Acres

Roydhouse, Shelley HD8 8LR

Tel.: (01484) 602606 - Fax: (01484) 608411
e-mail: 3acres@globalnet.co.uk - Website: www.3acres.com

   VISA **AE**

 Timothy Taylor Landlord, Black Sheep, Tetley Bitter

Looking from a distance across the moor, you'd expect this traditional, stone-built inn to be a sleepy little place, but few inns are like the Three Acres. Vibrant, buzzy and extremely popular, the same positive mood holds sway throughout: some people have come for a beer in the bar, or have heard about the lovely integral deli selling lots of oils, pestos and other fine foods, but the real centre of the pub is the dining room. Any number of framed menus, not to mention fun food and wine-themed curiosities and collectables, suit the characterful, enthusiastic atmosphere and prompt the appetite for a wide-ranging menu with a broad, classic base. Comfortable bedrooms with some nice individual touches are divided between the pub and the adjacent block.

Food serving times:
Monday-Sunday:
12pm-2pm, 6.30pm-9.45pm
Closed 25 December-
3 January
(booking essential)
Prices:
Meals: a la carte 23.50/30.00
🛏 **20 rooms:** 60.00/80.00

Typical Dishes

Grilled goat's cheese on cider apples

Lemon sole, spinach

Black Forest truffle torte

6.25mi Southeast of Huddersfield by A629 on B6116
Parking

Silsden

038 The Grouse

Keighley Rd, Silsden BD20 0EH
Tel.: (01535) 657788 - Fax: (01535) 655742

VISA M©

Timothy Taylor Golden Best, Landlord

A buzzy pub, refurbished in late 2003, at the bottom of the town: in the latter part of the 18C, there were three cottages here but for many years it's served as an inn. As you approach, the modernisation is apparent, announced by frosted glass and aubergine coloured signs. Inside, halogen lighting, wood floors, muted tones and stark browns reflect the zeitgeist. David, the manager, and Matthew, the chef, are brothers whose teamwork gels smoothly. Diners order drinks at the small bar and eat at the uncovered tables; light lunches give way to handsomely endowed dinners, whose more formal character still manages to satisfy the local demand for steaks. Main courses might include Moroccan style seven vegetable and chickpea tagine, or breast of Gressingham duck with a beetroot, orange and red onion compote.

Food serving times:
Tuesday: 6pm-9.30pm
Wednesday-Saturday:
　12pm-2pm, 6pm-9.30pm
Sunday: 12pm-2pm
Prices:
Meals: a la carte 16.00/25.00

Parking

Typical Dishes

Aparagus, Serrano ham

Duck, beetroot and orange compote

Lemon tart, raspberry sorbet

Sowerby Bridge

039 **The Millbank**

Mill Bank Road, Sowerby Bridge HX6 3DY

Tel.: (01422) 825588

e-mail: themillbank@yahoo.co.uk - Website: www.themillbank.com

Tetley Bitter, Timothy Taylor Landlord

Here's a proper pub with flagged floors and exposed stone in an invigorating position in the Pennines. It caters just as readily for drinkers as for those who've come in to eat, even though its modernised interior certainly puts it firmly into the dining pub league. Chunky wooden tables and chairs, a ready warmth of service, allied to interesting modern cooking, guarantee customers from far and wide, and booking is essential. A neat little terrace helps take the strain. You might want to try pheasant breast suffed with pistachios, fondant potato, creamed cabbage and bacon or Goosnargh duck breast, with potato and mushroom Anna, apricot and cardamon chutney: whatever you choose, a Michelin Bib Gourmand award guarantees good food at a modest price. Recently completed, well-kept bedrooms add to the inn's reputation.

Food serving times:
Tuesday-Thursday:
    12pm-2.30pm, 6pm-9.30pm
Friday-Saturday:
    12pm-2.30pm, 6pm-10pm
Sunday: 12pm-4.30pm
Closed first week January and first 2 weeks October (booking essential)
Prices:
Meals: a la carte 18.95/32.95

Typical Dishes

Smoked chicken ravioli

Sea bass, celeriac

Hot chocolate fondant cake

2.25mi Southwest by A58
Parking on the road in front of the pub

Thunder Bridge

040　Woodman Inn

Thunder Bridge HD8 0PX

Tel.: (01484) 605778 - Fax: (01484) 604110
e-mail: thewoodman@connectfree.co.uk - Website: www.woodman-inn.co.uk

   VISA MC

 Timothy Taylor Landlord, Best, Tetleys, Websters Best

Take the road south from Huddersfield and you're soon in 'Last of the Summer Wine' country, the ideal setting for this 19C inn of Yorkshire stone which, nearly a decade ago, was extended by the owners to include the adjacent old weavers' cottages. Thus was created a host of well thought out, sizable bedrooms, the perfect final destination after an invigorating day in the nearby Southern Pennines. Bars and restaurant are of more recent vintage, having both been refurbished in 2003. You can eat formally, at linen-clad tables, in the latter, while scrubbed tables and a more free and easy ambience set the mood for dining in the rest of the pub. Tasty, unfussy dishes appear on an appealing menu that utilises freshly prepared, local ingredients in a traditional manner.

Food serving times:
Monday-Saturday:
　　　12pm-3pm, 6pm-9pm
Sunday:　　　12pm-6pm
Prices:
Meals: 10.95 and a la carte
16.00/24.00
🛏 **12 rooms:** 45.00/65.00

Typical Dishes
Seafood timbale
Chicken with chorizo and
black pudding
Strawberries, Champagne
sorbet

5.75mi South East of Huddersfield by A629, after Kirkburton follow signs to Thunder Bridge. Parking

*W*indswept peaks and misty lochs from the pages of Burns and Scott or the urban grit of modern film and fiction? Visitors could be forgiven for wondering what to expect, in this country of contrasts, but it's all here: the wild beauty of Wester Ross and the Neoclassical elegance of Edinburgh's New Town, the fishing villages of the East Neuk, sheltering on the North Sea coast, the lush gardens of Inverewe, warmed by the Gulf Stream in the west, as well as the vibrance of straight-talking Glasgow. This is a land where tradition can mean etiquette and fellowship on the first tee or the raw energy of Shetland's Viking fire festival, centuries of pre-eminence in British science and letters, or a turbulent social history which has left its mark on every part of life. There's a difference in town and country pub culture, too. Perhaps more than anywhere else in Britain, inns in the remote countryside are often the centres for a widespread community : pub, hotel, restaurant and even shop in one, with a wise word behind the bar on anything from fishing lures to football scores. In Glasgow and Edinburgh, however, dining pubs are only a tiny part of a busy year-round cultural life, which hits fever pitch with the creativity and sheer variety of the summer festivals. One thing is for sure, century-old inns and modern gastropubs take equal pride in their national specialities: smoked or fresh salmon and trout, Loch Linnhe prawns, seafood soups like Cullen Skink and Partan Bree, prime beef, Highland game and haggis.

Yell Unst

Shetland

Hillswick
Sandness
Mainland Lerwick
Sumburgh

Bergen
Aberdeen
Stromness

Westray
Rousay Sanday
Mainland Stronsay
ness Kirkwall
Wick

Pentland Firth
Aberdeen

N O R T H

142 Banff Fraserburgh
Keith A 96
105 Peterhead
A 96
ey Bergen
Stromness
Lerwick
1 Aberdeen
eins Stonehaven
90 68
94 Montrose
Arbroath
Andrews
Forth
orth Berwick
ngton
15 Berwick-upon-Tweed
Tweed
Coldstream
burgh 119
Alnwick
Wall A 696
Blyth
Newcastle Tynemouth Bergen
upon-Tyne South Shields Stavanger
Gateshead Sunderland
Durham Hartlepool
Middlesbrough
Darlington Whitby

S E

M E R

D U

N O

Netherley

001 ## Lairhillock Inn

Netherley AB39 3QS

Tel.: (01569) 730001 - Fax: (01569) 731175
e-mail: lairhillock@breathemail.net - Website: www.lairhillock.co.uk

 🍴 ✂ **VISA** **AE** **①** **MC**

Timothy Taylor Landlord, Courage Directors and a selection of Isle of Skye ales

Beautiful Deeside country stretches away to either side, and the Granite City is only a 15-minute drive, but tearing yourself away from a ramble in the hills is not an altogether bad idea when the wonderfully atmospheric front snug bar is the destination. A former coaching inn, the Lairhillock remains the beating heart of the village, and the snug exerts a gravitational pull. It's an invariably busy and friendly bar, but if you find the bustle a bit too much, then there are other areas to discover: there's a lounge with an altogether more relaxed feel, and a conservatory with open fires, which is the place to dig into a good choice of satisfying, rustic dishes chock full of local produce: Gourdon langoustines, salmon from the Dee and Don, Highland venison and boar, and Shetland mussels.

Food serving times:
Monday-Thursday:
12pm-2pm, 6pm-9.30pm
Friday-Saturday:
12pm-2pm, 6pm-10pm
Sunday: 12pm-2pm,
5.30pm-9pm
Closed 25-26 December and 1-2 January
Prices:
Meals: a la carte 19.15/32.55

Typical Dishes
Grilled pigeon salad
Salmon, pepper and parmesan crust
Cranachan and shortbread tower

5mi North of Stonehaven by B979, then Northeast 1.5mi on Portlethen rd.
Parking

Crinan

002 Crinan

Crinan PA31 8SR

Tel.: (01546) 830261 - Fax: (01546) 830292
e-mail: nryan@crinanhotel.com - Website: www.crinanhotel.com

 rest **VISA** **AE** **MC**

Velvet, Belhaven

Superbly located in a commanding position with exceptional views of Loch Crinan and Sound of Jura, this elegant, whitewashed building has picture windows that let guests take in superb views of fishing boats chugging out towards the Hebrides. Naturally enough, the bar has a nautical theme, while there are two homely lounges to sit and watch the world go by. There's a Gallery bar, too, which overlooks the loch. With all this natural beauty in abundance, make sure you get to eat where you can take in the vista. The split-level restaurant is smart with linen clad tables, and the menus have an interesting, modern feel to them. Try, maybe, roast scallops, cauliflower puree and raisin vinaigrette for starters; skate salad with haricot verte, or fillet of beef, cubed celeriac and red wine jus for a main. Stay in pleasant, bright bedrooms.

Food serving times:
Monday-Sunday:
   12pm-3pm, 6.30pm-8.30pm
Closed Christmas-New Year
Accommodation rates include dinner
Prices:
Meals: a la carte 13.85/15.50
20 rooms : 140.00/340.00

Typical Dishes

Oak smoked salmon

Loch Crinan prawns, Skye salad

Isle of Orkney ice cream

8mi Northwest of Lochgilphead by A816 and B841.
At the end of Crinan canal on the edge of Loch Crinan. Parking

Kintyre - Kilberry

003 Kilberry Inn

Kintyre-Kilberry PA29 6YD

Tel.: (01880) 770223 - Fax: (01880) 770223
e-mail: relax@kilberryinn.com - Website: www.kilberryinn.com

 VISA **MC**

 Arran

Between the wooded heights and the widening Sound of Jura stands a whitewashed cottage on a long country road. It's as simple as you could wish: a parlour for lunch and dinner and a little beamed lounge in stone and pine, with local landscapes on the walls, a fire in the hearth and local whiskies behind the bar. Oh, and a few gold discs awarded to the owner's son, the drummer in Travis! The blackboard menu changes every day, but the fortifying home cooking always has a real local flavour to it and the ingredients are all found close to home. It's the efforts of the staff that really make the place, though, with a nice, upfront informality setting the tone. The three bedrooms are cosy and usefully equipped: you'll need a good night's sleep before touring Arran or following the Islay and Jura whisky trail!

Food serving times:
Tuesday-Saturday:
    12.30pm-2pm, 7pm-8pm
Sunday: 12.30pm-2pm
Closed end October-end March. Open Bank Holiday Mondays

Prices:
Meals: a la carte 15.00/25.00
🛏 **3 rooms :** 42.50/85.00

Typical Dishes

Smoked haddock chowder

Salmon with pesto and parmesan crust

Arran cheese plate

15mi West of Tarbert on B8024. Parking

Strachur

004 **The Creggans Inn**

Strachur PA27 8BX

Tel.: (01369) 860279 - Fax: (01369) 860637
e-mail: info@creggans-inn.co.uk - Website: www.creggans-inn.co.uk

 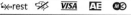

A wide selection of ales offered

The enviable delights of Loch Fyne in wild and remote Argyll and Bute provide a haunting and spectacular backdrop to this whitewashed, roadside inn. The Creggan has a well-established and hard-earned local reputation, built up by years of smoothly run service. There's a cosy bar and small wicker-chaired conservatory, and two lounges, one of which has a fine outlook. You can eat at the bar, or the spacious dining room with its wood floor and warm colour scheme. Dishes are flavoursome and full of fine Scottish ingredients. Walks in the area are guaranteed to bring on a very restful state, and the Creggan comes up trumps with delightful, cottage style bedrooms.

Food serving times:
Monday-Sunday:
  12pm-2.45pm, 6pm-8.45pm
Closed 25-26 December
(bar lunch)/dinner
Prices:
Meals: 28.00 and a la carte
15.00/30.00
14 rooms : 80.00/140.00

Typical Dishes

Tomato and pepper soup

Poached sea bass

Lemongrass and ginger panna cotta

On A815 on shores of Loch Fyne.
Parking and 2 moorings for boats

Tayvallich

005 Tayvallich Inn

Tayvallich PA31 8PL
Tel.: (01546) 870282 - Fax: (01546) 870330
Website: www.tayvallich.com

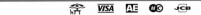

Calky

In glorious isolation stands Tayvallich in the Sound of Jura. It's a little coastal hamlet with cosy harbour and Gulf Stream-nourished palm trees close to the shores of Loch Sween; the Tayvallich Inn, quite rightly, is the hub of the community. Believe it or not, it was the local bus garage until the early 1970s, when it was converted into its present incarnation. It has an enviable lochside setting and a smart whitewashed exterior with pleasant summer decking at the front. Inside, at the large bar in plump cushioned chairs, is a great place to mingle with the locals. Next door the pine furnished dining room has windows on three sides for the views, and interesting menus, which rely on fresh supplies of prawns, scallops and the local catch to underpin creative dishes.

Food serving times:
Monday-Sunday:
　　12pm-2pm, 6pm-10pm
Closed November-March
Prices:
Meals: a la carte 12.40/24.95

On B8025 on the shores of Loch Sween. Parking

Typical Dishes

Scallops on black pudding

Mushroom and parmesan pasta

Crème brûlée

Swinton

015 The Wheatsheaf

Main Street, Swinton TD11 3JJ

Tel.: (01890) 860257 - Fax: (01890) 860688

e-mail: reception@wheatsheaf-swinton.co.uk - Website: www.wheatsheaf-swinton.co.uk

     VISA

Deuchars IPA, Broughton Greenmantle

This cosy, attractive village inn on the Scottish borders has a welcoming stone façade, but the main delight here comes when you step through the entrance into the firelit bar with its fine array of real ales and wander through to the adjoining rooms whose nooks and crannies throw up subtle changes of character. The stylish restaurant is well renowned locally. It sources fresh seafood from Eyemouth Harbour, just 12 miles away, as well as borders beef, lamb and organic pork from local, traditional butchers. For dinner, you might try peppered breast of Gressingham duck in a thyme scented sauce with pink peppercorns, or baked fillet of local salmon with tarragon and prawns.

Food serving times:
Monday-Sunday:
    12pm-2pm, 6pm-9pm
Closed 24-26 December, 31 December-1 January and Sunday dinner December-January

Prices:
Meals: a la carte 15.00/33.00

🛏 **7 rooms :** 62.00/120.00

Typical Dishes

Asparagus with pancetta on toast

Lamb, basil and mustard

Pear, ginger pudding

6mi North of Coldstream on A6112. Parking

Gatehead

006 **Cochrane Inn**

45 Main Rd, Gatehead KA2 0AP
Tel.: (01563) 570122

No real ales offered

A golfer's paradise: that's this traditional East Ayrshire pub, surrounded by a phalanx of courses, including the nearby Royal Troon, only five miles away on the coast. It's a fine place to relax after playing a round: the rustic stone interior or well-tended garden are ideal spots for recounting those putts that got away. The bar area boasts plenty of Scottish ales, and you can drink at little tables made from beer barrels. The separate dining room won't win any design awards, but that's how the locals like it: nice and simple, with exposed stone walls. Experienced staff serve hearty, honest, good value, well-cooked dishes with a Scottish accent and lacking any superfluous frills: try Cumberland sausage with pink peppercorn sauce and Cheddar mash, or traditional haggis with neeps and tatties.

Food serving times:
Monday-Sunday:
    12pm-2pm, 5.30pm-9pm
(booking essential)
Prices:
Meals: a la carte 16.00/20.00

Typical Dishes

Pickled Arctic herring, beetroot

Beefsteak and sausage pie

Sticky toffee pudding

3mi Southwest of Kilmarnock on A759.
Parking

Sorn

007 Sorn Inn

35 Main St, Sorn KA5 6HU

Tel.: (01290) 551305 - Fax: (01290) 553470
e-mail: craig@sorninn - Website: www.sorninn.com

VISA MC JCB

Arran ales, Bavarian Weihenstephaner

This traditional, family run whitewashed inn nestles enviably in the heart of the Ayrshire countryside. There's a small bar which is popular with locals and which offers the "Chop House" menu of steaks and simpler dishes. The real hub of the inn, though, is the rear dining room clothed in smart linen-clad tables and with a small lounge offshoot. It specialises in modern British cooking that's particularly good value for the accomplished cooking on offer, which specialises in using locally sourced meat, fish and game. Worth looking out for are breast of pigeon on sarladaise potato, bok choi, light Madeira and juniper berry jus, or sea trout on crushed new potatoes, pea and mint velouté. To round things off, there are four simple but modern and comfy bedrooms with showers and even DVD players.

Food serving times:
Tuesday-Friday:
12pm-2.30pm, 6pm-9pm
Saturday: 12pm-9pm
Sunday: 12.30pm-7.30pm
Open Bank Holiday Mondays
Prices:
Meals: 14.00/34.00 and a la carte 14.00/34.00
4 rooms : 40.00/90.00

Typical Dishes
Scallops, rum and raisin dressing
Beef with horseradish couscous
Ravioli of chocolate

9mi West of Muirkirk on B743.
Parking

Glasgow

008 Babbity Bowster

16-18 Blackfriars St, Glasgow G1 1PE
Tel.: (0141) 552 5055 - Fax: (0141) 522 7774

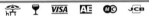 VISA AE MC JCB

 Deuchars IPA, Peters Well Addlestone Cider and a regularly changing guest ale

A well-regarded Glasgow favourite in a carefully renovated townhouse, more informal than the neo-Classical façade might lead you might expect. Simple gingham-clothed tables and sketches and photos of city life set the tone in a laid-back, open-plan bar, where a short lunchtime menu of warming, substantial dishes includes Cullen Skink and stovies - meat and potato casseroles – as well as French bistro standards and croques monsieur. Upstairs, the restaurant's evening menu is a touch more formal but every bit as robust and tasty, choosing Scottish produce for its oat-crusted venison or sea bass in brandy butter. Oh, and the origin of the name? An old country dance which, like all the best folk songs, has at least two risqué interpretations to it. The friendly staff are happy to oblige with an explanation, or maybe even a rendition…

Food serving times:
Monday-Sunday:
12pm-10.30pm
Closed 25 December
Prices:
Meals: a la carte 12.95/25.85
🛏 **6 rooms :** 40.00/60.00
☕ 6.00

Typical Dishes

Scallops with red pepper

Saddle of red deer

Clootie dumpling with toffee sauce

Parking for hotel guests only ➤

Glasgow

009 **Rab Ha's**

83 Hutcheson St, Glasgow G1 1SH

Tel.: (0141) 572 0400 - Fax: (0141) 572 0402
e-mail: management@rabhas.com - Website: www.rabhas.com

VISA **AE** **M©**

No real ales offered

Built on the New World tobacco trade, the exchanges, halls and warehouses of Merchant City are finding a new lease of life as shops, living space and, yes, gastropubs. After the magnificence of Hutcheson's Hall and the Victorian City Chambers around the corner, Rab Ha's rather blank façade looks like a bit of a let-down. Inside, though, it's far more inviting, lively and modern and, on a cold night, discreetly cosy: there's a bit of relaxed 'take-us-as-you-find-us' about the place, but if anything the service is actually more efficient and friendly for it. As students and local businessmen squeeze onto chairs and benches, you can clink lagers and weigh up a bar menu running from Thai curry to haggis with the trimmings. A more formal restaurant selection is more likely to take in cod with leek and tomato or beef in thyme and port sauce.

Food serving times:
Monday-Sunday:
          12pm-10.30pm
Closed 25 December and
1 January
(bar lunch)
Prices:
Meals: 19.95 and a la carte
19.95/28.95
🛏 **4 rooms :** 65.00/75.00

Typical Dishes

Scallops, bacon and avocado relish

Spice-crusted lamb

White and dark chocolate parfait

Parking on the street or in nearby NCP car park in Glassford Street

Achiltibuie

010 **Summer Isles**

Achiltibuie IV26 2YG

Tel.: (01854) 622282 - Fax: (01854) 622251
e-mail: info@summerisleshotel@aol.com - Website: www.summerisleshotel.co.uk

Orkney Dark Island, Isle of Sky Red Cuillin

An idyllically named establishment for an idyllic setting – this super bar and hotel faces the eponymous isles, far away from the madding crowd at the end of a 20 mile single track road. The bar is the 'village pub', attached to the hotel but separate from it. Its simple, rustic ambience is perfect for the setting: sit in wooden booths and take in the wild, untouched landscape. You'll dine on seafood platters and rustic dishes such as casseroles and lamb shank; in the summer, don't miss the chance to eat al fresco. If you plump for the hotel, you'll be sampling precisely judged cuisine which has earned a Michelin Star for its excellence. There's every chance you'll stay the night: look forward to bedrooms ranging from simple and restrained to smart and sophisticated.

Food serving times:
Monday-Sunday:
12pm-3pm, 6pm-9pm
Closed 25 December and
1 January
No food service mid
October-Easter - Seafood -
(bookings not accepted)
Prices:
Meals: a la carte 15.00/28.00
13 rooms : 75.00/180.00

Typical Dishes

Antipasti, Parma ham and salami

Seafood platter

Warm fruit crumble with custard

Parking

Applecross

024 Applecross Inn

Shore St, Applecross IV54 8LR

Tel.: (01520) 744262 - Fax: (01520) 744400
e-mail: applecrossinn@globalnet.co.uk - Website: www.applecross.uk.com

     VISA MC JCB

Isle of Skye Red Cuillin, Black Cuillin, Hebridean Gold, Blaven, Young Pretender

Not only one of the most remote pubs in the UK, but one of the trickiest to drive to as well – nevertheless, a visit to this cheerful hostelry, with stunning views to Skye's Cuillin Hills, is a truly rewarding experience. Approach via the hair-raising 'Pass of the Cattle', or the 24 mile single track road from Shieldaig: neither journey will be forgotten in a hurry. The inn is an old fisherman's cottage on the side of the loch. Its no-nonsense bar has pine panelling, exposed stone and lots of windows affording properly breathtaking views. Seafood, from extremely local sources, is the backbone of the menus: it's very fresh and certainly the thing to choose, though, local venison or sausages are also on the list. It gets busy, so be early or book! If you can't face the return journey just yet, they have bright and comfy bedrooms.

Food serving times:
Monday-Sunday:
                    12pm-9pm
Closed 25 December and 1 January
(booking essential)
Prices:
Meals: 28.00 (fixed price dinner) and a la carte 16.00/22.00
🛏 **7 rooms :** 28.50/70.00

Typical Dishes

Haggis flambéed in Drambuie

Prawns in garlic, lemon and herbs

Raspberry cranachan

From Kishorn via the Bealach nam Bo (Alpine pass), or round by Shieldaig and along the coast. Parking

Badachro

019 Badachro Inn

Badachro IV21 2AA
Tel.: (01445) 741255 - Fax: (01445) 741319
e-mail: lesley@badachroinn.com - Website: www.badachroinn.com

Black Isle Yellow Hammer, Red Kite, Isle of Skye Black Cuillin, Young Pretender, Houston Killellan, Peter's Well

Food serving times:
Monday-Sunday:
    12pm-3pm, 6pm-9pm
Closed 25 December
Prices:
Meals: a la carte 10.00/20.00

Probably rather easier to get to by boat than by car, this pleasant little whitewashed pub has rather wisely invested in two moorings for visiting yachts. It's in a delightfully sheltered and remote location, right on the seashore of this small inlet, close to a little group of local houses. A cosy, lawned area with tables sits adjacent to the water. Inside, it's equally compact and traditional, with an open fire, beams, minuscule bar and local maritime charts on the walls. The nicest place to eat is the conservatory, with Loch Gairloch lapping its sides. Go for dishes from the daily changing menus featuring local seafood: all very fresh, simply prepared, and, in the majority of cases, homemade. Or take your lunch on a sunny day onto the 'terrace' and watch the world go quietly by – perfect!

Typical Dishes

Smoked haddock chowder

Gairloch prawns, salad and dip

Chocolate marquise

On B8056 on shores of Loch Gairloch. Parking and 2 moorings for boats

Cawdor

011 Cawdor Tavern

The Lane, Cawdor IV12 5XP

Tel.: (01667) 404777 - Fax: (01667) 404777
e-mail: cawdortavern@btopenworld.com - Website: www.cawdortavern.com

 Highland IPA, Tomintoul Stag, Cairngorm Gold and guest ales

Only a few miles from Loch Ness and Moray Firth, this country inn has a tourist attraction of its own – it's only five minutes from the local castle. In fact, its links in this respect go somewhat deeper than mere proximity: it's set within the Cawdor Estate, in what used to be the joiner's workshop for the castle itself. It's now a very personally managed pub, and the owners run a tight ship. There are three separate rooms: one with pool table, one for smokers, one for non-smokers, and old oak panelling from the castle can be found here. Well-marshalled young staff serve a wide ranging menu with plenty of choice, featuring top-notch local fish, game and meats.

Food serving times:
Monday-Saturday:
    12pm-2pm, 5.30pm-9pm
Sunday: 12.30pm-3pm,
    5.30pm-9pm

Closed 25-26 December and 1-2 January
(booking essential Saturday-Sunday)
Prices:
Meals: a la carte 18.50/26.95

Typical Dishes

Scallops, bacon salad

Loin of lamb with lovage jus

Belgian chocolate tart, honey cream

5mi Southwest of Nairn on B9090. Parking

Glenelg

012 Glenelg Inn

Glenelg IV40 8JR
Tel.: (01599) 522273 - Fax: (01599) 522283
e-mail: christophermain7@glenelg-inn.com - Website: www.glenelg-inn.com

VISA AE D MC

No real ales offered

Idyllically set off the beaten track in its own extensive grounds in a quiet hamlet by the lochside, this cosy inn was, in a previous incarnation, a couple of wee cottages. The Inn gloriously overlooks Glenelg Bay and the Isle of Skye. There's a very pubby bar, full of character: the locals have an amiable habit of turning it into the centre of the universe. It also boasts a beamed ceiling, dark wood panelling, and plenty of local photos on the walls. Blackboard menus offer a tried-and-tested, classic selection, utilising much local produce, of which fish and seafood are the speciality. If you're staying overnight, you can look forward to comfy, individually decorated bedrooms, followed by great Highland breakfasts in the morning.

Food serving times:
Monday-Sunday:
    12.30pm-2pm, 7pm-9pm
Closed Christmas
Closed Sunday dinner to non residents - (booking essential) - accommodation rates include dinner
Prices:
Meals: 29.00 (fixed price dinner)
🛏 **7 rooms :** 158.00/218.00

Typical Dishes

Carrot and coriander soup

Red mullet, sweet red pepper

Chocolate torte

Come off A87 at Shiel Bridge. Parking

Plockton

013 Plockton

41 Harbour St, Plockton IV52 8TN

Tel.: (01599) 544274 - Fax: (01599) 544475
e-mail: info@plocktonhotel.co.uk - Website: www.plocktonhotel.co.uk

 😐 🍷 ✑ ✗ **VISA** **AE** **MC** **JCB**

🍺 *Deuchars IPA, Hebridean Gold*

F ine views of Loch Carron are a more than adequate reason to visit this attractive little National Trust village near the Kyle of Lochalsh. The eponymous inn – a delightful pair of wee cottages on the lochside – is the place to indulge the views while supping a pint with the locals, who flock here. The bar's the centre of activity, but if you're after a quieter environment, then you can retreat to the small rear terrace or the recently installed restaurant, where it's quite possible you'll be able to order a corn on the cob, alongside an impressive list of local seafood. Plockton isn't renowned for its road network, so for those making the wise move of staying overnight, there are plenty of recently refurbished, well-kept, comfy bedrooms to tempt you.

Food serving times:
Monday-Sunday:
    12pm-2.15pm, 6pm-10pm
Closed 25 December and
1 January
Prices:
Meals: a la carte 13.00/30.00
🛏 **15 rooms :** 45.00/90.00

6mi Northeast of Kyle of Lochalsh.
Parking 100 yards away

Typical Dishes

Talisker pâté

Scallops, chilli and garlic sauce

Raspberry cranachan

Plockton

014 Plockton Inn

Innes Street, Plockton IV52 8TW

Tel.: (01599) 544222 - Fax: (01599) 544487
e-mail: stay@plocktoninn.co.uk - Website: www.plocktoninn.co.uk

 rest **VISA** **MC** **JCB**

2 regular ales offered

In the middle of a pretty harbour town on Loch Carron, this neighbourhood favourite without airs and graces is the place to come for good, unfussy seafood: platters of simply prepared shellfish and tasty dishes of locally landed fish are definitely the speciality, but they also do a good homemade hamburger! If you feel like some after-dinner entertainment, there might be a traditional music session in the bar next door. They also offer neat bedrooms in bright patterns; five of them are to be found in the annexe across the road.

Food serving times:
Monday-Sunday:
  12pm-2.30pm, 6pm-9.30pm
Closed 25-26 December
Check food service times in winter
Prices:
Meals: a la carte 14.00/22.00
14 rooms : 35.00/70.00

Typical Dishes
Smoked seafood
Chicken with butter beans and chorizo
Ice cream, raspberries and whisky

6mi Northeast of Kyle of Lochalsh. Parking

Waternish

016 ## Stein Inn

MacLeod Terr, Stein, Waternish IV55 8GA

Tel.: (01470) 592362

e-mail: angus.teresa@steininn.co.uk - Website: www.steininn.co.uk

 VISA **MC** **JCB**

 Red Cuillin, Reeling Deck, Deuchars IPA, Orkney Dark Island, Aviemore Tradewinds, Harviestoun Bitter and Twisted

In a breathtakingly beautiful spot on Loch Bay, the oldest inn on Skye is run with great warmth and dedication by a chatty husband and wife team. At the heart of the place is a tiny pine-clad locals bar and a lounge with rough stone walls, tall settles and an open fire; it's good for soup, sandwiches and a local ale, but it would be a shame not to try something more substantial in the little dining room – well-prepared seafood dishes, like fresh prawn tails and halibut and chips, are the pick of a tasty menu which also includes Highland venison. But for pure relaxation and peace of mind, take one of their 90 malts down to the grassy bank or the benches looking west over the bay and watch the sun set beyond the headland. Guests staying in the cosy, well-kept bedrooms – a snip at the price – can compare the view in the morning.

Food serving times:
Monday-Sunday:
12pm-4pm, 6pm-9.30pm
Closed 25 December,
1 January and Mondays in winter
- Seafood specialities -
Prices:
Meals: a la carte 10.65/21.65
5 rooms : 25.00/66.00

Typical Dishes

Skye scallops on mixed leaves

Casserole of Highland venison

Chocolate mousse

23mi Northwest of Portree by A850 on B886.
On the shore of Loch Bay. Parking

Howgate

017 **The Howgate**

Howgate EH26 8PY

Tel.: (01968) 670000 - Fax: (01968) 670000
e-mail: peter@howgate.com - Website: www.howgate.com

 VISA **AE** **D** **MC** **JCB**

No real ales offered

What was at one time a stabling facility for race horses, and more recently a dairy producing Howgate cheeses, is now a characterful establishment with two distinct areas. There's a tartan carpeted bistro with bar, open log fire and stone walls with framed newspaper articles, that specialises in simple, tried-and-tested dishes; and then there's the formal restaurant, which serves slightly more adventurous cuisine, but generally covers well-rehearsed, traditional territory. Menus are generous and extensive: daily specials, which range from home-made fishcakes to dishes with locally sourced beef, lamb and venison, should appeal to those who appreciate more traditional favourites.

Food serving times:
Monday-Sunday:
 12pm-2.30pm, 6pm-9.30pm
Closed 25-26 December and
1 January
Prices:
Meals: a la carte 15.00/30.00

Typical Dishes

Salmon fishcake, oriental dressing

Sirloin steak, pepper and brandy sauce

Banoffee pudding

Southwest 0.75mi on A6094.
Parking

Glendevon

018 The Tormaukin Country Inn

Glendevon FK14 7JY

Tel.: (01259) 781252 - Fax: (01259) 781526
e-mail: enquiries@tormaukin.co.uk - Website: www.tormaukin.co.uk

  rest **VISA**

Timothy Taylor Landlord, Fuller's London Pride, Harviestoun Bitter & Twisted

This extended 18C drovers' inn is tucked away in the picturesque "hidden glen" of Glendevon, with the Ochil Hills providing a splendid distant backdrop. Although a roadside establishment, it still manages to convey a character in sympathy with its surroundings. There's rustic charm in abundance: beams, flagged floors, plush softly lit bar, and log fires. A handy place for the golfing community, who create a pleasant feel, mingling with walkers and locals. You can eat in the atmospheric bar or cosy restaurant. Menus may not set any new gastronomic standards, but have earned a deserved standing locally: a smooth mix of popular Scottish favourites with more modern options. Ramblers – or golfers – too tired to continue can stay in comfortable bedrooms.

Food serving times:
Monday-Saturday:
12pm-2.15pm,
5.30pm-9.30pm
Sunday: 12pm-9.30pm
Closed 25 December and 2nd week January
Prices:
Meals: a la carte 13.65/30.95
12 rooms: 60.00/90.00

Typical Dishes

Coronation chicken salad

Trout fillets with almond and whisky

Nougat parfait

6mi South of Auchterarder on A823.
Parking

Ardeonaig

020 Ardeonaig

South Rd, Ardeonaig FK21 8SU

Tel.: (01567) 820400 - Fax: (01567) 820282
e-mail: info@ardeonaighotel.co.uk - Website: www.ardeonaighotel.co.uk

 rest **VISA**

No real ales offered

This family-run inn has its origins in the 17C, standing serenely in a wooded meadow on the south shore of Loch Tay. Its tranquil aspect is enhanced with a large garden – an ideal spot to relax in – or the library, which offers fine views. The homely, snug bar has walls filled with fishing memorabilia, and if you wander into the welcoming dining room you'll understand why: freshwater fish is a key element to the menus, alongside interesting dishes with a South African influence: the owner himself is a Springbok. There's also an enclosed courtyard, which, on a sunny day, is an ideal place to dine. Afterwards, delight in Highland walks or a slow drive alongside the Loch.

Food serving times:
Monday-Sunday:
8am-10pm
Prices:
Meals: a la carte 17.00/45.00
20 rooms : 45.00/220.00

Typical Dishes

Smoked Loch Tay salmon

Beef in black pepper and whisky sauce

Summer pudding

6.75mi Northeast of Killin.
Parking

Killearn

021 **The Black Bull**

2 The Square, Killearn G63 9NG

Tel.: (01360) 550215 - Fax: (01360) 550143

e-mail: sales@blackbullhotel.com - Website: www.blackbullhotel.com

    ⸺room *VISA* AE M©

 Deuchars, Brains SD and regularly changing guest ales

Set in the centre of a small village half-an-hour from Glasgow and 20 minutes from Loch Lomond, this extended former coaching inn is a good base for touring the heart of Scotland. Its focus is a contemporary styled bistro/brasserie in rather striking modern browns with a large dispense bar and wood floor. Most of the locals, though, head for the adjacent pub bar which mirrors the bistro's modish style, and also allows you free reign at the extensive, popular menus, typified by steak pie, seared trout fillet, escalope of beef with fries and salad or wild mushroom and Parmesan risotto. The bedrooms are of varying shape and size but similar modern furnishings.

Food serving times:
Prices:
Meals: 12.95 and a la carte 21.00/35.00
🛏 **12 rooms :** 65.00/90.00

Typical Dishes
Smoked salmon salad
Salmon on hot and sweet peppers
Chocolate and raspberry mousse

20mi North of Glasgow by A81 on A875.
Parking

Kippen

022 The Inn at Kippen

Fore Rd, Kippen FK8 3DT

Tel.: (01786) 871010 - Fax: (01786) 871011

e-mail: info@theinnatkippen.co.uk - Website: www.theinnatkippen.co.uk

 VISA MC JCB

Harviestoun Bitter and Twisted

Spacious, contemporary and open-plan, this fully refurbished village inn may not be quite what you were expecting. High-backed leather chairs and banquettes, smart glassware and casually uniformed staff set a determinedly modern tone, but it's not all out-with-the-old: framed black-and-white photos from the early 1900s show a very different way of life in this town on the edge of the Gargunnock Hills. The same wide choice is available at lunch and dinner, in the dining rooms and the rear bar, and ranges from surefire pub standards to slightly more elaborate restaurant dishes, still with a robust and straightforward style. Decorated in co-ordinated colours, the four bedrooms, named after local parishes, have a comfortable country feel to them.

Food serving times:
Monday-Sunday:
   12pm-3pm, 6pm-9.30pm
Closed 1 January
Prices:
Meals: a la carte 18.95/25.00
4 rooms : 40.00/70.00

Typical Dishes

Trio of Scottish salmon, herb pancakes

Loin of venison, sloe gin sauce

Vanilla crème brûlée

9.5mi West of Stirling by A811 on B822.
Parking

Linlithgow

023 The Chop and Ale house

Champany, Linlithgow EH49 7LU

Tel.: (01506) 834532 - Fax: (01506) 834302
e-mail: reception@champany.com - Website: www.champany.com

 Belhaven Ale

A restaurant within a restaurant, the intimate Chop and Ale House does away with most of Champany Inn's formality. Ancient exposed stone, closely set tables and a crackling log fire can't have changed much since this was the inn's public bar, while bridle bits and equestrian brick-a-brac mirror the muted prints of local squires and their prize horses. Forget dropping in for just a pint – it's cosy and relaxing, but it's just not that kind of place – but do come for well-sourced cooking, all appetising and popular with a strong Scottish flavour and a few unexpected variations. Aberdeen Angus steaks, hearty burgers and sausages, as well as piquant pickled herrings, are served with quiet professionalism by a friendly team.

Food serving times:
Monday-Friday:
12pm-2pm, 6.30pm-10pm
Saturday-Sunday:
12pm-10pm
Closed 25-26 December and 1 January
Prices:
Meals: a la carte 17.40/29.40
16 rooms : 115.00/125.00

Typical Dishes

Italian bean salad, chorizo

Chargrilled ribeye

Hot malted waffles, maple syrup

2mi Northeast of Linlithgow on A803 at junction with A904.
At the Champany Inn. Parking

"*H*iraeth"– the longing for home – and pride in the life of the nation take their source in many parts of Welsh identity. Unity is rooted in the very language of the Cymry, or "comrades", and the strength of community famously finds its voice in the songs of an eager rugby crowd. But above all, love of Wales is inseperable from a love of the land itself. The emblematic peaks of Snowdon and Cadair Idris and the steep streets of the Rhondda live long in the memory, but the full picture is wide enough to take in Lleyn's hidden coves and holy islands, the craggy stacks of the Pembrokeshire coast, the dominating towers of King Edward's castles and the fantasia of Portmerion, a playful dreamscape of domes and colonnades. Though long overlooked, Welsh cuisine is now making up for lost time and offering a taste of home, from rare delicacies like Wye and Usk salmon to world-famous lamb, Caerphilly, cawl cenin – a leek soup – and the humble Bara Brith; increasingly diverse real ales, and even Welsh whisky, mean there's always something new to try: Iechyd da!

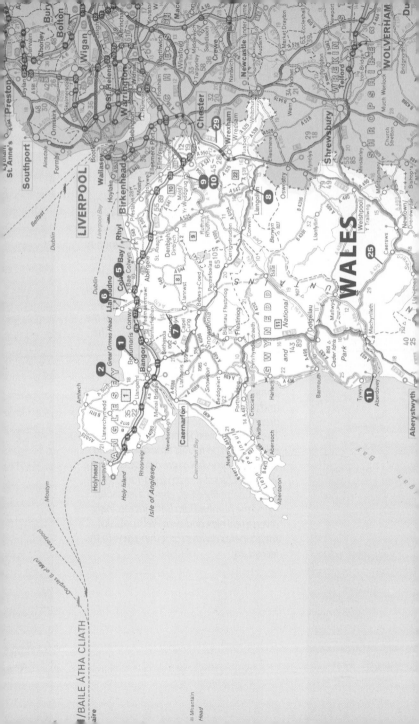

Beaumaris

001 Ye Olde Bulls Head

Castle St, Beaumaris LL58 8AP

Tel.: (01248) 810329 - Fax: (01248) 811294

e-mail: info@bullsheadinn.co.uk - Website: www.bullsheadinn.co.uk

room VISA AE MC JCB

Bass, Worthingtons, Hancocks

A classic market town inn and a good start for anyone crossing the Menai Straights for the first time – smart and spacious rooms are nicely maintained, but the same right-minded professionalism is in evidence throughout and a devoted following gives the restaurant an even stronger local reputation. Unlike the well-kept bar, which retains much of its old-style pub character, the brasserie has been tastefully restyled; an airy and comfortable place with seagrass matting, neat linen, soft lilac tones and lights around the sand-coloured beams. Sound, tasty cooking follows the modern lead and dishes like scallops with puy lentils and chorizo or beef with wild rice and shallot tarte Tatin are whisked from the kitchen by an efficiently drilled team.

Food serving times:
Monday-Sunday:
12pm-2pm, 6pm-9pm
Prices:
Meals: a la carte 12.50/17.50

Typical Dishes

Thai chilli squid

Roast sea bass, caramelised lemons

Jellied terrine of summer fruits

In the centre of town.
Parking on the main street

Red Wharf Bay

002 Ship Inn

Red Wharf Bay LL75 8RJ

Tel.: (01248) 852568 - Fax: (01248) 851013

VISA · MC

Greene King, Adnams, Imperial, Tetleys Mild, Marston Pedigree

The neat, white-painted Ship Inn is a welcome enough sight in itself, but what makes it really special is its fabulous view: down on the shore of Red Wharf Bay, it looks out across the sands, over every play of afternoon light on the water and out to the galloping "white horses" in the open sea. In the height of summer, an empty table on the large terraces won't be free for long, but if you can tear yourself away, take a look inside. Pews and benches line the bare stone walls, which have gathered a collection of old beer adverts, pub mirrors and photographs to go with their nautical bric-a-brac, while the dining room provides a more formal setting on Saturday nights. A large menu offers anything from a lunchtime sandwich to sea bass on herb rösti or grilled pork with mustard sauce and apple compote.

Food serving times:
Monday-Sunday:
12pm-2.30pm, 6pm-9.30pm
Prices:
Meals: a la carte 10.00/20.00

2.5mi Southeast of Benllech by A5025. Parking

Typical Dishes

Mussels, leeks and Gorau Glas cheese

Lamb shank, celeriac and black pudding

Rhubarb crumble

Salem

003 **Angel Inn**

Salem SA19 7LY
Tel.: (01558) 823394

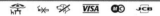

VISA *MC* *JCB*

Buckleys Best and fortnightly changing guest beers

Y ou'll find the welcome extended here to be as wide as the village of Salem is small; the owners took over in 2002 and their infectious enthusiasm has helped build a solid local following. Get here down a narrow road; you can't miss it, it's next to the chapel. Sink into one of the bar lounge sofas and place your order; there's a blackboard menu at lunchtimes and a more elaborate, printed a la carte in the evening. It's a spacious place, the Angel, and the sympathetic extension that is the restaurant offers large, well spaced tables, a wood floor and a subtle Victorian or Edwardian feel. By now, you'll have come to anticipate the warm, chatty service. What might surprise you are the rather complex dishes, featuring a host of local ingredients. Menus might include cannelloni of crayfish tails, Welsh spring lamb or Usk Valley venison.

Food serving times:
Tuesday-Saturday:
   12pm-2pm, 7pm-9pm
Sunday: 12pm-2pm
Closed 1 week January
Closed Tuesday lunch
Prices:
Meals: a la carte 24.00/30.00

Typical Dishes

Crayfish tail ravioli, fennel fondue

Welsh lamb, celeriac and Carmarthen ham

Semifreddo of coffee

3mi North of Llandeilo by A40 off Pen y bane road. Parking

Aberaeron

004 ## Harbour Master

Quay Parade, Aberaeron SA46 0BA

Tel.: (01545) 570755 - Fax: (01545) 570762
e-mail: info@harbour-master.com - Website: www.harbour-master.com

    VISA **MC**

 Buckleys Best, Brains SA

Appealingly situated on an attractive quayside in West Wales, this listed building is painted in deep, bold blue and was, indeed, the harbourmaster's home nearly 200 years ago. It's a fine place to relax and watch the sun set over Cardigan Bay, or, if you're feeling more energetic, to take a bracing walk along the coastal path at the front door. You can eat in the bar with the locals, or in the smart, nautically themed restaurant, which specialises in local produce with a pronounced seafood bias: feast yourself on locally caught lobsters, crab, seabass and mackerel. Beef and lamb are from the land surrounding Aberaeron. For another option of watching the setting sun, climb the listed Georgian spiral staircase and stay in one of the stylish and individual bedrooms.

Food serving times:
Monday-Saturday:
    12pm-2pm, 6pm-8.30pm
Sunday: 12pm-2pm
Closed 24 December-10 January
Closed Monday lunch
Prices:
Meals: a la carte 25.00/30.00
9 rooms : 55.00/115.00

Typical Dishes

Aberaeron prawns

Chargrilled fillet of Welsh black beef

Espresso crème brûlée

In town centre overlooking the harbour.
Parking

Colwyn Bay

005 Pen-y-Bryn

Pen-y-Bryn Rd, Upper Colwyn Bay, Colwyn Bay LL29 6DD

Tel.: (01492) 533360 - Fax: (01492) 536127

e-mail: pen.y.bryn@brunningandprice.co.uk - Website: www.penybryn-colwynbay.co.uk

 VISA AE MC

 Thwaites Bitter and up to 4 guest ales

On the way to the local zoo, this ordinary looking 1970s pub really doesn't promise too much. But hold your horses (and your elephants and leopards). Inside there's something of a transformation, with very spacious and comfortable surroundings forcing you to change your perspective. There are oak wood floors, polished tables and tasteful décor, comprising a host of old pictures of the promenade and local scenes; one wall's packed with books and there's a real fire. To the rear is a sloped garden with benches, and a fine view of the bay is possible from some inside vantage points. A young, enthusiastic team runs the place, preparing an extensive menu, printed and replicated on a large blackboard. Welsh cooking combines with tasty international dishes, plus good pub staples. Carefully prepared, generous portions all round.

Food serving times:
Monday-Sunday:
12pm-9.30pm

Prices:
Meals: a la carte 18.00/24.00

Typical Dishes

Goat's cheese, roast leeks, peppers

Lamb with redcurrant sauce

Belgian waffles

1mi Southwest by B5113.
Parking

Glanwydden

006 Queens Head

Glanwydden LL31 9JP

Tel.: (01492) 546570 - Fax: (01492) 546487
e-mail: enquiries@queensheadglanwydden.co.uk - Website: www.queensheadglanwydden.co.uk

▼ 🥄 *VISA* ⓜⓒ

Tetleys, Abbot, Firkins, Kilderkin, Burton

I f popularity is the yardstick of a good pub, then here is a league champion. Holiday-makers frequent this smart, cream painted pub in droves and most of them are within the premises as there are only a few tables dotted around the tarmac outside. It's a cosy, comfortable place (if you can get a seat) with the traditional appeal of low beamed ceilings, polished wooden tables, burgundy velour sofas and walls decorated with old maps and locally inspired paintings. Menus fit neatly into the tried-and-tested category but they contain plenty of local ingredients and are invariably well cooked. Dishes you might find are goat's cheese and onion tart, baked haddock with salad and bread, and homemade sticky toffee pudding. Despite the numbers, service is notably efficient.

Food serving times:
Monday-Saturday:
    12pm-2.15pm, 6pm-9pm
Sunday: 12pm-9pm
Closed 25 December
Prices:
Meals: a la carte 15.65/26.40

Typical Dishes

Goat's cheese tart

Pork belly, creamed Savoy cabbage

Panna cotta, berry compote

3mi Southeast of Llandudno by A470 off Penthyn Bay rd.
Parking

Tyn-y-Groes

007 Groes Inn

Tyn-y-Groes LL32 8TN
Tel.: (01492) 650545 - Fax: (01492) 650855
e-mail: thegroesinn@btinternet.com - Website: www.groesinn.com

 VISA AE ⓓ Ⓜ JCB

Tetley, Burton Ale

On the eastern edge of the Snowdonia National Park and south of Conwy, this lays claim to being the oldest pub in Wales, and it bears its age with great charm, character and no little sense of style. There are lovely bar areas finished with great taste: historic bric-a-brac, beamed ceilings, polished oak furniture, relaxing garden and fine views. A cloth-clad dining room and conservatory are the places to dine: you'll find popular, tried-and-tested menus making good use of ingredients from North Wales. Staying overnight proves a popular option here: the bedrooms are stylish and furnished with fine fabrics; many boast superb countryside views, while two have the added distinction of a terrace.

Food serving times:
Monday-Sunday:
   12pm-2pm, 6.30pm-9pm
Prices:
Meals: 15.50/28.00 and a la carte 15.00/20.00
🛏 **14 rooms :** 79.00/95.00

Typical Dishes

Trio of Welsh sausage salad
Conwy seafood platter
Bara brith and butter pudding

From Conwy Castle take the B5106 towards Trefriw; the inn is about 2mi on the right. Parking

Llangollen

008 **The Corn Mill**

Dee Lane, Llangollen LL20 8PN

Tel.: (01978) 869555 - Fax: (01978) 869930

Website: www.brunningandprice.co.uk

   ⚘ ☂ ⚒=rest ⚓

Timothy Taylor Landlord and up to 5 guest ales offered

A cleverly restructured conversion with a strong imprint of original industrial chic: joists span the spacious rooms over three levels, wooden cogs and drivewheels are braced to the rafters of the bar, period prints of riverbank landscapes hang on rough, limewashed walls and glass blocks, set into the floor, give glimpses of the old workings of the mill. Best of all, a decked terrace juts out over the fast-flowing river Dee, and on still summer days you may just hear the restored steam engines chugging up the hill to Carrog. Bold and generous cooking adds a few international influences to a British base and offers plenty of choice, including lighter bites and a big sharing platter of starters. In July, the International Eisteddfod's fringe festival of arts and world music centres on the theatre around the corner.

Food serving times:
Monday-Saturday:
12pm-9.30pm
Sunday: 12pm-9pm
Closed 25-26 December
Prices:
Meals: a la carte 18.00/25.00

Short walk from railway and public parking ❯❯

Typical Dishes

Home-made pâté

Shoulder of lamb, root vegetable mash

Welsh cheeses

Mold

009 Glas Fryn

Raikes Lane, Sychdyn, Mold CH7 6LR
Tel.: (01352) 750500 - Fax: (01352) 751923
e-mail: glasfryn@brunningandprice.co.uk - Website: www.glasfryn-mold.co.uk

 Timothy Taylor Landlord, Flowers Original, Phoenix Arizona, Spitfire, Hopback Summer Lightning

This large red-brick pub, handily placed for visitors to the North Wales coast and Chester, may not look too promising from the outside - apart from its pleasant terrace and garden - but inside is a different story. Its modern feel is lent character by lots of old bottles, sepia photos and shelves of books, all of them lovingly kept and neatly exhibited. Institutions of local prominence are based nearby, so expect to rub shoulders at the bar with actors, lawyers, farmers, technicians and theatre-goers. There's a good choice of food with a global influence and the menu, both printed and on the blackboard, reflect traditional and modern tastes.

Food serving times:
Monday-Saturday:
                    12pm-9.30pm
Sunday: 12pm-9pm
Closed 25 December
Prices:
Meals: a la carte 15.00/26.70

Typical Dishes

Chorizo with houmous bruschetta

Grilled trout, potato salad

Waffles, ice cream

1mi North by A5119 on Civic Centre rd.
Parking

Mold

010   The Stables (at Soughton Hall)

Mold CH7 6AB

Tel.: (01352) 840577 - Fax: (01352) 840382
e-mail: info@soughtonhall.co.uk - Website: www.soughtonhall.co.uk

      VISA AE

Plassey Bitter, Grooms Tipple

Where do you go for a decent pint in an extravagant 18C Italianate mansion? The summer house? The servants' quarters? Not quite. As relaxed and unfussy as the house is grand, the converted stable block gets slap-bang down to earth with a rustic interior of old brick and bare beams: horses' names on brass stable-plates, set into the tables, are a light-hearted touch. The approach to dining is just as informal: take your pick from sandwiches and light dishes or more substantial mains, some on the specials board - Welsh rarebit pork on a mound of apple and mustard mash sums up the generous country style here. There's also an interesting wine shop upstairs, which can only help to boost an excellent local following

Food serving times:
Monday-Saturday:
     12pm-9.30pm
Sunday: 1pm-9.30pm
(booking essential)
Prices:
Meals: a la carte 20.00/29.00
  14 rooms :   170.00

Typical Dishes

Venison and duck pâté

Lamb shank, minted creamed potato

Orange chocolate truffle torte

2.5mi North by A5119 on Alltami Rd. Parking

Aberdovey

011 **Penhelig Arms**

Aberdovey LL35 0LT

Tel.: (01654) 767215 - Fax: (01654) 767690
e-mail: info@penheligarms.com - Website: www.penheligarms.com

  VISA **MC**

Regularly changing guest ales

In the 1700s, The Little Inn was a quaint meeting place for locals in this beautiful part of West Wales. Nearly 300 years later residents and visitors are still coming, but the inn itself has grown out of all proportion, and now the Penhelig Arms, handsomely extended, stares regally out at the waters of the Dyfi Estuary. On one side is the Fisherman's Bar, where the locals gather round a log fire in the winter months. When it's warmer, you can go and sit at the sea wall. A separate dining room sports bay views, sympathetically painted light blue walls and a laid back feel. Menus change regularly and reflect the latest catch. Meat, too, comes from local sources. Try rack of local lamb, cooked pink, with aubergine chutney and rosemary gravy, or roast fillet of cod with mustard mash and prawn velouté. Cottagey bedrooms boast sea vistas.

Food serving times:
Monday-Sunday:
12pm-2pm, 6pm-9.30pm
Closed 25-26 December
Prices:
Meals: a la carte 18.00/26.00
 15 rooms : 45.00/110.00

Typical Dishes
Mullet with chilli, lemon and ginger

Cod, prawns, fennel and star anise

Chocolate cheesecake

On A493.
Parking

Llandenny

012 Raglan Arms

Llandenny NP15 1DL

Tel.: (01291) 690800 - Fax: (01291) 690155
e-mail: raglan.arms@virgin.net

Adnams, Wye Valley Bitter, Dorothy Goodbody, Brecon County Ale, Tomos Watkins

The owners' years of experience go a long way to explaining the popularity of this friendly village pub that works hard to keep everyone happy, and generally succeeds. Regulars rule the roost in one half of the central bar, reserved for pool, pints and slot machines, but the other side is given over to dining. Pine tables and chairs squeeze in around leather sofas for a share of the fireside warmth, but book in good time and there's always a space, here, in the pleasant conservatory or out on the decked terrace in good weather. You risk a crick in the neck from scanning the ample blackboard menu, but it's well worth it: fairly priced dishes like duck rillettes with homemade pear chutney or a pair of sea bass fillets with garlic and coriander are typical of the refreshingly simple and ably judged cooking.

Food serving times:
Tuesday-Saturday:
12pm-3pm, 7pm-11pm
Sunday: 12pm-3pm
Closed last week March, 1st week July and 1st week October
Prices:
Meals: a la carte 16.75/26.50

Typical Dishes

Duck rillettes, apple and cider chutney

Sea bass, garlic, lemon and parsley

Lemon tart

4.25mi North East of Usk by A472 off B4235. Parking

Llandewi Skirrid

013 ## The Walnut Tree Inn

Llandewi Skirrid NP7 8AW

Tel.: (01873) 852797 - Fax: (01873) 859764
e-mail: francesco@thewalnuttreeinn.com - Website: www.thewalnuttreeinn.com

 No real ales offered

One of the most famous establishments in Wales, the Walnut Tree has been something of a landmark for a number of years. Perched on a hillside overlooking the impressive Monmouthshire countryside, its location seems perfectly suited to the rustic nature of its cooking, albeit of another land. A small bar with fireplace sets the scene upon entry; the cosy, compact proportions continue in the restaurant, so do book ahead. The walls are full of pictures by local artists; in contrast, the tables are uncovered. Owner Francesco, invariably hospitable, makes sure of attentive service. He oversees a predominantly Italian menu, extensively pasta based, that might include tortelli di ricotta and spinach with butter and sage, or truffle gnocchi with baby vegetables and rucola. Fine Welsh ingredients – lamb, beef, cheese – also vie for attention.

Food serving times:
Tuesday-Saturday:
  12pm-2.30pm, 7pm-9.30pm
Sunday: 12pm-2.30pm
(booking essential)
Prices:
Meals: 19.50 and a la carte 30.00

Typical Dishes

Lasagne bolognaise

Sea bass with Parma ham

Banana tart Tatin

3.75mi North East from Abergavenny on B4521 (Skenfrith rd). Parking

Nant-Y-Derry

014 The Foxhunter

Nant-Y-Derry NP7 9DN

Tel.: (01873) 881101 - Fax: (01873) 881377
e-mail: info@thefoxhunter.com - Website: www.thefoxhunter.com

~~☐~~ **VISA** **MC** **JCB**

 Old Speckled Hen, Brains SA, Marstons Pedigree

An unlikely change of use by any standards: what started life as Victorian station master's office is now a pleasant, quietly prospering pub-bistro, with appetite-awakening food-themed prints and huge arrangements of lillies taking the place of leaves on the line. The pleasant service is probably a change for the better too. Stripped back to its basics – polished floorboards, exposed timbers and original brickwork – it looks the picture of carefully styled gastropub, though the well-separated, bare wooden tables untypically allow their diners plenty of space. A wide-ranging choice with roots in rustic European cuisine spans cod goujons with aïoli, spinach and ricotta ravioli, even a choucroute garni.

Food serving times:
Tuesday-Saturday:
12pm-2.30pm, 7pm-9.30pm
Closed 25-26 December and
2 weeks February
Prices:
Meals: 22.00 and a la carte
25.00/35.00

Typical Dishes

Suckling pig, artichokes
Salt cod, cuttlefish and white
beans
Crème Catalan

5mi Northwest of Usk by B4598.
Parking

Raglan

015 Clytha Arms

Raglan NP7 9BW

Tel.: (01873) 840206
e-mail: clythaarms@tiscali.co.uk • Website: www.clytha-arms.com

 rest 🚭 **VISA** **AE** **O** **MC** **JCB**

Bass, Hook Norton, Felinfoel, traditional cider and regularly changing guest ales

This relaxed and unassuming country pub is one for the traditional, 'everyday hero' category. Under the roof of the old dower house, you'll glimpse a few framed prints, a dartboard and skittles and the gleam of bar taps through a crowd of chatting locals, while the broad inglenook in the comfy lounge bar next door comes complete with a drowsy pub cat. Though the menu of familiar standards, served in the more formal dining room, is prepared with due care and attention, the food at the Clytha Arms is really at its most appealing when it forgets its restaurant manners. With greater simplicity of presentation come direct and refreshing flavours, so find a seat on the refectory benches in the bar and get started on a generous plate of faggots with peas and sauté potatoes, or grilled pineapple with coconut sorbet.

Food serving times:
Monday-Saturday:
12.30pm-2.30pm,
7pm-9.30pm
Sunday: 12.30pm-2.30pm
Closed 25 December
Closed Monday lunch
Prices:
Meals: 18.95 and a la carte 17.00/37.00
🛏 **4 rooms :** 50.00/90.00

Typical Dishes

Leek and laverbread rissole

Turbot, orange sauce

Sauternes cream with prunes

3mi West on Clytha rd.
Parking

Rockfield

016 **Stonemill**

Rockfield NP25 5SW

Tel.: (01600) 716273 - Fax: (01600) 715257
Website: www.thestonemill.co.uk

  VISA

  No real ales offered

A massive millstone from the original press is the centrepiece of this old cider mill, which produced its first vat of scrumpy back in Tudor times. Most of the orchards are long since felled, but this is still a beautifully rural spot and the bar and dining room alike, all stone flags and broad timbers, have bags of charm, character and originality. A raised, almost galleried lounge with comfy leather sofas connects to a dining area with well-spaced painted wooden tables. Flavourful, unfussy cooking suits its dishes to the moment: try Toulouse sausage salad or roast salmon on tomato fondue. Chatty and unflappable, the mill's owner takes the lead in the service, bringing just the kind of hospitable warmth a place like this needs.

Food serving times:
Tuesday-Saturday:
   12pm-2.30pm, 6pm-9.30pm
Sunday: 12pm-2.30pm
Closed 2 weeks January
Prices:
Meals: a la carte 25.00/30.00

Typical Dishes

Chargrilled squid, salad

Herb-crusted lamb

Caramel panna cotta, raspberries

6.25mi Northwest of Monmouth on B4233.
Parking

Skenfrith

017 **The Bell**

Skenfrith NP7 8UH
Tel.: (01600) 750235 · Fax: (01600) 750525
e-mail: enquiries@skenfrith.co.uk · Website: www.skenfrith.co.uk

 VISA AE M© JCB

 Timothy Taylor Landlord, Hook Norton Best, Freeminer Bitter

A walk in the Monmouthshire countryside reaps rich rewards with a visit to this lovely pub: an overnight stay is highly recommended too. It's located by the river with flocks of sheep in the surrounding fields. A stylish country flavour imbues all areas: there's a stone floor, roaring log fire, bare wooden tables and chairs and lots of black-and-white photos of the locality in yesteryear. You can relax in comfy sofas or on the beautiful garden terrace. Everything, everywhere is spotlessly kept. A fresh, local and organic emphasis informs the menus, which adhere to a traditional base with modern overtones, and keen, friendly service can be relied upon. The inn's main strength, though, is its bedrooms; these are exceptional, from the inclusion of DVDs to luxurious toiletries, and practically define the term "country style".

Food serving times:
Monday-Sunday:
  12pm-2.30pm, 7pm-9.30pm
Closed late January-early February and Mondays November-March
Prices:
Meals: a la carte 24.00/29.00
⊨ **8 rooms :** 70.00/170.00

Typical Dishes

Tomato, basil and mozzarella salad

Duck breast, orange and coriander

Champagne jelly

11mi West of Ross-on-Wye by A49 on B4521. Parking

Tredunnock

018 The Newbridge

Tredunnock NP15 1LY

Tel.: (01633) 451000 - Fax: (01633) 451001
e-mail: thenewbridge@tinyonline.co.uk - Website: www.thenewbridge.co.uk

Brains SA, Bass, Hancock's Bitter

The fast-flowing River Usk is the sprightly neighbour to this smartly gabled, cream painted pub which, to complete the rural picture, overlooks a winding country road and, of course, the bridge. Inside, there's a lovely open, spacious feel with stylish contemporary touches sprinkled all around. The dining element here is strong and the prevailing ambience suggests restaurant at least as much as pub. A curved iron staircase connects two levels of chunky wood tables and chairs. Lots of blackboard specials to peruse; the cooking is modern and quite adventurous but not over embellished. Afterwards, you can stay in state-of-the-art bedrooms where no expense has been spared.

Food serving times:
Monday-Saturday:
 12pm-2.30pm,
 6.30pm-9.30pm
Sunday: 12pm-3pm,
 7pm-8.30pm
Closed 26 December
Prices:
Meals: a la carte 25.00/35.00
6 rooms : 90.00/100.00

Typical Dishes
Guinea fowl, duck and foie gras
Pork, spinach and baby carrots
Hot chocolate souffle

Northeast of Caerleon on the banks of the River Usk. Parking

Stackpole

019 The Stackpole Inn

Jasons Corner, Stackpole SA71 5DF

Tel.: (01646) 672324 - Fax: (01646) 672716
e-mail: www.stackpoleinn.com

Brakspear, Felinfoel Double Dragon

A real fixture of the landscape, this rural pub feels as if it might almost have grown up out of the Pembrokeshire countryside: sturdy wooden slabs frame the bar-room, hops stretch their shoots towards the courses of bare brick and pint glasses shine on a Welsh slate bar. The owner, a natural hostess, superintends service with great warmth of personality and with her son in charge of the kitchen, it's a co-operative family effort. His straightforward, modern-classic cooking draws on seasonal Welsh ingredients to flavourful effect: winter in particular brings fortifying plates of warming and unfinicky country food like poached chicken with vegetable broth.

Food serving times:
Monday-Sunday:
    12pm-2.30pm, 6pm-9pm
**Closed Sunday dinner
November-March**
Prices:
Meals: a la carte 15.00/25.00

Typical Dishes

Thai fishcakes, chilli sauce

Beef with wild mushrooms

Raspberry brûlée

5mi South of Pembroke by B4319

Brecon

020 Felin Fach Griffin

Felin Fach, Brecon LD3 0UB

Tel.: (01874) 620111 - Fax: (01874) 620120
e-mail: enquiries@eatdrinksleep.ltd.uk - Website: www.eatdrinksleep.ltd.uk

 ℅room **VISA** **MC**

 Tomos Watkins OSB, Cwrw Haf

The wonderfully relaxed atmosphere starts in the open bar of this converted farmhouse: antiques and reclaimed furniture, bright modern colours, sofas by the log fire and a politely inquisitive pub dog make this an easy place to feel at home in. It's the same story in the spacious bedrooms, all in light, restful tones, which prove that you can banish twee or designerish clutter and still have thoughtful extras close to hand: each has fine linens, European and Indian furniture and a selection of good books. Well-balanced cooking in a modern style makes intelligent use of local ingredients and only a very tasty breakfast, fresh from the Aga, could possibly tempt you out of such wonderfully comfortable beds!

Food serving times:
Monday-Sunday:
  12.30pm-2.30pm,
  6.30pm-9.30pm
Closed 25-26 December and 2 weeks January-February
Closed Monday lunch except Bank Holidays
Prices:
Meals: a la carte 15.00/26.00
🛏 **7 rooms :** 67.50/115.00

Typical Dishes

Scallops, black pepper butter

Rack of lamb, spring vegetables

Crème brûlée

4.75mi Northeast of Brecon by 4602 off A470.
Parking

Crickhowell

021 **Bear**

High St, Crickhowell NP8 1BW

Tel.: (01873) 810408 - Fax: (01873) 811696
e-mail: bearhotel@aol.com - Website: www.bearhotel.co.uk

 𝒴 **VISA** **AE** **M©** **JCB**

 Bass, Brains Reverend James, HB, Ruddles County

In a small town in the Black Mountains, The Bear is a traditional coaching inn dating from 1435 with bags of charm and character. The snug bar at the front, with its open fire and beams, leads into an area of nooks and crannies and the lounge: lots of rafters, comfy armchairs, antique settles, and a window seat letting you to see what's happening in the market square. Don't miss out on eating here; two separate dining rooms are handsome enough on their own, with plenty of antiques and curios, but when you add the delicious food they serve – classically based with first-rate local ingredients – then you should see why the place is perennially busy. Appetising, modern bar-bistro dishes use similarly fresh produce to flavourful effect. There's also a welcoming summer garden, and bedrooms are plush and spacious.

Food serving times:
Monday-Saturday:
12pm-2pm, 6pm-10pm
Sunday: 12pm-2pm, 7pm-9pm
25th December to non-residents
Restaurant Monday-Saturday evenings only
Prices:
Meals: a la carte 15.00/22.00
🛏 **33 rooms :** 58.00/130.00

Typical Dishes

Asparagus with blue cheese and pancetta

Welsh lamb cutlets

Bread and butter pudding

In the town centre.
Parking

Crickhowell

022 Nantyffin Cider Mill Inn

Brecon Rd, Crickhowell NP8 1SG

Tel.: (01873) 810775
e-mail: info@cidermill.co.uk - Website: www.cidermill.co.uk

 A selection of local real ales

This hugely characterful 16C cider mill in the heart of the Brecon Beacons is difficult to miss: apart from being a distinctive mill by a busy crossroads, it's painted in an evocative pink wash. Inside, the characterful features remain: its working parts are still in situ, and two snug bars boast open fires, comfy country style seating, rattan flooring and an interesting mix of antiques and curios. This was one of the first Welsh gastropubs, and a slightly more formal dining room is filled with old mill objects and simple wooden tables. Varied menus, apart from quite rightly highlighting cider, feature local fish and game with some prominence.

Food serving times:
Tuesday-Saturday:
    12pm-2.30pm,
    6.30pm-9.30pm
Sunday: 12pm-2.30pm
Closed 25 December and 1 week January
Open Sunday dinner and Monday during school summer holidays
Prices:
Meals: 12.95 and a la carte 16.50/28.00

Typical Dishes

Welsh goat's cheese salad

Grilled lamb steak, garlic sauce

Aromatic panna cotta

1.5mi West of Crickhowell on A40.

Hay-on-Wye

023 Old Black Lion
26 Lion St, Hay-on-Wye HR3 5AD
Tel.: (01497) 820841 - Fax: (01497) 822960
e-mail: info@oldblacklion.co.uk - Website: www.oldblacklion.co.uk

 Wye Valley Old Black Lion and 1 guest ale

Know your JK Rowling from your DH Lawrence? After a busy round of book bazaars and seminars in the bibliophile's capital of Britain, head for dinner at this part 13C and 17C inn. The main bar is long on charm and character, lit by a real log fire: you could settle in comfortably with a pint and a good page-turner at any time, and though there's a separate formal dining room, you can choose a table and eat here, too. A dependable traditional menu holds one or two light variations, but the list of chalkboard specials is arguably the better choice – honest, tasty and prepared with good culinary understanding. Immaculate bedrooms, some in the adjacent block, are far better than the average pub, but it goes without saying that you'll have to reserve in good time for the Festival.

Food serving times:
Monday-Sunday:
12pm-2.30pm,
6.30pm-9.30pm
Closed 25-26 December and 2 weeks January
Prices:
Meals: a la carte 20.50/28.00
10 rooms : 42.50/85.00

Typical Dishes

Goat's cheese and tomato tart

Rack of lamb, rosemary jus

Lavender crème brûlée

In the town centre.
Parking

Llanfrynach

024 **The White Swan**

Llanfrynach LD3 7BZ

Tel.: (01874) 665276 - Fax: (01874) 665362

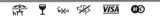 **VISA** Ⓜ©

 Hancocks HB, Robinson's

Though stylishly modernised, this pub in a picturesque setting still seems as much a part of the countryside as the adjacent church and fields. The sheltered rear terrace is perfect for making the most of warm summer afternoons but, in the evening, the softly lit bar and restaurant – in Welsh slate, timber and stone – is definitely the place to be. A well thought-out menu changes with the seasons and takes the organic option wherever it can: balanced, contemporary dishes might include a simple but flavourful goat's cheese quesadilla with salsa, good sea bass served with Oriental noodles and a satisfyingly nutty iced nougat. Good value.

Food serving times:
Wednesday-Sunday:
    12pm-2pm, 7pm-9.30pm
Closed 25-26 December and 1 January
Prices:
Meals: a la carte 17.00/24.00

Typical Dishes

Asparagus, tomato and blue cheese tart

Fillet of cod with cheese topping

Chocolate torte

3.5mi Southeast off Brecon by A40 Off B4558.
Parking

Pontdolgoch

025 **Talkhouse**

Pontdolgoch SY17 5JE

Tel.: (01686) 688919 - Fax: (01686) 689134

e-mail: info@talkhouse.co.uk - Website: www.talkhouse.co.uk

 Tetleys Cask and 1 guest ale

A cosy, unassuming exterior gives little away about the stylish going-on inside this 17C former coaching inn tucked away on a quiet road in rural mid-Wales. It's full of charm, with lots of curios, knickknacks and antiques adorning the rustic-styled bar, where you can slump into plush sofas in front of the log fire. French windows lead onto a lovely terrace and gardens for al fresco dining on warmer days. Eating here is a treat: considerate, personal service strikes just the right balance and a wide-ranging menu has a well-executed touch, as reassuring local produce comes together to create well-honed seasonal dishes. There are bedrooms too: an immaculate trio with a welcoming, individual style.

Food serving times:

Tuesday-Saturday:
12pm-2pm, 6pm-9pm

Sunday: 12pm-2pm

Prices:

Meals: a la carte 20.00/27.00

3 rooms : 70.00/95.00

Typical Dishes

Smoked haddock rarebit

Rack of lamb

Selection of Welsh cheeses

1.5mi Northwest of Caersws on A470. Parking

Talybont-on-Usk

026 ## Usk Inn

Station Rd, Talybont-on-Usk LD3 7JE
Tel.: (01874) 676251 - Fax: (01874) 676392
e-mail: stay@uskinn.co.uk - Website: www.uskinn.co.uk

Hancocks HB, Bass, Felinfoel Double Dragon

With a blend of friendliness and professional know-how, the hospitable husband-and-wife owners can take a lot of credit for the inviting atmosphere of this rurally set inn. The generous welcome is the same if you're staying in one of the rooms – individually styled and pine-furnished – or feel like whiling away an hour in the big public bar with a drink, a light snack and a seat in one of the deep, teak-brown leather armchairs. For bigger appetites, there's the restaurant, where the native Welsh influence is unmistakeable, local produce forming the core of an extensive menu that changes through the year. If you're new to this part of Powys, you'll find no shortage of ways to explore it: a canal cruise, cycling on the Taff Trail or your first steps into the Brecon Beacons.

Food serving times:
Monday-Saturday:
  12pm-2.30pm, 6.30pm-9pm
Sunday: 12pm-3pm
Closed 3 days at Christmas
Prices:
Meals: 9.95/23.95 and a la carte 18.00/24.00
11 rooms : 65.00/100.00

Typical Dishes

Smoked duck salad
Venison, port and liquorice jus
Ginger rum cheesecake

On the edge of the village, opposite the former railway station and yard. Parking

Llanrhidian

027 The Welcome To Town

Llanrhidian SA3 1EH

Tel.: (01792) 390015 - Fax: (01792) 390015
Website: www.thewelcometotown.co.uk

✕ ✕ **VISA** **M©**

No real ales offered

The Welcome to Town is more of a goodbye to the city – if you're in need of the perfect mid-week escape, a ten-mile drive takes you out into the rural peace of the Gower peninsula and straight to the front door of this old pub, where the owner's enthusiasm and experience is writ large…in the framed certificates and awards decorating a traditionally styled dining room. Able, pleasant service, with the formality of a restaurant, strikes the right note, while locally influenced cooking brings out appealing, seasonal flavours, a considered, rather classical approach underpinning it all. The specials board changes by the day, and it's worth asking about their good-value lunches.

Food serving times:
Tuesday-Saturday:
 12pm-2pm, 7pm-9.30pm
Sunday: 12pm-2pm
Closed 25-26 December and second 2 weeks February
Prices:
Meals: 14.95 and a la carte 14.95/30.00

Typical Dishes

Laverbread with crispy pancetta

Salt marsh lamb with ratatouille

Rhubarb parfait

10.5mi West of Swansea by A4118 and B4271.
Parking

East Aberthaw

028 **Blue Anchor Inn**

East Aberthaw CF62 3DD

Tel.: (01446) 750329

Website: www.blueanchoraberthaw.com

Wadworth 6X, Theakstons Old Peculier, Marstons Pedigree, Buckley's Best and guest ales

An absolutely charming 14C thatched pub, bright with overflowing hanging baskets in summer. Inside, the warren of little firelit rooms and massive walls in local stone give it character to spare. Looking its age in the very best sense, it's cosy, effortlessly pleasing and, once you get comfortable, very hard to leave, but the chatty staff wouldn't dream of hurrying you along. As you might expect, there's an extensive menu built on sound, homely foundations; restorative, traditional dishes like tomato and basil soup or minted lamb chops seem to go down well with the locals.

Food serving times:

Monday-Saturday:
  12pm-2.15pm, 7pm-9.30pm
Sunday: 12pm-2.15pm

Prices:
Meals: 13.75 and a la carte
13.00/25.00

Typical Dishes

Mushroom millefeuille

Pheasant wrapped in bacon

Rhubarb crumble

5mi West of Barry by B4265. Turn at the cement factory and follow the road for approximately 1 mile. Car park opposite the pub

Gresford

029 Pant-yr-Ochain

Old Wrexham Rd, Gresford LL12 8TY

Tel.: (01978) 853525 - Fax: (01978) 853505
e-mail: pant.yr.ochain@brunningandprice.co.uk - Website: www.brunningandprice.co.uk

 Timothy Taylor Landlord, Flowers, Weetwood Old Dog, Thwaites

To get an idea of this pub's vintage, look at the Tudor wattle and daub walls and timber in the alcove behind the inglenook fireplace. The Pant isn't just rather old, it's also rather vast, with several rooms running off the main bar. Overall, it's smart yet rustic, enhanced by lake views and a small model railway in the grounds. Its library bar has some dining tables, plus a good view of the lake, which makes it the pick of the rooms in which to eat. The menu is a printed sheet duplicated on the blackboard with a good choice of traditional and modern dishes ranging from light to very substantial; the cooking is robust and bold. Locally, this is a very well regarded place, but its bustling atmosphere just adds to the experience.

Food serving times:
Monday-Saturday:
12pm-9.30pm
Sunday: 12pm-9pm
Closed 25-26 December
(booking essential)
Prices:
Meals: a la carte 25.00/35.40

Typical Dishes

Roast chicken, pepper and fruit chutney

Lamb with lemon and almond couscous

Waffles, fudge sauce

3mi Northeast of Wrexham by A483 on B5445. Then 1mi South from Gresford.
Parking

With over a third of the country's population living in and around, Belfast is truly the focus of Northern Irish life. As the only city in Ireland to feel the rise and heavy fall of Britain's industrial empire, it has worked bravely to re-establish itself with a busy cultural life and a wave of new building, and perhaps it is in part the attitudes in the rest of Britain and Ireland that make us look elsewhere for easier symbols and images of the country. Though less intensely marketed than the Southern Ireland experience, the six counties contain some of the finest landscapes in the island. The incredible, innumerable columns of the Giant's Causeway, formed 60 million years ago by volcanic eruptions, attract thousands of visitors every year, while to the east lie the quiet, wooded bays of the Antrim coast and the deep inland glens. The beautiful Mourne and Sperrin Mountains stand as great Ulster landmarks, while Lough Neagh, the largest body of fresh water in the British Isles, lies in repose, a vast blue mirror in the heart of the province: here you'll find the working landscapes and the working people richly explored in Seamus Heaney's poetic memories of his youth. From the cultivated splendour of Mount Stewart Gardens or Castle Coole to the earth-magic of Beaghmore, from the whale-backed islands of Strangford Lough to the leaping salmon and pike in Lough Erne, a feeling for the natural world of Northern Ireland goes straight to the heart.

Belfast

001 The Errigle Inn
312-320 Ormeau Rd, Belfast BT7 2GE

Tel.: (028) 9064 1410 - Fax: (028) 9064 0772
e-mail: philip@errigle.co.uk

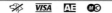

 No real ales offered

Seventy years in the business, this big, traditional Belfast bar remains a pub landmark in the city. Hungry newcomers can be forgiven for edging awkwardly around the maze of rooms at first: the no-nonsense Pinewood bar is really the locals' stamping ground for a beer and a smoke, but remember that the bustling Tom McGurran bar always keeps a little space for diners. For a bit more restaurant comfort, though, you're better off surrounded by handsome dark wood and green leather in the Oak Room, or in the dining room upstairs on a Friday or Saturday. Dinner dishes along traditional lines are tasty, generous and carefully prepared, whether you choose roast lamb with spinach and cabbage or pork with Thai-spiced noodles; lunches tend to be more basic: baps, grills, pastas and that dietician's nightmare, the mighty Ulster Fry.

Food serving times:
Monday-Thursday:
    12pm-3pm, 5pm-9.30pm
Friday-Saturday:
        12pm-10pm
Sunday: 12pm-8pm
Closed 25 December
Prices:
Meals: a la carte 12.95/23.25

Typical Dishes
Asparagus risotto
Cod, spinach and crème fraiche
Blueberry croissant butter pudding

South side of city centre.
Parking on the street

Bushmills

002 Distillers Arms

140 Main St, Bushmills BT57 8QE

Tel.: (028) 2073 1044 - Fax: (028) 2073 2843

e-mail: simon@distillersarms.com - Website: www.distillersarms.com

 🍷 🚭 **VISA** Ⓜ️Ⓒ

 Theakstons Best

The smart conservation village of Bushmills has its very own smart – and stylish – pub, set conveniently on the high street. Once home to owners of the local distillery, it's seen some very plush interior renovations creating an open-plan bar and comfortable lounge with shiny wood floors, elegant coolie lampshades and chunky brown leather sofas. The rear dining area is spacious enough for groups taking in the delights of the north Antrim coast and the menus are decidedly, sometimes ambitiously modern. Typically, you could try grilled fillets of sea bass with Asian spices, wilted greens, boiled potatoes and chilled tomato, garlic and anchovy sauce or pan-seared chicken supreme, aubergine, basil couscous, tomato and red onion salsa. A Michelin Bib Gourmand award winner for the quality and value of its cooking.

Food serving times:
Monday-Sunday:
12.30pm-3pm, 5pm-9pm
Closed 25 December and Monday in winter
Tuesday-Friday dinner only in winter
Prices:
Meals: a la carte 20.00/25.00

Typical Dishes

Whiskey cured salmon
Herb marinated sea bass
Vanilla cheesecake

In the town centre.
Close to Bushmills whiskey distillery

Annahilt

003 ## The Pheasant

410 Upper Ballynahinch Rd, Annahilt BT26 6NR

Tel.: (028) 9263 8056

e-mail: thepheasantinn@aol.com

 No real ales offered

Even in midweek the little public bar is bustling by lunchtime: the old floorboards, mock Tudor windows and a smouldering peat fire suggest a place happy to keep 21C fads at arm's length, for the moment at least. Press through and find a table, either along the colourful banquettes or in one of the booths, and allow yourself an aperitif while you look through the menu. You'll have time for a half at least; the choice is vast – too wide, perhaps – but you're assured of generous helpings. Steak, deep-fried whitebait, pork and bacon pie, and plates of smoked salmon and smoked halibut can usually be found on a list of tasty, no-nonsense classics, served up with brisk, capable cheeriness by a young bar team.

Food serving times:
Monday-Sunday :
    12pm-2.15pm, 5pm-9pm
Closed 25-26 December and 12-13 July
Prices:
Meals: a la carte 12.00/25.00

Typical Dishes

Chicken in Parma ham

Pork fillet on bacon mash

Pear tarte Tatin

4mi Southeast of Hillsborough on B177 then 1mi North of Annahilt on Lisburn rd.
Parking

Ballynahinch

004 **The Primrose**

30 Main St, Ballynahinch BT24 8DN

Tel.: (028) 9756 3177 - Fax: (028) 9756 5954

e-mail: info@primrosebar.co.uk - Website: www.primrosebar.co.uk

 No real ales offered

Nothing particularly draws you in to The Primrose, just one of a pretty average string of buildings along Main Street: only inside do you notice that little extra thought and effort that raises this small-town pub above the norm. Several small rooms around the double bar are all brightly decorated and feel surprisingly welcoming: you can expect an encouraging turn-out in the evening, and even at lunchtime there's a pleasant buzz of conversation from the locals, happy to have escaped the shop or the office for an hour or two. They come for burgers, steaks and baguettes, one or two daily specials or a list of well-presented dishes that includes internationally influenced choices – teriyaki beef or Indian-spiced lamb with chick peas – as well as classics like smoked salmon and prawn salad. Attentive service.

Food serving times:
Monday-Sunday:
  12pm-2.30pm, 5pm-8.45pm
Closed 24-26 December
(bar meals Monday-Friday)
Prices:
Meals: a la carte 15.00/24.00

Typical Dishes

Indian prawns, naan bread

Chicken with prosciutto and sage

Home-made cassata

In the town centre.
Parking on the street

Donaghadee

006 **Grace Neill's**

33 High St, Donaghadee BT21 0AH

Tel.: (028) 9188 4595 - Fax: (028) 9188 2553

e-mail: info@graceneills.com - Website: www.graceneills.co.uk

      VISA **AE** **MC**

No real ales offered

Reputed to be the oldest pub in Ireland, the 17C Grace Neill's has certainly seen some changes in its time. True, the traditional front bar, propped up on its massive timbers, looks as charming and timeless as ever; it's a place for slow pints and unhurried chat, with families snacking and drinking in the lounge. But at the back, the new split-level brasserie is chic, formal and uncompromisingly contemporary: silk cushions, elegant storm lamps, subtle shades of chestnut and aubergine and banquettes à la parisienne. The service, even for a light lunch of omelette Arnold Bennett and lemon parfait, can get rather earnest and solicitous, but there's no mistaking the good intentions behind it.

Food serving times:

Tuesday-Saturday:
  12pm-2.30pm, 6pm-9.30pm
Sunday: 12pm-2.30pm

Closed 25 December and 12 July

Prices:

Meals: a la carte 12.00/24.00

Typical Dishes

Ham hock terrine

Coconut chicken, mango noodles

Passionfruit panna cotta

18mi East of Belfast on A2. Parking

Donaghadee

007 **Pier 36**
36 The Parade, Donaghadee BT21 0HE
Tel.: (028) 9188 4466 - Fax: (028) 9188 4636
e-mail: info@pier36.co.uk - Website: www.pier36.co.uk

 VISA **MC**

 No real ales offered

Never less than busy, this family-run harbourside pub is a real local favourite. The door opens into a thronging front bar, which manages to be comfortable and gloriously cluttered at the same time, while the semi-raised dining area, in stripped pine and bare brick, has an almost country-cottage feel to it – perhaps it's the smell of bread and home cooking from the stove. Chatty, well-marshalled bar staff keep things moving briskly, serving up enjoyable, ultra-simple seafood from plaice with lemon to lobster Thermidor, as well as tasty grills and slow-cooked roasts. It's not called Pier 36 for nothing, and a pre-dinner stroll along the waterfront can be a lovely way of sharpening the appetite.

Food serving times:
Monday-Sunday:
12pm-2.30pm, 5pm-9.30pm
Closed 25 December
- Seafood specialities -
Prices:
Meals: a la carte 13.00/35.00

Typical Dishes
Sauteed crab claws, garlic butter
Panfried hake, bubble and squeak
Apricot brioche

18mi East of Belfast on A2. Parking

Dundrum

008 Buck's Head Inn

77-79 Main St, Dundrum BT33 0LU

Tel.: (028) 4375 1868 - Fax: (028) 4481 1033
e-mail: buckshead1@aol.com - Website: www.thebucksheadinn.co.uk

      VISA AE MC JCB

Krombacher, Erdinger

Local watercolours on the brick walls lend a touch of intimacy and originality to this relaxing, everyday pub, where you can choose informal dining or something closer to restaurant style. Consistent and simply presented cooking with a seafood base strikes an appealing balance between traditional pub meals and more elaborate styles: dishes range from local scampi and chips and baked smokie topped with Gruyère to seared turbot on Mediterranean couscous or a light rhubarb and almond flan. There's plenty to see and do after lunch, too: visit Dundrum's ruined castle or head south into the lovely rolling landscape of the Mourne Mountains, driving the picturesque coast road or striking out on foot along part of the Ulster Way, which passes a few miles from here.

Food serving times:
Monday-Saturday:
  12pm-2.30pm, 7pm-9.30pm
Sunday: 12pm-2pm,
                       7pm-8.30pm
Closed 24-25 December and
Monday October-March
- Seafood specialities -
Prices:
Meals: 15.50/24.50 and a la carte 15.00/24.50

Typical Dishes
Thai style mussels
Venison, clove and cinnamon marrmalade
Vanilla and buttermilk panna cotta

Northeast of Newcastle on A2.
Parking on the street

Hillsborough

009 The Plough Inn
The Square, Hillsborough BT26 6AG
Tel.: (028) 9268 2985 - Fax: (028) 9268 2472
e-mail: derekpatterson@barretro.com - Website: www.barretro.com

🍷 **VISA** **AE** **①** **MC**

No real ales offered

In such a quiet town, The Plough Inn keeps itself surprisingly busy: there's a little coffee shop over to one side, a smarter, more modern first-floor bistro – Bar Retro – and the traditional main bar at the hub of things below. Here, the stripped floorboards and no-frills approach set a simple tone, but there are no complaints from a regular crowd of neighbourhood drinkers and diners, who can take their pick from a list of snacks and sandwiches or a broad, appealing menu with a sound Irish base: even by local standards, the portions are immense. Service may slow down a little as the lunchtime rush picks up, but the polite good humour never flags.

Food serving times:
Monday-Sunday:
    12pm-2.30pm, 5pm-9.30pm
Closed 25 December
(bar meals Monday)
Prices:
Meals: a la carte 15.00/21.50

Typical Dishes
Tempura shrimps
Calves liver on cauliflower crème
Blackberries and vanilla crème

In centre of town.
Parking

Holywood

005 **Cultra Inn**

Cultra Station Rd, Cultra BT18 0EX

Tel.: (028) 9042 5840 - Fax: (028) 9042 6777

No real ales offered

On a more intimate scale than the commanding 19C mansion on the hill, but still part of the Culloden Hotel estate, the contemporary-rustic Cultra Inn stands in its gardens. With all its clean, polished, new wood, it can feel a bit bare without the friendly sound of its regulars, but fortunately that's a pretty rare occurrence: people come in good numbers, clustering near the log fire for a moment on colder days, before sitting down to hearty lunches and dinners. A simple midday menu, beginning with potatoes and panini, extends to chicken with mushroom and bacon sauce or real classics like boiled bacon and champ or a steak sandwich on soda bread – good with a pint and live Six Nations on the big screen. A more elaborate evening choice – minus the rugby – could include pine nut and chorizo pasta or monkfish with dill cream and spinach.

Food serving times:
Monday-Saturday:
   12pm-2.30pm, 6pm-9.30pm
Sunday: 12.30pm-2.30pm,
                     6pm-9.30pm
Closed 25 December
Prices:
Meals: a la carte 14.00/18.00

Typical Dishes

Crispy Thai beef salad

Chicken, mushroom and bacon sauce

Sticky toffee pudding

1.5mi East on A2.
In the grounds of the Culloden Hotel.
Parking

545

*W*ell deserving of its old epithet, 'The Emerald Isle', Ireland conjures up images of dewy fields and distant mountains. Wondrous, ever-changing cloudscapes do haul in rainfall on an almost industrial scale, accounting for the fresh atmosphere and luminous look of the landscape, but this picture of gentle, unpeopled tranquillity does no justice to the country's variety: sandy strands, flora-rich peatland and, at the westernmost edge of Europe, the natural phenomenon of the Cliffs of Moher, a five mile spectacular of shale and sandstone bounded by the Atlantic breakers and the Burren. Peaceful Cashel and Clonmacnoise evoke the spirit of Celtic Christianity and kingship, while Southern Ireland's towns and cities throb with life, culture and chatter: Galway has grown into a buzzing university and cathedral city alongside its thriving port while Killarney, near the wild south-west tip, has been attracting visitors for over 200 years. Dublin remains the heart of the nation, a fascinating focus of literary association with a vital blend of street, café, bar and restaurant life: the addictive craic of the "fair city" is played out to an accompaniment of Georgian elegance and the stunning background of the Wicklow Mountains. Away from the capital, too, friendly pubs serve up not only good stout and even better conversation, but also wholesome favourites like Irish stew, colcannon and coddle and imaginative new cuisine showcasing the finest produce the country has to offer.

Liscannor

001 Vaughan's Anchor Inn

Liscannor

Tel.: (065) 7081548 - Fax: (065) 7086977
e-mail: info@vaughansanchorinn.com - Website: www.vaughansanchorinn.com

~~~ ~~~ **VISA** **MC**

No real ales offered

Conveniently placed for the cliffs of Moher and the beach, this is a long-standing pub, seriously well-regarded by the locals. It boasts a charmingly unique interior: the front counter acts as a shop where you can buy corn flakes and coffee, while the walls are filled with fishing paraphernalia: nets, photos, ships' wheels and the like. Simple wooden tables make it seem like a bistro; a mix of simple and complex dishes means there's always something of interest on the menu. The more involved options might include seared scallops on a bed of crisp-fried smoked haddock and scallion mash with a white wine sauce. It gets very busy, so be prepared to wait for your dish to arrive.

Food serving times:
Monday-Sunday:
              12pm-9.30pm
Closed 25 December
- seafood -
Prices:
Meals: a la carte 25.00/50.00
🛏 **3 rooms :** 60.00

Typical Dishes

Steamed black sole, buttered samphire

Roasted lobster

Bread and butter pudding

On coast road 1.5mi West of Lahinch on main route to Cliffs of Moher. Parking

Newquay

002 **Linnane's Bar**

New Quay Pier, Newquay

Tel.: (065) 78120
e-mail: linnaneslobsterbar@hotmail.com

No real ales offered

On the crags overlooking Galway Bay, this little white-painted pub is traditional, friendly and totally relaxed. If the clouds are setting in, you can always find a table in the modest bar, decorated with black and white photos, but if there's even a hint of sun, make straight for the lovely terrace overlooking the water. A concise, all-seafood menu, concentrating on prime fresh shellfish, keeps it delightfully simple; they're open all day in summer, so you can while away the afternoon with open sandwiches, chowders, lobster, scallops, oysters, chilled Sancerre and plenty of fresh sea air! There's more seafood for sale at the pier shop. If you can tear yourself away, drive through the strange, barren Tolkien-scape of The Burren to Lahinch beach or the breathtaking Cliffs of Moher.

Food serving times:
Monday-Sunday:
12.30pm-9pm
Closed October-March
- Seafood -
Prices:
Meals: a la carte 18.50/ 38.00

Between Kinvarra and Ballyvaughan off N67.
Parking

Typical Dishes

Seafood chowder
Crab cakes
Apple crumble

Castletownshend

003 ## Mary Ann's

Castletownshend

Tel.: (028) 36146 - Fax: (028) 36920
e-mail: maryanns@eircom.net - Website: www.maryannsbarrestaurant.com

 No real ales offered

First find this sleepy coastal village, then follow the row of terrace houses until you come to a pleasant little 19C pub. With fifteen years' experience, the friendly owners are old hands by now, taking real pride in their tasty, traditional home cooking and preferring not to cut corners when it comes to the important things. There's a familiar ring to much of the large menu, as well as the blackboard specials – this is food to satisfy, rather than surprise or impress – but homemade soups, good homebaked rolls, local cheeses and their real speciality, seafood, are all clearly well above the norm. If it's sunny enough, the friendly people behind the bar will offer you a seat in the garden.

Food serving times:
Monday-Sunday:
   12pm-2.30pm, 6pm-9pm
Closed 24-26 December and 1-2 January
(bookings not accepted)
Prices:
Meals: a la carte 17.00/45.00

Typical Dishes

Mini seafood platter

Fish and chips

Assiette of desserts

Between Clonakilty and Skibbereen off N71.
Parking on main street

Clonakilty

004 ## An Sugán

Wolfe Tone St, Clonakilty

Tel.: (023) 33719 - Fax: (023) 33825
e-mail: ansugan@eircom.net - Website: www.ansugan.com

 🍷 ⚔ 🚫 **VISA** Ⓜ️©

 No real ales offered

Personally run for ages, the unpretentious An Sugán welcomes hungry visitors as well as locals, dropping in to sink a pint and catch up on Clonakilty's news and current affairs. It's worth making time for a half in the characterful bar, all dark polished wood and frosted glass, before heading upstairs to the restaurant, decorated with memorabilia and old photos. A traditional blackboard menu doesn't try to reinvent the wheel, but offers sound, tasty home cooking with an appealing pub flavour: crisp, fresh scampi are well worth trying. Relaxed and friendly service.

Food serving times:
Monday-Sunday:
12.30pm-9.30pm
Closed 25 December and Good Friday
Prices:
Meals: a la carte 17.00/ 32.00

Typical Dishes

Terrine of black and white pudding

Salmon in wine cream

Bread and butter pudding

In the town centre.
Parking available on the street ➤

Cork

005 The Douglas Hide

63 Douglas Street, Cork

Tel.: (021) 4315695
e-mail: info@douglashide.com - Website: www.douglashide.com

 No real ales offered

Somewhere, indeed, to hide away in Cork – this late Victorian pub is tucked into its cosy niche on Douglas Street, just five minutes from the city centre. The intimate little bar, with its clusters of regulars, opens out into an altogether brighter, more open area with heavy pine tables and chairs. Modern artwork, appropriately food and drink themed, adorns the walls and basks in the warm glow from candles burning on each table. County Cork is a rich provider of free range and organic produce: fish, meat, cheeses, vegetables and herbs arrive from suppliers close to hand and all the pub's desserts, breads and ice creams are made on the premises. Recent recommendations include cauliflower and soft cheese roulade with watercress salad followed by celeriac and Cashel blue cheese mousse on a turnip and thyme gratin.

Food serving times:
Monday-Friday:
    12pm-3pm, 5.30pm-9pm
Saturday: 5.30pm-9pm
Sunday: 12pm-3pm
Closed 25 December and Good Friday
Closed Monday dinner
Prices:
Meals: a la carte 20.00/ 40.00

Typical Dishes

Duck, mushroom and blue cheese tart

Scallops on cabbage, yoghurt dressing

Lemongrass brûlée

Five minutes walk from town centre over Parliament Bridge. Street parking or White Street car park 5 minutes walk

Kinsale

006 Dalton's

3 Market St, Kinsale

Tel.: (021) 4777957
e-mail: fedalton@eircom.net

Kinsale Landers Ale

Moist, tasty crab cakes with pineapple salsa, chicken satay and Cajun popcorn prawns: here's a globe-trotting chef and landlord who is determined to bring a little unexpected variety to Kinsale's dining. A loyal local following suggests he must be doing something right, and while they still offer a good pie and pint for the traditionalist, it's the more ambitious dishes which set the place apart from the countless other pubs in town. It just goes to show that you can't go by appearances, for apart from the eyecatching purple façade, the line of bar stools, the tan banquettes, the tiled floor and the glowing fire are as traditional as the easygoing ambience and the cheerful welcome.

Food serving times:
Monday-Friday:
12.30pm-3pm
Closed 24 December-
6 January, Easter week and
Bank Holiday Mondays
Prices:
Meals: a la carte 13.50/
19.00

Typical Dishes

Chowder

Fish special

Assiette of desserts

2 minutes away in St Multose car park

Dublin

007 **The Cellar Bar**

Upper Merrion St, Dublin D2

Tel.: (01) 603 0600 - Fax: (01) 603 0700
e-mail: info@merrionhotel.com - Website: www.merrionhotel.com

No real ales offered

One of Dublin's favourite places for lunch is hidden away behind the elegant façade of an old Georgian town house, now the Merrion Hotel. The superbly restored wine vaults are now a smart destination bar by night, a bar-brasserie by day, and a city institution all round, so beat the lunchtime rush and find an alcove table under the brick and granite arches or pull up a spare stool at the long bar. Even on the busiest days, smiling, super-efficient bar staff keep things moving, serving up everything from hot roast beef sandwiches and Caesar salad to bacon and cabbage or Irish stew; plum frangipane tart with deliciously smooth ice cream is an occasional special and deserves to be tried.

Food serving times:
Monday-Saturday:
12pm-2pm
(live music Sunday brunch)
(carving lunch)
Prices:
Meals: a la carte 23.00/28.00

At the Merrion Hotel. Parking on meters nearby available at a charge of 20Euro per night for guests staying at the hotel.

Typical Dishes

Chilli marinated chicken wings

Mushrooms, cheese, bacon and salad

Chocolate fondant

Ballinasloe

008 **Tohers**

18 Dunlo Street, Ballinasloe

Tel.: (090) 9644848 - Fax: (090) 9644844

No real ales offered

A bustling market town like Ballinasloe ensures that this converted pub on the high street sees its fair share of local life: Tohers' ground floor bar is a buzzing place to be. It has a rustic charm befitting its proximity to the market square, and the marina is only a short walk away. Upstairs, the atmosphere's slightly more refined: three rooms make up the restaurant with its simple linen covered tables and understated rural décor. Menus contrast sharply: bar lunches are simple but tasty – everything from freshly baked baguettes to chicken fajitas – while upstairs in the evening, ambitious dishes with global inspiration make an appearance. Menus might include spring roll of gingered crab with a marinated carrot and fennel salad; or slow cooked Moroccan spiced lamb shank with lemon and garlic couscous.

Food serving times:

Monday-Saturday:
   12pm-3pm, 6pm-9.30pm

Closed 25 December, 1 January, 10 October-27 October and Bank Holidays

Closed Monday dinner

Prices:

Meals: 25.00 and a la carte 23.50/37.50

Typical Dishes

Fried Brie, salsa

Aromatic duck, orange and ginger

Chocolate and orange pudding

In the town centre.
Street Parking

Clonbur

009 John J. Burkes

Clonbur

Tel.: (094) 9546175 - Fax: (094) 9546290
e-mail: tibhurca@eircom.net - Website: www.burkes-clonbur.com

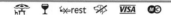

No real ales offered

Between two of Ireland's finest fishing waters, it's no surprise to find cabinets and cases displaying the ones that didn't get away. The brown trout in Lough Corrib and Lough Mask are legendary, the perch and pike no less so, and where better for food and drink after a long day out than this friendly pub, still owned by the Burke family. The tiny, unassuming shopfront opens up into a big, characterful bar and simply set rear dining room, as popular with the locals as with the anglers who flock to the West Coast in the height of the season. Simple, fortifying meals will set you up for the great outdoors: try cod and chips, a pint of stout and a generous slice of home-made apple pie.

Food serving times:
Monday-Sunday:
12pm-9.30pm
Closed midweek November-March
(live music Friday-Sunday)
Prices:
Meals: a la carte 25.00/ 50.00
5 rooms : 60.00/80.00

Typical Dishes

Timbale of crab, salad
Sirloin steak
Dutch apple tart, ice cream

3.5mi West of Cong on R345.
In the town centre.
On street parking

Kilcolgan

010 ## Moran's Oyster Cottage

The Weir, Kilcolgan

Tel.: (091) 796113 - Fax: (091) 796503
e-mail: moranstheweir@eircom.net - Website: www.moransoystercottage.com

 No real ales offered

When you see the thatched roof of this pretty cottage, your mind might flash to a typical English country inn, but instead you're across the Irish Sea in a sleepy Galway village. Moran's is set in a delightful waterside location and you can watch the swans sail serenely past. Inside, this charming 18C building is full of nooks and crannies in the front bar. Settle down in one of the beamed snugs and parlours or go through to the very large dining area at the back where the walls are decorated with photos of famous customers. Local seafood dishes, unsurprisingly, make up the widely renowned menus: native oysters from their own oyster beds, lobster, mussels, crab salads, smoked salmon and seafood cocktails. Expect fairly fast and furious service from staff who are used to being busy.

Food serving times:
Monday-Sunday:
12pm-10pm
Closed 3 days at Christmas and Good Friday
- Seafood -
Prices:
Meals: a la carte 30.00/ 70.00

Typical Dishes

Seafood chowder

Seafood special

Cheesecake

> 5 minutes from the village of Clarenbridge. Parking

Kinvara

011 Keogh's Bar
The Square, Kinvara

Tel.: (091) 637145 - Fax: (091) 637028
e-mail: keoghsbar@eircom.net - Website: www.kinvara.com/keoghs

VISA **AE** **MC** **JCB**

No real ales offered

Kinvara is a pretty harbour village on the Galway coast, renowned for the quality of its Atlantic fishing catch. Gateway to the Burren, its colourful character is echoed in this bright yellow-fronted pub whose busy bar constantly buzzes to the sound of locals chattering over a pint of dark stout. At the back is a spacious, slightly more formal dining room, which still maintains a warm, pubby ambience. The Keoghs have been here for many years, and they serve simple, well-prepared and tasty dishes, based around the plentiful supplies of local seafood. On offer, typically, are prawns, salmon, crab, mussels and seafood chowder, cooked in a hearty and traditional style.

Food serving times:
Monday-Sunday:
12pm-10pm
Closed 25 December and Good Friday
Prices:
Meals: a la carte 17.00

Typical Dishes

Black pudding salad

Cod with pesto and herb crust

Bread, butter and whiskey pudding

In the centre of the town. Parking

Cahersiveen

012 The Point

Renard Point, Cahersiveen
Tel.: (066) 947 2165 - Fax: (066) 947 2165

No real ales offered

As the beautiful Ring of Kerry runs south, hold your course to the tip of the Iveragh peninsula: down at the quay, looking out across the harbour to Valencia Island, is a neatly kept little bar that's definitely worth going a little further for. Between them, a charming couple, owners of long standing, keep the place shipshape, pull the pints and prepare a short hot and cold supper menu of local seafood; all well chosen and as fresh as it comes, as you'd expect with a fish shed next door! It's a good place for a relaxed pint and a chat – there's no food at all at lunchtime – but if you arrive in the afternoon with time to spare, just take a seat on the little pavement terrace and wait for 5.30 to roll around!

Food serving times:
Monday-Sunday:
5.30pm-10pm
Closed 1 August. Restricted opening in winter
- Seafood - (bookings not accepted)
Prices:
Meals: a la carte 30.00

Typical Dishes

Hot crab claws

Pan fried hake, garlic and olive oil

Irish coffees

1.75mi Southwest by N70. Parking

Listowel

013 Allo's Bar

41 Church St, Listowel
Tel.: (068) 22880 - Fax: (068) 22803

≒rest 🚭 **VISA** **AE** **MC**

No real ales offered

A discreetly set institution in the centre of Listowel, this is a wonderfully relaxed pub that proves very popular with locals and tourists alike. It's the other half of Allo's restaurant with rooms, the two gelling in a smooth and seamless symmetry. The bar is a narrow room with lots of original 19C charm. Walls feature exposed brick and the wooden bar and floor are thickly varnished; small booths and stools at the bar provide a most convivial and traditional feel. Menus change on a weekly basis and offer a good range of popular snacks and sandwiches alongside hearty daily specials. Booking really is a must, as it invariably gets packed here.

Food serving times:
Tuesday-Saturday:
12pm-9.15pm
Closed 25 December
(booking essential)
Prices:
Meals: a la carte 20.00/35.00
🛏 **3 rooms :** 50.00/70.00

Typical Dishes

Seafood chowder

Baked Clonmel ham with parsley sauce

Crème brûlée

Just off Market Pl.
Parking at the rear ❯❯

Carrick-on-Shannon

014 The Oarsman

Bridge St, Carrick-on-Shannon

Tel.: (071) 9621733 - Fax: (071) 9621734
e-mail: info@theoarsman.com - Website: www.theoarsman.com

No real ales offered

No boating experience necessary, of course, but the town's club eights have been known to drop in, along with sea-anglers and tour rowers, back from a long day's pull up to Lough Key. They come for the spirited, upbeat atmosphere, light lunches and fresh, tasty dinners combining modern classics and a few popular Irish favourites; even when it's busy, alert and helpful staff will do their best find you a table in the main bar or up in the mezzanine, though propping up the bar for a half is no hardship here. Refurbished in traditional style, with some unlikely bits of bric-a-brac hanging from its exposed timbers and stone, it's an enjoyable place and worth seeking out.

Food serving times:
Monday-Wednesday :
12pm-3.30pm
Thursday-Saturday:
12pm-3.30pm, 7pm-9.30pm
Closed 25 December and
Good Friday
Prices:
Meals: a la carte 24.50/37.50

Typical Dishes

Scallops with oyster tempura

Loin of lamb, polenta and herb crust

Strawberry sponge

In the town centre.
Disc parking adjacent to pub

Terryglass

015 The Derg Inn

Terryglass

Tel.: (067) 22037 - Fax: (067) 22297
e-mail: derginn@eircom.net - Website: www.derginn.ie

No real ales offered

Not, perhaps, typically pubby from the outside – sandwiched between the post office and Paddy's Bar – this is in fact an unmistakeable and friendly place once you're through the front door. Enthusiastically run by keen owners, it has wood and flagged floors, rafters, open fires and pot stoves; dotted round the central wood bar are chunky pine tables and an assortment of chairs, benches and pews, and there's outside seating in the summer months. As much local and organic produce appears on the menus as possible: classic Irish favourites alongside more modern dishes served in an invariably friendly manner. After which, all that remains is to take that brisk constitutional down to beautiful Lough Derg.

Food serving times:
Monday-Sunday:
11am-10pm
Closed 25 December and Good Friday
Prices:
Meals: a la carte 21.00/37.00

Typical Dishes

Goat's cheese, leek and spinach tartlet

Pork, prune, apricot and juniper sauce

Raspberry brûlée

South of Portuna by N52 on R493. Parking in village

Dunmore East

016 **The Ship**
Dock Rd, Dunmore East
Tel.: (051) 383141 - Fax: (051) 383144
e-mail: theshiprestaurant@eircom.net

 VISA Ⓓ ⓂⒸ

🍺 *No real ales offered*

A small, stone-built pub happily nestling in a pleasant fishing village, The Ship's corner position makes it one of Dunmore East's most recognisable institutions and it's well received locally. There's a strong element of delightful pubby character inside: big bar, polished wood floors, beams, pillars, and lots of open fires. Nautical memorabilia, too, is spot-on for the location. Sit down at simple tables and 'barrel' shaped chairs and tuck into menus that are not, surprisingly, dominated by seafood: you'll find meat plays an equally prominent part in the soundly cooked range of dishes. Blackboard options, though, are firmly centred on fish specials.

Food serving times:
Monday-Saturday :
      12.30pm-2.15pm,
      7.30pm-10pm
Sunday: 12.30pm-2.15pm
Closed Monday and Tuesday October-March
- Seafood -
Prices:
Meals: 25.00 and a la carte 30.00/47.00

Typical Dishes

Scallop and prawn salad, cider dressing

John Dory, saffron potatoes

Orange panna cotta

12mi Southeast of Waterford on R684. Near the harbour

Lismore

017 **Buggys Glencairn Inn**

Lismore

Tel.: (058) 56232 - Fax: (058) 56232
e-mail: info@buggys.net - Website: www.lismore.com

   VISA **MC**

 No real ales offered

This "pretty as a picture" cottage style inn is most homely: it even has a picket fence. A country pub writ large, it boasts everything from a little fire-lit bar to charming bedrooms with an old-world feel. The quaint bar is a good place to settle down with a pint of stout and enjoy freshly prepared dishes off a limited choice menu; or, if you prefer, the same options are on offer in a couple of small dining rooms, charmingly set up with a stylish country informality. The food is heartily rustic in nature: on the menu, you might find pot-roasted fillet of pork and apricots, or fish landed at Helvick, cooked in butter, olive oil and lemon juice. The owner is a talented artist, and it's easy to appreciate just how much of his inspiration has gone into the pub's appeal, not to mention his popular menus.

Food serving times:
Monday-Sunday: 7pm-9pm
Closed 23 December-
2 January
Prices:
Meals: a la carte 31.00/
37.00
🛏 **5 rooms :** 70.00/130.00

Typical Dishes

Rabbit in cider

Brill in butter and lemon

Strawberries, pepper and
orange juice

3mi Southwest by N72.
Parking

Carne

018 **Lobster Pot**

Carne

Tel.: (053) 31110 - Fax: (053) 31401

🍷   ✄   ✄   *VISA*   AE   MC

No real ales offered

Engagingly quirky and genuinely welcoming, this personally owned seaside pub has been over 20 years in the making: it's now covered with old metal signs on the outside, and the intimate snugs and parlours are crammed with nauticalia and pasted with old posters and advertisements from days gone by. There's also a dining room at the back and, come the evening, they add an extensive list of grills, steaks and locally landed fish to the lunchtime chowders, salads and sandwiches. The real treat, though, is the huge seafood platter, an aquarium's worth of home-smoked salmon and mackerel, freshly dressed crab, poached salmon and prawns Marie Rose, served with bushels of salad. Try it with freshly baked brown scones and a glass of stout!

Food serving times:
Tuesday-Sunday:
12pm-9pm

Closed 25 December, 2 January-11 February and Good Fridays. Open Bank Holiday Mondays
- Seafood - check opening times in winter

Prices:
Meals: a la carte 26.00/50.00

Typical Dishes

Garlic mussels

Dover sole

Selection of cheeses

South of Rosslare Harbour. Parking

Arklow

019 Kitty's of Arklow

56 Main St, Arklow

Tel.: (0402) 31669 - Fax: (0402) 31553
e-mail: conor@kittysofarklow.com - Website: www.kittysofarkow.com

No real ales offered

One of Arklow's most recognisable sights: that's the fondly regarded red building in the centre of the town. Locals flock here, and the downstairs bar is constantly bustling, the pints of stout flowing freely. It seems a shame to leave, but then again, there are two dining rooms upstairs, both rich in easy-going rustic character, decorated with everything from books and old farm equipment to pictures for sale. Arrive early for one of the most sought-after tables, which overlook the high street. Simple lunchtime menus range from panini to specials; in the evenings, more structured and elaborate options prevail; service is cheerful, efficient and as smooth as clockwork.

Food serving times:
Monday-Sunday:
    12pm-3pm, 6pm-10pm
Closed 25 December and
Good Friday
Prices:
Meals: 20.00/37.00 and a la carte 20.00/37.00

Typical Dishes

Goat's cheese tart

Tiger prawns, tomato and basil

Chocolate fondant, Baileys sauce

In the town centre. Public parking nearby.

Index of towns

Y